Praise for

'A thoroughly original and gripp[...] Tudor London, via dragon-like early steam engines, from pioneering reformers to outrageous scoundrels, and finally to the lives of modern Londoners, perplexed as to why Thames Water has yet again had to close a road, to replace cast-iron Victorian pipework with blue tubes, this is a lucid, hugely readable account of the struggle to supply clean water to one of the world's first megacities. The conflicts between private profit and public interest, which go back to Jacobean times, carry on today. Anyone interested in the real London needs to read this'   – *Andrew Marr*

'The first biography of liquid London is a pacey yet scholarly tale of greed versus altruism. Nick Higham breaks new ground in analysing the history of that most fundamental metropolitan element – its water supply'
     – *Sarah Wise*

'An enthralling guide to London's most neglected and under-exploited asset. Its day must surely come'   – *Simon Jenkins*

'London has been called the city of rivers, but for more than a century the capital's watery powers have been built over and then disregarded. In this multi-faceted work, Higham swims through the centuries to show how integral water has been to the creation of an industrial powerhouse, and how the historic struggle between private enterprise and public good continues to float the market. A masterful achievement'
     – *Judith Flanders*

'A painstakingly researched account of how contemporary incompetence and private-interest greed in the water industry is reflected in a long and fascinating history of adventuring, double-dealing, political corruption and short-termism set against the efforts of visionary engineers and prophets. Beyond that, a story told with cracking momentum. And great respect for the charms of our lost and culverted rivers'   – *Iain Sinclair*

'*The Mercenary River* is a gruesome yet fascinating tale of how London came to be supplied with water'   – *Adrian Tinniswood, Daily Telegraph*

Nick Higham is a journalist who has always been passionate about history. He spent 15 years as the BBC's arts and media correspondent, then a further 15 years there as a generalist, whenever possible smuggling history onto the air under the guise of news. Nick also presented 'Meet the Author' on the BBC News Channel for many years. He lives in London.

THE
MERCENARY
RIVER

Private Greed, Public Good:
A History of London's Water

NICK HIGHAM

HEADLINE

First published in 2022 by
HEADLINE PUBLISHING GROUP

First published in paperback in 2023 by
HEADLINE PUBLISHING GROUP

1

Cataloguing in Publication Data is available from the British Library

ISBN 978 1 4722 8386 3

Offset in 11.5/14pt Baskerville MT Pro by Jouve (UK), Milton Keynes

Printed and bound in Great Britain by Clays Ltd, Elcograf S.p.A.

Headline's policy is to use papers that are natural, renewable and recyclable
products and made from wood grown in well-managed forests and other
controlled sources. The logging and manufacturing processes are expected
to conform to the environmental regulations of the country of origin.

HEADLINE PUBLISHING GROUP
An Hachette UK Company
Carmelite House
50 Victoria Embankment
London EC4Y 0DZ

www.headline.co.uk
www.hachette.co.uk

Contents

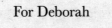
For Deborah

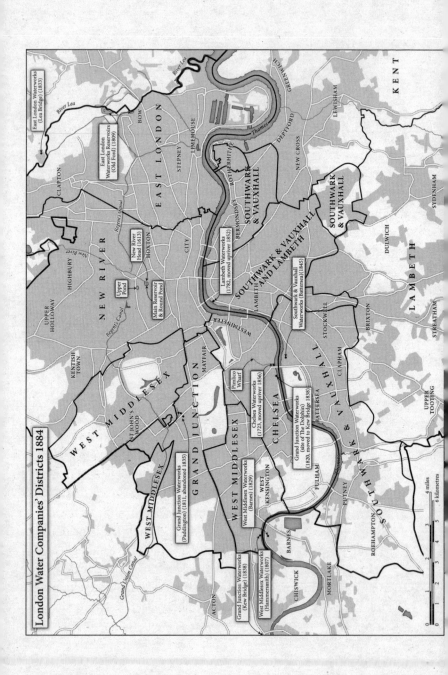

London Water Companies' Districts 1884

East London Waterworks (Lea Bridge) (1833)

East London Waterworks Reservoirs (Old Pond) (1809)

River Lea

River Lea

River Lee

Thames

BOW

LIMEHOUSE

STEPNEY

EAST LONDON

CLAPTON

Regent's Canal

GREENWICH

DEPTFORD

ROTHERHITHE

BERMONDSEY

NEW CROSS

LEWISHAM

KENT

SYDENHAM

New River

New River Head (1613)

HOXTON

CITY

HIGHBURY

NEW RIVER

Upper Pond

Main Reservoir & Round Pond

Regent's Canal

SOUTHWARK & VAUXHALL

SOUTHWARK & VAUXHALL

SOUTHWARK & VAUXHALL

DULWICH

LAMBETH

Lambeth Waterworks (1782, moved upriver 1852)

SOUTHWARK & VAUXHALL AND LAMBETH

LAMBETH (1845)

Southwark & Vauxhall Waterworks (Battersea) (1845)

STOCKWELL

BRIXTON

STREATHAM

UPPER HOLLOWAY

WESTMINSTER

KENTISH TOWN

ST JOHN'S WOOD

WEST MIDDLESEX

GRAND JUNCTION

MAYFAIR

Pimlico Wharf

Chelsea Waterworks (1723, moved upriver 1856)

CHELSEA

Grand Junction Waterworks (site of The Dolphin) (1820, moved to Kew Bridge 1838)

BATTERSEA

CLAPHAM

SOUTHWARK & VAUXHALL

UPPER TOOTING

Grand Junction Waterworks (Paddington) (1811, abandoned 1835)

WEST MIDDLESEX

West Middlesex Waterworks (Barnes) (1829)

WEST KENSINGTON

FULHAM

PUTNEY

WEST MIDDLESEX

Grand Junction Waterworks (Kew Bridge) (1838)

West Middlesex Waterworks (Hammersmith) (1807)

ACTON

Grand Union Canal

BARNES

CHISWICK

MORTLAKE

ROEHAMPTON

SOUTHWARK & VAUXHALL

0 1 2 3 4 miles
0 1 2 3 4 5 6 Kilometres

A Note on Style and Sources

This is a book for the general reader not the specialist historian. In quoting historical documents from the late eighteenth century onwards, I have modernised spelling, punctuation and the use of capitals to improve under-standing. I have used City (i.e. with a capital C) to refer to the City of London and its institutions; the city (all lower case), however, refers to the wider metropolitan area. I prefer the River Lea to Lee.

I have tried to keep endnotes and references to a minimum. So while, as a general rule, I have aimed to give the source of all substantial quotations and of detailed information that might otherwise be hard to find, and I have also referenced information from archive documents or contemporary publications, I have attempted to do so without overburdening the text. Documents in the London Metropolitan Archives are indicated by the letters LMA. Where I refer to pictures that are available online, I have given a website address. And I have indicated the principal secondary sources for each chapter as I have gone along.

In quoting from books and articles, I have made exten-sive use of online resources, such as the Wellcome Collection and Project Gutenberg. Page numbers cited refer to the original printed source, not to the online version, where they differ.

In citing weights and measures, I have used those current at the time. Supplying the metric equivalent on every occasion would clog the text hopelessly. A gallon in the UK is roughly equivalent to 4.5 litres, a mile to 1.6 kilometres, a yard to 0.9 metres and an inch to 2.5 centimetres. There are 12 inches to a foot, three feet to a yard and 1,760 yards to a mile. Other measures (such as rods) I have explained in the text. The bushel and the chaldron (which were not standard measures), however, require dedicated footnotes to elucidate.

I have not attempted to convert prices and costs to modern values. All historians agree, and it is true, that it is extremely difficult to make meaningful comparisons, because wages, prices, the purchasing power of money – and what there was to purchase – changed so radically over time, but I have occasionally indicated what a particular sum might have felt like to contemporaries. In pre-decimal days, there were 12 old pence to a shilling and 20 shillings to a pound and I have adopted the abbreviations common in the nineteenth century, i.e. £12 4s 7d. A guinea was £1 1s.

Introduction

On the morning of Monday, 15 January 1877, the residents of the Thames-side town of Richmond woke to find they had no water.

Failures of the water supply were not unknown in Victorian London: mains burst, pumping engines broke down. But this was different. This was planned. One of London's eight private water companies had deliberately decided to stop supplying an entire town with piped water.

The deed was done secretly, at night: the company's chief engineer went round the neighbourhood disconnecting the mains, accompanied by men with pickaxes. He acted even though he and the company's directors knew the households they were cutting off had no alternative source of water, nor would they have for many weeks and perhaps months.[1]

It was an act of ruthless self-interest, even vindictiveness, on the company's part, displaying (to our modern sensibility) grotesque disregard for the welfare of customers. The people of Richmond were left without water to cook with or wash with or drink.

The company was the Southwark & Vauxhall Waterworks, and its action was the culmination of a long-running feud with the local authority in the town, known as the vestry.* Richmond's vestry wanted to replace the company's water supply with one of its own, thus threatening to deprive the company of revenue.

Few episodes in the history of London's water supply crystallised more clearly the conflict that lay at the heart of the water business for three centuries – and which, after an eighty-five-year interregnum, during which the supply was in public hands, re-emerged in the 1990s. On the one hand stood the consumers and the public at large, who needed and expected a reliable supply of clean, affordable water. On the other were the shareholders and investors in private water companies – on whom the metropolis depended for the complex and expensive infrastructure that brought the water to their customers, but whose interest lay in keeping costs as low and profits as high as possible. By 1877 debates about how to resolve this conflict had been raging for three-quarters of a century – and would only be resolved at the start of the next century.

This book tells the story of that conflict and what led up to it. It focuses on the drama and scandals that arose when the interests of capitalists and the public clashed, and on the running battle fought by the companies throughout the nineteenth century with campaigners and legislators, who believed the water companies owed a duty to the public as well as to their shareholders. (Though by no means did all legislators agree – the ones with water company shares often took a contrary view.)

---

* Vestries were so called because they originated as assemblies of property owners who met to manage local affairs in the vestry of the parish church. They were the forerunners of district and borough councils.

It is also the history, from the medieval period onwards, of an increasingly sophisticated and pioneering industry. The challenge of supplying clean(ish) water to the world's fastest-growing city, Europe's first modern metropolis, taxed governments, administrators, engineers, scientists and businessmen alike. It prompted impressive technological innovation: London's water industry was among the first to introduce iron mains, after the engineer Thomas Simpson had found a way to stop them leaking; it pioneered new techniques for cleansing and purifying water, such as the slow sand filters introduced by Simpson's son, James, also an engineer, which are still used, uniquely among cities in the developed world, to purify two-thirds of London's water; and it was at the forefront of the Industrial Revolution, as an important market for the latest steam-powered technology which drove its pumps.

There were organisational innovations too, which if anything were even more revolutionary. London water companies invented the concept of the networked utility: the city was probably the first place in the world to turn piped water supply to the home into a profit-making business. One of the world's first modern business corporations was a London water company, and the story of London's water is also the story of the way the modern public company evolved – that flawed engine of growth, employment and consumption, without which it seems the developed economies of the modern world cannot function.

It also produced one of the world's first organised consumer movements: by modern standards, the supply with which Londoners struggled to keep themselves washed and watered in the eighteenth and early nineteenth centuries was absurdly inadequate, dirty and malodorous, not to mention costly. Consumer fury reached a peak when the companies, which up until then had competed to supply the capital, reached a series of secret agreements – between 1815 and 1817, north of the Thames, and in 1843, south of the river – and carved up the territory between them, raising prices as they did so. The resulting cartel or oligopoly remained in existence until the companies were taken over by the Metropolitan Water Board in 1904.

This is also a book about our changing relationship with water, and the way we use it. For much of human history, and in London well into the nineteenth century, water had to be rationed and stored at the point of use in tanks and other receptacles, which all too often became dirty and polluted. It was the cause of much heavy labour, most of it undertaken by women, and involved a great deal of fetching and carrying, whether for washing, cooking or doing the laundry. The poor suffered most, forced to rely on polluted parish pumps or on standpipes in courts and alleys for grossly inadequate supplies.

And then there was the problem of getting rid of the stuff. When water became available in increased quantities, and especially after the introduction of flushing water closets which rapidly overwhelmed traditional cesspits, the city faced both a public health crisis and a political challenge that was only resolved by the creation of London's first, albeit imperfect, city-wide local authority and by the reluctant intervention of central government.

The man generally credited with solving London's sewage problem is Joseph Bazalgette, who, as chief engineer of the Metropolitan Board of Works, designed and built the system of intercepting sewers that kept human filth out of the River Thames in central London and diverted it downstream. He is justly celebrated as one of London's heroes. But this book also identifies some of the other men whose foresight and energy had equally far-reaching impacts on the city, but whose contributions are much less well-known. Among them are a Jacobean goldsmith and an early Victorian engineer.

The goldsmith, Hugh Myddelton, built the New River, which is neither new nor a river but a man-made canal snaking south out of Hertfordshire; more than 400 years after its completion it still supplies around ten per cent of London's drinking water each day.

The engineer, James Simpson, did not wait to be told that the river water his employers supplied was dirty and not truly fit for human consumption, but, on his own initiative, took two bold steps to address the problem. In 1829 he introduced his slow sand filter. And, in the 1840s, he persuaded the directors of the Lambeth Waterworks to move their intake from the polluted tidal Thames to Seething Wells, upstream from Teddington Lock and beyond the reach of the tide, in search of cleaner water. In 1852 legislation required all the London water companies to follow suit: Simpson, unprompted, had shown the way.

*

London is a city of rivers. Many – such as the Effra, the Fleet, the Tyburn – have been 'lost', covered over and converted long ago into sewers. Another, the Lea, figures significantly in this story as a frequently compromised source of drinking water. But even the nineteenth century pollution of the Lea was as nothing compared with the condition of the Thames before 1860: at the heart of the city's life for centuries, the Thames was taken for granted, exploited and abused. Yet astonishingly it survived and recovered, thanks to government intervention, and still today supplies the bulk of the capital's water.

Journalists often like to describe some little-known fact they have stumbled across as a 'well-kept secret'. I used to be a journalist and I am tempted to use the phrase myself. But, in truth, there is nothing secret about London's water history: it's just that it is too often overlooked and under-appreciated. This book is the first comprehensive modern attempt to tell the whole story – to explain what happened, and why it mattered then and still matters today.

*

Some of London's water history is still visible, scattered across the capital. There are reservoirs, built to store the water long enough for the muck it contained to sink to the bottom, and to ensure there were supplies on hand during periodic droughts. There are pumping stations, which sucked water out of the Thames and Lea and from deep wells, using steam engines of formidable power, and then forced it under pressure into the mains, through which it flowed into customers' homes. And there are filter beds, man-made ponds designed to strain water through sand and gravel and biologically purify it.

Many of the early filters and reservoirs have disappeared, their value as essential infrastructure outweighed by their value as building land. But a few of the old places are still in use, still serving their original function, and others sur-vive repurposed as wildlife sanctuaries and boating lakes.

Many of the pumping stations have also survived, some housing compact modern pumps that are dwarfed by the cavernous spaces originally built to house massive steam engines; others have been converted to homes, businesses or visitor centres. Often they are fine buildings in their own right: the Victorians in particular knew how to make industrial buildings that were beautiful as well as functional. A handful, such as the former pumping station at Kew Bridge, which is home to the London Museum of Water and Steam, accommodate restored steam engines, mysterious but potent assemblies of iron and brass and steel, fired up from time to time by men of a certain age in boiler suits. Though large, their movements are precise, even delicate; though powerful, they are surprisingly quiet (the engines, that is – though the men don't tend to say much either).

I began the research for this book by exploring the New River, which nowadays ends at two reservoirs near my home in Stoke Newington, but originally went as far south as New River Head on the borders of Islington and Clerkenwell next to Sadler's Wells Theatre. The name Clerkenwell recalls the Clerks' Well, which was an earlier component of London's water supply; Sadler's Wells commemorates another historic water feature. The story of London's water shaped not just the city's physical appearance but also the names we give it.

The New River's original length was over forty miles, as it hugged the 100-foot contour to the west of the River Lea. Today its extravagant meanders have been straightened out, after four centuries of tunnelling and embanking, rerouting and general meddling. It runs through London's sprawling northern outskirts, sometimes like a knife cut into its thick suburban crust, sometimes rather as if G. K. Chesterton's rolling English drunkard had switched his efforts from road-making to canal cutting.[2] It takes you past residential suburbs and shopping centres, trading estates and schools: most of the way you can follow a path provided by Thames Water.

There are ducks and swans and moorhens to watch, back gardens to peer into, long stretches of urban drabness interspersed with woodland and fields of grazing horses. You might see a kingfisher, or a rat. Sometimes the walk takes you above the surrounding houses; even on flat ground there is a perceptible raised bank on the eastern (downhill) side, which prevents the water making a break for freedom and the Lea.

The river ceased to run south of Stoke Newington in 1946. From there to New River Head it is merely a ghostly presence on the map. Its course must be imagined from surviving hints and fragments: an embankment and a dog-leg of open water in Clissold Park; a strip of allotments; wide grass walks in Petherton Road and in Colebrook Row. In New River Walk it has become a narrow ornamental park guarded by a heron, a cordon sanitaire keeping the imposing Victorian villas of Canonbury apart from Islington council's Marquess Estate.

Travelling north, the river might offer a palimpsest of London's development, a cross-section through the city's history – except that London doesn't work like that. Where you might expect an orderly succession of historical developments like geological strata, instead you get constant anachronisms, the remains of ancient villages subsumed by the urban sprawl, fossils in the city's timeline.

North of Enfield, London ought by rights to end and farmland begin. Instead the city stretches a long tentacle out into the deep countryside, following the course of the

Lea and the A10 and the railway to Hertford and Harlow. For part of the way, the New River marks this built-up area's western boundary. Then, beyond Broxbourne, it drifts east, close to the course of the Lea.

To find its source, take the slow train (there are no fast ones) from Liverpool Street to Hertford East, an implausibly imposing terminus at the end of a humdrum commuter route. From there you can walk along the Lea Navigation downstream towards Ware. A thousand yards along the towpath, surrounded by water meadows, is the New Gauge. A four-square, two-storey brick building, it has an inlet beneath the towpath and an outlet at the back. Inside is a contraption to regulate the flow. Through this portal, constructed in 1856, gushes a maximum of 22.5 million gallons of water a day. To all intents and purposes the New River originates here, as a kind of reverse tributary of the Lea, and it has been taking water from the Lea since Hugh Myddelton's time.

But, as originally conceived, the river began not at the Lea but at the springs of Amwell and Chadwell. Great Amwell, three miles downstream from New Gauge, has a street of old houses, a good pub and a characterful church, and below them an island in the New River adorned with classical statuary. The spring here has long since dried up. But Chadwell still functions. Up until a few years ago it was possible to stroll across the meadows from the Lea and stand beside the spring, tucked under a low escarpment next to the graffiti-scarred concrete viaduct that carries the A10 over the river. The valley is filled with the noise of traffic.

Today the spring is fenced off. But you can still look down on a waterscape of ditches and disused gravel pits with the Lea in the distance. In the foreground is a circular pool, and a channel flowing sinuously east and curving out of sight beyond a thicket. Here, where the scrappy edgelands of Hertford merge into the greater edgelands of Greater London, is the New River's original source. And here, like the water bubbling up from the chalk aquifer, the modern history of London's water really began.

1

Conduits and Cobs

William Campion makes only one appearance in the
pages of history, but it is a memorable one. The unlucky –
or villainous, or perhaps just thirsty – Campion lived in
Fleet Street and, in the chilly month of November 1478,
was convicted by the Lord Mayor and Aldermen of stealing water. He had surreptitiously tapped the public conduit
near his house and diverted part of the flow to his own
use, thereby depriving his neighbours.

The word 'conduit' in medieval London described two
different but related things. One was a pipe that carried
water into the City from springs outside the walls; the
other was the building, also known as a conduit house, at
which the pipe terminated and from which residents could
collect water free of charge for household use. Campion
may have tapped the pipe itself, or he may have found a
way to siphon water from the nearest conduit house at the
corner of Fleet Street and Showe Lane.

His punishment was public, uncomfortable and apt.
After a spell in gaol, he was brought out and 'being set upon
a horse, a vessel like unto a conduit [house] was placed
upon his head, and kept filled with water, which ran down
his person from small holes made for the purpose'. In this
condition he was paraded round the City and his offence

proclaimed as a warning to others. At the end of the circuit he was returned to gaol, presumably humiliated and unquestionably cold and damp.[1]*

Few things reveal more clearly the gulf that separates you, dear reader, from your medieval ancestors than your attitude to water. You work on the comfortable assumption that clean, potable water is always available, readily heated, and equally readily disposed of: your daily life depends on it. Perhaps before sitting down to read this chapter you put the kettle on for a cup of tea, filling it by the simple act of turning a tap. Perhaps you started today with a shower. Perhaps you're looking forward to ending it with a soak in a hot bath. No doubt you have used a lavatory – though you may call it a toilet or loo or WC or john or one of a score of other euphemisms – and then flushed your waste away with the contents of a cistern that will rapidly and automatically refill itself. Quite possibly you have a dishwasher – and you almost certainly have access to a washing machine.

There is a cost to this, but it is a financial and an environmental one: in the modern developed world, water involves us in little physical labour. This is not true in much of the global south, where water – not always clean – must still be fetched from common wells or standpipes and carried home, nor in places where population growth combined with climate change, mismanagement and geopolitical tensions has created water shortages. But in most

---

* Campion's punishment could have been worse: in 1262 in Siena, a woman accused of deliberately poisoning the fountains was flayed alive and burned (Roberta J. Magnusson, *Water Technology in the Middle Ages*, p. 160).

of Europe and North America, we have forgotten what it is to have to work for our water.

In medieval London water was a scarce resource of questionable cleanliness and purity. It was used sparingly because there was barely enough to go round, and it had to be fetched and carried – either from a private well in the backyard or from some more distant source – and then put on a fire to heat. Water is unforgiving stuff, inconveniently heavy and using it in quantities is laborious and fatiguing.

As a result, patterns of medieval water use were very different from today's. Plenty of water was of course drunk, but mostly indirectly, as ale or beer; only the desperate drank water neat, because the only water available was usually tainted. Commercial brewers were among the heaviest industrial users of water, though a lot of brewing also went on in the home. Water was used in large quantities by butchers and fishmongers, and in larger quantities still by tanners and dyers. It was given to the animals who powered the city and its transport. But it was not used for flushing human waste away – solids went mainly into cesspits, which had to be periodically emptied, while pots of urine were sometimes tipped into the open drain, or 'kennel', that ran down the middle of the street.

Many people without their own well got their water by dipping a bucket in the Thames – we know this because the City's records show that they periodically drowned in the process, and because the owners of wharves and stairs beside the river had to be stopped from charging people for access. The river was clean enough for salmon, which only disappeared in the early nineteenth century, but the water was still of questionable quality: for every ordinance forbidding people from throwing rubbish into the river there was another instructing butchers, for instance, to load their offal into boats and dump it midstream. And the river was tidal, so fresh water coming downstream mingled at certain states of the tide with salt seawater coming up: during a bad drought in 1325–6, when the fresh water flow was much reduced, people complained that their ale tasted salty.

Conduit city

The conduits were the medieval city's response to its perennial water shortage. One of London's earliest historians, William Fitzstephen, writing in the late 1100s, praised the 'sweet, wholesome and clear springs' on the city's northern outskirts, and described their water rippling brightly over the pebbles.[2] But these natural springs on the city's fringe produced nowhere near enough water, so the conduits were constructed from the thirteenth century onwards: the earliest, the Great Conduit, was begun in 1236, when royal letters patent were issued, allowing the city to tap springs next to the river Tyburn, near the modern Bond Street tube station. The springs were a gift from Gilbert de Sandford, and the water was to be 'for the profit of the city and the good of the whole realm thither repairing: to wit, for the poor to drink, and the rich to dress their meat.'[3]

A reservoir was built to provide a 'head', i.e. sufficient pressure to force water through a pipe. The modern South Molton Street may mark the start of the pipe's route. From there it may have run due south towards Buckingham Palace and then east to Charing Cross, or (accounts vary) in a south-easterly direction past today's Conduit Street.

Either way, it then went along Fleet Street and up past Newgate to a rectangular conduit house in Cheapside, the city's principal shopping street. Since the conduit flowed downhill as far as the River Fleet and then up Ludgate Hill, it's clear the medieval engineers understood the principle of the inverted siphon, which dictates that a liquid that fills a pipe will re-emerge at or just below the level at which it enters it, even if the pipe dips in between (the commonest form of inverted siphon in our world is the ubiquitous plumber's U-bend).

Part of the conduit house still exists, a hidden relic of the medieval city. It rested on an arched stone undercroft, which was rediscovered in 1899, and rediscovered again and excavated in 1994: it lies beneath a manhole cover carrying the City of London's crest and a commemorative inscription.

Later a second outlet, known as the Little Conduit, was erected along the route of the pipe in West Cheap, just north of St Paul's, and the system was extended to other locations around the city. A map of 1585 shows a gothic structure labelled 'ye lytle cundit', surrounded by 'tankards' for distributing water resting on the ground, waiting to be filled: made of wooden staves hooped with iron, the tankards look like enormous water jugs with wide flat bottoms and narrow mouths and each held three gallons.[4]

As the number of conduit houses increased (eventually there were sixteen, many in the middle of the narrow streets where they obstructed the traffic), the flow became weaker and new sources were pressed into service, initially at Tyburn, later at Paddington, where the springs were leased from Westminster Abbey for an annual rent of 2lb of pepper. More springs were tapped in Finsbury and

Highgate, in Hackney and Dalston. One conduit house was constructed at the bottom of Snow Hill, next to the bridge where Holborn crossed the River Fleet; it was rebuilt in 1577 by a gentleman called William Lambe, and the water came from springs in Bloomsbury, near what is now Lamb's Conduit Street.*

Another much older conduit ran parallel to Lamb's. It was called the White Conduit, from the chalk used to construct it, and served the Greyfriars in Newgate rather than the general public. One of its sources was known as the Chimney Conduit after the open shaft or chimney that rose up next to the arched roof of the collecting tank. It was still in place behind 20 Queen's Square in Bloomsbury in 1910, when an antiquary exploring it fell in and was obliged to swim. But two years later it was dismantled and, in 1924, was re-erected in the grounds of the Metropolitan Water Board's headquarters at New River Head. The MWB building has now been converted to upmarket flats, but the old structure is still there in the communal garden, complete with its shaft or chimney, squatting like a miniature church among the residents' sun-loungers.

Another white conduit, also private, supplied the Charterhouse on the city's northern fringe from springs in the modern White Conduit Street, now a scruffy little road between a Sainsbury's carpark and Islington's Chapel Market. The Charterhouse supply was constructed in 1430

---

* You can still see a functioning medieval water conduit in the market place at Wells in Somerset, fed from springs in the grounds of the Bishop's Palace – a town meeting point and a vital artery, now reduced to a picturesque tourist attraction.

and a plan of it – the oldest surviving plan of any London building – was drawn up between 1442 and 1457: the document's existence testifies to the cost and complexity of the system, which must have needed frequent maintenance. Hydraulic engineering was among the more sophisticated technologies available to medieval Europeans, and this is a user's manual: it shows the pipes in schematic form – including the point at which they intersect with a similar conduit taking water to St John's Priory. Today the Charterhouse is one of the most atmospheric historic spaces in London. The greater part of the original monastery disappeared when the site was rebuilt as a mansion in Elizabethan times, but one side of the cloister survives, complete with the doorway to one of the monks' two-storey cells and the hatch next to it through which food was delivered. The main water pipe led to a conduit house in the middle of the cloister from which subsidiary pipes fanned out to give each monk his own supply from a tap in his cell's back garden.

The public conduit houses were neighbourhood centres, places for exchanging gossip and news: the 'water-coolers' of their day. The poor could fetch water themselves, the wealthier could send their servants or wait to buy it from one of the water carriers who hawked it round the streets in the aforementioned tankards or in horse-drawn water carts. The carriers, also known as tankard-bearers, had a guild, the Fraternity of St Christopher, but they sound a rough lot. At one stage in 1541, the Lord Mayor banned them from carrying clubs and staves because of the fights that broke out over who was first in the queue at the conduit. In 1569, they were described by the City chamberlain as men 'of the greatest disorder, simplest of discretion and most troublesome.'[5]* Nor did they make much money. The water bearer who appears in Ben Jonson's *Every Man In His Humour*, Oliver Cob, is a gobby stage clown and stereotypical cockney who engages in backchat with the posher characters and exits after his first scene with the cheery line: 'Helter skelter, hang sorrow, care will kill a cat, uptails all, and a pox on the hangman.' But he lives in a mean house, and another character describes him disparagingly as 'a tankard-bearer, a thread-bare rascal, a beggar, a slave that never drunk out of better than piss-pot metal in his life'. He is last seen beating his wife. Later writers often claim 'cob' was a generic term for a water carrier, but there seems to be no evidence for this before Jonson's play: was Oliver called Cob because he was a cob; or were cobs later called cobs because of Oliver?[6]

Remarkably, the conduits were a public service and the water was free: the expense of building and maintaining them was born by the City Corporation or by benefactors anxious to save their souls with good works. They were

---

* A much-reproduced image purporting to show a London water carrier with two barrels hanging from a yoke across his back may be misleading. It appeared in Marcellus Laroon's *Cries of London* in 1687. But all written references to London water carriers speak of tankards carried on one shoulder. Laroon is said to have sketched his likenesses from life, but he was of Dutch origin and you wonder if, in this case, he slipped in a picture he'd made of some water carrier in the Netherlands. If he did, then his London readers weren't fazed: Pepys, who owned a copy of the book and annotated eighteen of the images with the names of the original street personalities, made no comment on this one. Ted Flaxman and Ted Jackson, in an appendix to *Sweet & Wholesome Water*, call the picture 'an unexplained puzzle'.

kept in repair and locked up at night by officials appointed
by the City: a ten-year experiment in contracting out
the management of the Great Conduit in 1367 was not
repeated. The development of this civic water supply was
an impressive achievement of London's medieval city
government.

But the system suffered from considerable strain and
the strains grew harder to contain as the city grew. Between
1500 and 1600 the population increased at least four-fold,
from around 50,000 to around 200,000. What had once
been an insignificant backwater in the stream of European
history had become one of its largest urban centres, on a
par with Paris and Naples.

Keeping it clean

The ways in which people used water also changed, meaning they needed more of it. Medieval Londoners lived a
dry life: they cooked and heated their homes with wood
fires, and every aspect of their existence must have been
perfumed by the smell of wood smoke, but their living
spaces could be kept clean with nothing more elaborate
than a brush. By the 1570s population growth had made
firewood in London enormously expensive: more people
meant there was a demand for more fuel and it needed to
be brought from further away.

This crisis in the supply of firewood paralleled the similar crisis in the water supply and occurred at roughly the
same time. London had outgrown the capacity of its
immediate neighbourhood to support it. The solution in
the case of water was, as we shall see, to find new sources

further from the city and to apply new technology to the exploitation of an existing source, the Thames. In the case of firewood, the solution was enormous quantities of a replacement fuel, 'sea coal', brought down the North Sea coast from the coalfields around Newcastle. Londoners had been burning coal at least since the thirteenth century, but in modest amounts. Despite periodic attempts to limit coal burning, on account of the smoke it produced, or even to ban its import to the city, by 1610 Parliament was describing it as the 'ordinary and necessary fuel' of the city, and so it remained.[7]

In time London became synonymous with coal-burning, the only major European capital of which this was true, but one drawback of the new fuel was that the greasy soot and smuts that coal fires produced made everything filthy. For the first time water was needed to wash down walls and floors in interior spaces, and the mop and the flannel joined the brush, broom and besom in the housewife's armoury. The diarist John Evelyn, in 1661, complained that coal smoke was 'superinducing a sooty Crust or Furr upon all that it lights, spoyling the moveables, tarnishing the Plate, Gildings and Furniture, and corroding the very Iron-bars and hardest stones with those piercing and acrimonious Spirits which accompany its Sulphure.'[8] An eighteenth century Swiss traveller was struck by the fact that affluent Londoners had their houses washed 'from top to bottom' twice a week, and kitchens, staircases and entrances every morning: coal made that essential.*

---

* The Swiss visitor was impressed with the sophistication of London's water supply and by its abundance, but struck by some of the ways Londoners used it. 'Absolutely none of it is drunk,' he wrote.

Coal also helped transform the way food was cooked: more water was required in the kitchen. Sticky pottages and risotto-like frumenty, made from grains with the odd vegetable or bit of meat, were staples of medieval cookery. The simplest of these dishes – such as pease pottage, made with dried peas – were cheap food for the poor; the more elaborate were unquestionably elite concoctions, full of rare and expensive ingredients. This kind of cookery worked well with wood fires that burned fiercely for a while to bring the pot to the boil and then subsided leaving the contents to simmer and absorb relatively modest amounts of water slowly. But coal burned hotter for longer, and food like this would need constant stirring to prevent it sticking and burning. So it was gradually replaced by less labour-intensive dishes that could be left to cook in the long, rolling boil of a pot on a coal fire or cast-iron range. Which, arguably, was how the likes of steamed puddings and boiled vegetables became synonymous with British cuisine.

One thing that water was not much used for in medieval and early modern London was washing people, other than their hands and faces. Opinions vary as to whether that meant people smelled bad; much depended on how often their linen underclothes were washed.

There were (a few) baths. Some royal palaces were fitted with wooden tubs, and there were public 'stews' modelled on Turkish baths, supposedly introduced by returning crusaders. Many were owned by William Walworth, Richard II's Lord Mayor of London, in

_____

(cont.) 'The lower classes, even the paupers, do not know what it is to quench their thirst with water.' (Hugh Barty-King, *Water – The Book*, p. 69).

Southwark and on Bankside, but in due course they were shut down for immorality, and by Shakespeare's time 'stew' and 'bagnio', the Italian for bath, had become synonymous with 'brothel'.

The standard view used to be that, in the words of one historian writing in the 1960s, 'With the sixteenth century England went into a dirty decline'.[9] And it is not hard to find evidence to support that contention. Tudor and early Stuart writers advised against washing the body, on the grounds that it opened the pores and left the skin dangerously vulnerable to invasion by 'venomous ayre' that might 'infecte the bloode'.[10] Elizabeth I was said to take baths despite this injunction – but only once a month and 'whether she need it or no'. Samuel Pepys's diary makes just one mention in nine years of his wife taking a bath, when she went 'with her woman to the hot house to bathe herself, after her long being within doors in the dirt, so that she now pretends to a resolution of being hereafter very clean. How long it will hold I can guess.'[11] A few days later his wife banned Pepys himself from the marital bed until he had 'cleaned himself with warm water': perhaps he'd made the mistake of telling her what he thought of her bathing and she was getting her revenge?[12]

But more recently the view that everybody must have smelled bad because they washed themselves so rarely has been challenged. The social historian Ruth Goodman, who specialises in recreating the living and working environments of the past on television, argues that people may not have washed their bodies but they did wash their linen, which absorbed sweat and dirt and so helped to keep unpleasant body odours at bay. She quotes the seventeenth-century self-styled Water Poet, John Taylor, who combined versifying with his trade as a Thames waterman. His poem, 'In Praise of Cleane Linen', was dedicated to the laundress Mrs Martha Legge, who washed the clothes of the young men studying at the Middle Temple:

> Remember that your laundress paines is great,
> When labours only keep you sweet and neat . . .
> By her thy linnen's sweet and clenely drest,
> Else thou would'st stink above ground like a beast.[13]

And the irrepressible Goodman has tried living like an unwashed denizen of the sixteenth and seventeenth centuries herself, twice, on one occasion going without a bath or shower for three months but changing her linen smock and hose daily. Nobody noticed, she maintains, and she remained smell-free – 'even my feet'. On the second occasion she spent six months living and working on a 'Tudor' farm for a television series, changing her woollen hose just three times in that period and her linen smock once a week – a regime presumably more typical of the average working Londoner. She was doing hard physical work and concedes there was 'a slight smell', but that her colleagues, including the camera crew, did not find it offensive. And in any case it was masked by the odour of wood smoke.[14]

Water pressures

By the Tudor period, nothing could disguise the fact that London as a whole was running out of water: there was never quite enough to go round. The records are full of complaints about the quantities being taken by brewers and fishmongers, even after those wanting water for purposes of trade were made to pay a fee. And sometimes the conduits failed, because of drought or thanks to human intervention. In December 1560 two men were whipped for stealing lead pipes: the theft meant all but one of London's conduits had had no water on 30 November. The elaborate sentence handed down to William Campion is evidence of how serious an offence it was to misuse water in this environment.

Campion, as we saw, had broken the law, but there were others who enjoyed a private water supply from the public conduits who were effectively above the law. Many city mansions and the riverside palaces of aristocrats along the Strand seem to have had their own 'quills' – so called because the branch pipe from the conduit was meant to be no wider than a goose's quill. Status counted for a lot in medieval and early modern London and it could be hard to resist a request from the powerful, whether for a privileged supply of water or anything else. But it's a measure of how severe London's water crisis had become that, by the early 1600s, the Lord Mayor was turning down requests from aristocrats for quills: Lord Cobham and Lord Fenton were told that the conduit supply was inadequate to meet the needs of the city's wider populace. Even the widow of the Earl of Essex got short shrift in 1601: the mayor refused to let her keep her quill because he said Essex House had been wasting the better-quality conduit water, using it not just for cooking but for doing the laundry and in the stable, in place of well water or river water. (He may of course have been emboldened by the fact that her husband had just been executed for treason.)

Things got so bad that, in about 1621, the water carriers presented a petition to Parliament, pointing out that it was against the law to divert any of the flow in the conduits for private purposes and complaining about 'private branches and cockes' leaving too little water for everyone else. And the cobs named names. Not for the last time the public interest of Londoners at large was being weighed against that of private individuals, such as Lady Swinnerton, who, the petition alleged, was allowed two gallons an hour from the conduit (which was regrettable enough), but had a pipe so large that it yielded more than thirteen gallons an hour, most of which ran to waste. The quantities of water involved are minuscule by modern standards: two gallons is roughly half the amount a modern garden tap delivers in a single minute.[15]

The pressures increased as the available water sources became increasingly polluted. In the sixteenth century the River Fleet, which joined the Thames at Blackfriars, had become a notorious repository for the noxious effluvia of tanneries, slaughterhouses and Smithfield livestock market, along with domestic privies. In 1589 the City spent a thousand marks diverting the springs on Hampstead Heath into the Fleet in an effort to clean and scour the channel: it had no effect. In 1612 Ben Jonson likened the Fleet to the River Styx, which the dead must cross en route to hell. He imagined two men trying to row up to Holborn in a waterman's wherry, past floating turds, dead cats, overhanging privies and all-encompassing stench:

> Row close then slaves. Alas, they will beshite us.
> No matter, stinkards, row. What croaking sound
> Is this we heare? Of frogs? No, guts wind-bound,
> Over your heads: Well, row . . . [16]

The lines come from a mock-heroic satire called 'On the Famous Voyage', 196 lines of classical allusion and vigorous toilet humour, an epic of disgust.

By Jonson's day Fitzstephen's sweet, wholesome and clear water rippling brightly over the pebbles had become almost irretrievably contaminated and fouled. Nor was the rest of London much cleaner or sweet-smelling. The typical Londoner lived in a four-room house on a cramped irregular site. From the 1570s onwards, all houses were supposed to have their own privy (also known as a house of office, house of easement or boghouse) and a stone-lined cesspit; the privy was usually at the end of the garden or yard if the house had one, or upstairs in a garret, where it connected with the cesspit via a lead funnel. Every alley was meant to have at least two privies, and there were also communal houses of easement – including one at the Vintry, endowed by Dick Whittington with 128 seats, and another with eighty seats at Queenhithe.

Until they were emptied these cesspits must have smelt strongly. And there was none of the rigorous separation of people and their waste to which we are accustomed today. In October 1660 Samuel Pepys reported an unpleasant discovery in his basement: 'I put my foot into a great heap of turds, by which I find that Mr Turners house of office is full and comes into my cellar, which doth trouble me.'[17]

Privately enterprising

The answer to the water shortage turned out to be a species of privatisation, in effect licensing entrepreneurial individuals to invest in water infrastructure, in theory at their own expense. Unlike their medieval predecessors, they hoped not for rewards in heaven but for profit on earth, and they harnessed capital, technology and market forces in a new way.

The first major effort was called the London Bridge Waterworks. In 1581 a Dutch or German engineer called Peter Morice* began paying the City ten shillings a year on a 500-year lease to rent the northernmost arch of London Bridge. He installed a waterwheel that pumped Thames water up into a tank, from where it was distributed in a network of wooden pipes. He brought with him the latest German technology, perhaps developed in Danzig, and his pump was powerful: as proof of concept, Morice had staged a demonstration in which he succeeded in sending a jet higher than the spire of nearby St Magnus Martyr church. And he was selling a service: his customers were actively encouraged to take quills from his pipes – provided they paid.†

Before long Morice had rented a second arch and in due course his successors took more, until, by 1767, there

---

* The name also appears as Moritz, Morris, Moris, Morrys, Morryce, Moryce and Maurice: early modern spelling was not a precise science, particularly when foreign names were involved.

† The notion of water fountaining over St Magnus Martyr makes a good story, even if the top of the tower of the medieval church was a good deal lower than the steeple of Wren's replacement, built after the Great Fire. But it may not be true: John Stow says only that Morris 'conveyed Thames water in pipes of lead over the steeple of St Magnus church . . . and from thence into divers men's houses', suggesting it was in fact pumped up and over a standpipe on or at the same height as the tower (John Stow, *The Survey of London*, 1603 edition, p. 169).

were five waterwheels occupying three arches and driving sixty-four pumps, plus another wheel in an arch at the Southwark end to supply the south bank. The London Bridge Waterworks survived until the old bridge itself was demolished in 1831, though by that stage it had been taken over by its great rival, the New River Company, and was in poor shape. In 1821, shortly before the takeover, the company's superintendent, giving evidence to a House of Commons inquiry, was disarmingly honest about the shortcomings of the product his waterworks supplied. Many inhabitants of the City preferred his water to the New River Company's, he said, because it was softer (and so better for doing the laundry). But was it drinkable, he was asked. 'I never think of drinking it,' he replied.[18]

Old London Bridge was a remarkable structure, lined with overhanging shops and houses, its pillars supported by massive stone 'starlings' or piers, which channelled the river water at ferocious speed between them. It was often pictured, and many of those pictures also show the waterworks – both the waterwheels themselves and the associated buildings on the river bank. The sound of the wheels and the wooden gears driving the pumps, combined with the water rushing between the starlings, made it a famously noisy place – so noisy that the playwright John Fletcher likened the talk of angry women to the 'noise at London-bridge'.[19]

From his waterwheel at the northern end of the bridge, Morice's pipes ran through much of the City, but not all of it. Their exact whereabouts was a mystery until a comprehensive survey in the middle of the eighteenth century: only when they burst was their location likely to be revealed. They were wooden, as all water mains in London were up until the early nineteenth century. But the head of pressure from the tank atop Morice's water tower was not enough to reach the northern parts within the City walls, let alone the suburbs that had grown up beyond them to the north, east and west.

From the outset Morice had the support of the City authorities and of leading citizens, and his construction costs were subsidised. The City's Common Council and Court of Aldermen considered that his work 'would profit the whole city, and be no hindrance to the poor water-bearers, who would still have as much work as they were able to perform'. Significantly (because it helped him generate support for his scheme), Morice was offering a free supply to some of the conduit houses, in particular one called The Standard at the City's highest point, the junction of Cornhill and Grace-church Street: equally significant, the business of selling water to private customers was described as merely 'by the way'. But it was also the case that Morice and his waterworks soon found it difficult to serve both the public and his private customers. The public supply suffered as more households signed up: the flow to the Standard was said to be 'much aslaked' in 1587 and to have run dry by 1603.[20]

*

The London Bridge Waterworks could claim three firsts. For the first time someone was using a mechanical pump (or 'engine') to supply water to Londoners; they were delivering water to individual consumers via a network of pipes; and they were doing so to make money: Morice and the City's government between them had invented the networked utility.

The launch of the business on Christmas Eve 1582 was a significant moment. Morice and his contemporaries would not have recognised it, but later historians certainly did. Frederick Clifford's *A History of Private Bill Legislation* has an unpromising title but is in fact a fount of information about the history of London's water supply. Clifford was writing in 1885, when the shortcomings of London's private water companies had long been evident and numerous attempts were being made to take them into public ownership. For him, with his late Victorian faith in municipal virtue and the benefits of sanitation, Morice's venture was the moment things started to go wrong:

> Such was the rise of the first private undertaking on record which supplied water for private profit . . . The water supply of London had rested solely with the Corporation, and was undertaken by them not for the sake of revenue but as a municipal duty which devolved upon all municipal bodies anxious to promote the health and comfort of their fellow-citizens. In furthering the plans of Morice and his co-adventurers the Corporation did not foresee, and could hardly be expected to foresee, how great a power they were beginning to transfer to private hands.[21]

The London Bridge Waterworks provided a partial solution to London's water crisis, but not a complete one.

Having licensed one entrepreneur to supply water commercially (and loaned him money), the City did the same for others. In 1593 a man called Bevis Bulmer set up a waterworks with a loan from the City at Broken Wharf near the modern Millennium footbridge; it survived until the eighteenth century, but Bulmer himself went broke because he used expensive horse-power rather than a waterwheel to drive his pump. At least three other water-works also came and went around this time.

But one stayed the course. It might be more accurate to describe Morice and Bulmer's ventures as public-private partnerships, since the City's loans were never fully repaid; but the company that transformed London's water business for ever was a different kind of beast. Hugh Myddelton's New River proved to be an infinitely more successful answer to the challenge of quenching London's thirst.

2

The Purchas'd Wave

All rivers have a source, a spring from which they flow, their *fons et origo*. The New River has several. But unlike most rivers, it also has origins that can be precisely dated: its beginnings are historical as well as geographical. And it had a readily identifiable originator: a soldier from Bath by the name of Captain Edmund Colthurst.

Colthurst was evidently a man of parts. He had seen active service in Ireland, defending a castle in County Waterford against the Queen's enemies. He was philanthropic enough and rich enough to donate Bath Abbey, which stood on his land, to the city of Bath. And he was ambitious and far-sighted, with connections at court.[1]

And to him we owe a remarkable piece of infrastructure, now more than 400 years old, which still fulfils the function for which it was designed and which delivers on any given day between 8 and 12 per cent of London's water. Contemporaries were impressed by it; later generations celebrated it – though for a long time its originator missed out on the credit due to him.

At some point in the 1590s, Colthurst came up with a plan for a kind of super-conduit to supply London with water. Though his contribution to the New River was ignored or downplayed for over three centuries, it was he who identified the springs at Chadwell and Great Amwell, on the slopes to the west and south of the River Lea near Ware in Hertfordshire, as possible sources of fresh water for London. And it was Colthurst who, in 1602, petitioned Queen Elizabeth for a charter to allow him to dig a channel or 'river' from the springs to the City, and when she died before giving final approval for the project, he successfully lobbied her successor, James I.

Colthurst's charter made clear that his scheme, like Peter Morice's London Bridge Waterworks, was a hybrid. Two-thirds of his water was to be used like that of the medieval conduits for public purposes, mainly flushing the stinking city drains: 'clensinge, scoweringe and keepinge sweete divers fowle and unsavoury ditches in and about our said Citties of London and Westminster, which at this present are a very great annoyaunce . . . and cause often tymes of sicknes.' The remaining third was for private sale, 'conveyed through pipes and other passages to particuler howses and places . . . for the necessary use . . . of persons who wante water.'[2]

It was Colthurst who determined the river's route, began negotiations with landowners along the way and, crucially, started digging. By early in 1605 he'd made a channel six feet wide some three miles south from Chadwell.

And then something happened. Perhaps Colthurst ran out of funds. Perhaps the City Corporation woke up to the fact that an outsider stood to make money from a project that might instead generate revenue for its own members. Either way, work stopped, and for the next four years nothing happened on the ground while rival projectors floated alternative schemes, City grandees plotted and two acts of Parliament were passed giving the Corporation, not

Colthurst, the legal right to dig a channel, now ten feet rather than six feet wide, and to construct brick or stone vaults and raised aqueducts.

At the end of it, Colthurst found himself supplanted by Hugh Myddelton. In effect, Colthurst's project fell victim to an early example of a takeover bid and it was Myddelton who ended up with the credit.

Happily, Colthurst was not frozen out completely. He had lobbied Parliament for compensation when it was debating the act that superseded his royal charter, and it was only passed on condition that the City compensate him. In the event, the compensation came from Myddelton, to whom the City devolved its powers under the act. The deal with Colthurst, under which two-thirds of the water was supposed to be for public use, lapsed.

In granting the right to build the river to Myddelton, the City demanded nothing in return, provided he agreed to assume the entire financial risk. Not everyone was happy about this. When the project faced further difficulties in 1611 mid-way through construction, one of the objections raised was that the City had handed over its statutory powers to a private individual, 'by which means that which was intended for a public good shall be converted into a private gain.'[3]

Myddelton and his supporters had a robust response to this: 'If the maior and citizens would not adventure upon so uncertaine a worke, Mr Middleton [sic] deserveth the greater comendacion in adventuringe his monie and travell for the good of the cittie, and if the cittie finde good and the countrie no hurt, though Mr Middleton gayneth by it, he deserveth well.'[4] From the start, the idea of putting public water supply in the hands of a private, profit-making enterprise made some people uneasy. The defence was usually some variant of Myddelton's on this occasion: that it was private investors who had been prepared to take the risk and put up the money, and that they deserved any profits as a result.

But commentators went on lamenting the decision to sign away the City's rights in the project, especially as, in due course, the New River Company became the dominant water company serving the City, and at the same time immensely profitable. In the nineteenth century, when the perception got about that the London water companies' dividends were excessive and the service they provided inadequate, the issue became politically charged and ultimately resulted in the companies' takeover. The arguments resurfaced in the 1980s, when Mrs Thatcher's government urged the privatisation of water on the grounds that, as with other utilities, it had been starved of investment under public ownership and that selling it off would give it access to much-needed private capital. The argument continues today.

The industrious goldsmith

Hugh Myddelton was a formidable man, the sort of character to whom the Victorians erected statues: three, in fact. The most prominent stands by Islington Green. Battered by time, traffic and acid rain, Myddelton stands in Jacobean doublet and hose, bearded and clutching a scroll, with an impressive chain about his neck. He might have stepped straight off the stage at Shakespeare's Globe. A second statue is on the Royal Exchange, across the road from the Bank of England, where he cuts a swaggering figure but is hard to see from the street. And the third – a modern replica of an original destroyed in the Blitz – is at one corner of Holborn Viaduct, where he appears as a man of business, with papers in his hand and his left arm up to his cheek (he could be on the phone).

You can judge what the viaduct's builders thought of Myddelton by the company he keeps at the other three corners: all towering figures in the early history of the City, all, like Myddelton, merchant princes remembered for their commitment to public service, all men without whom London's development might have been very different. Henry Fitzailwyn became the City's first mayor in about 1189. Sir William Walworth was the Lord Mayor who stabbed Wat Tyler in 1381, saving Richard II from his revolting peasants and preserving property and privilege. And Sir Thomas Gresham, a generation or two older than Myddelton, built the first Royal Exchange and endowed Gresham College, later the first home of the Royal Society.

Myddelton was sometimes taken by the Victorians to be an engineer, but he was in fact a goldsmith – the nearest thing in early modern London to a banker – and what we might nowadays call a venture capitalist. Goldsmiths tended to be rich, though much of their wealth was necessarily tied up in their stock-in-trade. Some idea of what that consisted of can be gleaned from the astonishing Cheapside Hoard discovered by construction workers in 1912. Probably buried in a cellar in Goldsmiths Row by the jewellers Francis and John Simpson, when they fled to join the king in Oxford at the start of the English Civil War, it contains more than 400 items, many of exquisite beauty, astonishing workmanship and tremendous value.[5] Though Myddelton may have acquired some of the skills needed to produce work like this during his apprenticeship, he was not really a craftsman but a retailer and dealer – a 'merchant goldsmith', one of four branches of the trade identified by the author of *The Gouldesmythes Storehowse* in 1604.

He was also a clannish City oligarch from Denbigh in North Wales, whose business associates included two of his eight brothers, who, like him, were City merchants and MPs. Another brother became governor of Denbigh Castle, a fourth high sheriff of Denbighshire and a fifth converted to Roman Catholicism and settled as a trader in Ghent. They were all active and successful men, but Hugh seems to have been especially driven and restless.

We know from the public record that he was a leading member of the Goldsmiths Company – he was twice prime warden, or master. He acted as a government adviser on metallurgical matters. He sold jewellery to both Elizabeth I and James I, and served as a member of numerous parliamentary committees. And – just when you think you have him conveniently pigeon-holed as a rather dull stick and a safe pair of hands – you discover he also invested in a buccaneering expedition to seize Spanish treasure ships in 1589, known as the Goldsmith's Voyage (though he stopped short of setting sail himself).

Myddelton remained close to his Welsh roots. He sat for Denbigh in Parliament, owned land in the area and was a burgess of both Denbigh and nearby Ruthin, to both of whose corporations he presented silver cups. He could write (and presumably speak) Welsh.

But as with most early modern figures, the man himself is elusive. There is a hint in a letter written in 1609. This was when his work on the New River was well under way, and Myddelton was predicting in the letter that it would cost him 'all my poore meanes'. Yet he was already contemplating his next project, exploiting some silver mines in Wales: 'I cannot be idell', he wrote.[6]

He had earlier tried and failed to exploit coal deposits around Denbigh, but the silver mines, in the west around Machynlleth and Aberystwyth, turned out to be extremely lucrative. The profits helped to extinguish the losses Myddelton incurred on the New River, which took a while to become profitable.

Less successful was a scheme to reclaim land from the sea at Brading Harbour on the Isle of Wight. Myddelton recruited Dutch engineers to undertake the work in 1620, but their dyke lasted only a decade. The sea returned in March 1630, and it was not until 1879 that a railway embankment succeeded where Myddelton had failed.

In 1625 he was invited by a gentleman in North Wales, Sir John Wynn of Gwydir, to undertake a similar scheme to reclaim 'drowned lands' from the sea at the mouth of Afon Glaslyn. Myddelton politely declined, in another of his rare surviving letters, on grounds of age and the risk of overstretching himself:

> As for myself, I am grown into years, and full of business here at the mynes, the river at London, and other places – my weeklie charge being above £200; which maketh me verie unwillinge to undertake anie other worke; and the least of theis, whether the drowned lands or mynes, requireth a whole man, with a large purse.[7]

Yet he did not shut the door entirely on Wynn's proposal, citing 'my love to publique works', though he died before he could take the idea further.

By the time the dyke at Brading collapsed in 1630, Hugh had sold his interest there – and had become a baronet, entitled to style himself 'Sir Hugh' and to pass the title on to his heirs, unlike a mere knight. Unusually – since the title of baronet had been invented by James I as a money-making wheeze – he didn't have to pay for it. The citation credited him with three achievements: the Welsh mines, the Brading reclamation, and bringing to the City of London 'with excessive charge and greater difficulty, a new cutt or river of fresh water, to the great benefitt and inestimable preservation thereof.'[8]

Myddelton's achievement at the New River impressed his contemporaries and posterity alike. He helped his reputation along with some judicious PR. When the work was completed in 1613, he staged a grand opening pageant at the terminal reservoir known as the Round Pond at New River Head. Sixty workmen paraded in green caps, along with the project's management team. One of them recited a celebratory poem commissioned from the playwright Thomas Middleton (no relation), which, among other things, stressed the cost of the project to Myddelton and the opposition he had had to overcome 'for the Citie's generale good':

> . . . after five years' dear expense in days,
> Travail and pains, besides the infinite ways
> Of malice, envy, false suggestions,
> Able to daunt the spirit of mighty ones
> In wealth and courage: this work so rare,

> Only by one man's industry, cost and care,
> Is brought to blest effect.

Then the floodgates were opened to the sound of drums, trumpets and the firing of mortars. There is no mention of the cost in the New River accounts: Myddelton appears to have paid for the event himself.[9]

A new adventure

Hugh Myddelton's scheme initially inherited the part-public, part-commercial status of Edmund Colthurst's. But as it evolved over the next few years, it took on a character unlike any previous water supply project. It became neither a public benefaction nor a partnership between the City and a private entrepreneur, but conceptually something quite original, built by a body of men – we would now call them shareholders, though they called themselves 'adventurers' – organised in a way that had only recently become possible. A century earlier it would have been inconceivable, in the simple sense that it would not have occurred to anyone to do things this way. 'The Governor and Company of the New River brought from Chadwell and Amwell to London', formally incorporated in 1619, six years after it started trading, represented a new way of doing business.

In the half century before the New River was first proposed, London's business community had acquired a taste for ambitious, even grandiose schemes, and had been developing clever new ways of financing and managing them. Myddelton's project took advantage of those developments, and Myddelton himself should be commemorated as a significant figure in the history of London not just because of his contribution to its water supply but for his role as a business pioneer.

A key date had been 1553, when a voyage promoted by the Italian navigator Sebastian Cabot to find a north-east passage to Cathay – a semi-mythical realm that we might identify as China – raised £6,000 in capital. London was a vigorous trading city, its river full of shipping, but the horizons of its merchants were limited. Most sailed no further than Antwerp, just across the North Sea, exporting woollen cloth to the great European market there, and buying in return merchandise from as far afield as the Mediterranean, Turkey and the East Indies. Trading with Antwerp and the other ports and cities of the Low Countries, or importing wine from Bordeaux, was never without risk, but the risks were known, the ports were mostly near at hand, and returns could be expected reasonably quickly. Merchants joined forces to hire ships, but the goods they carried belonged to individual members of the 'venture', and when the ship returned the venture was liquidated and each member was free to take his profits, along with his initial capital.[10]

Sailing north through the unknown seas of the Arctic to Cathay was a very different prospect, exceptionally challenging and uncertain. Cabot won backing for his project partly for reasons of national prestige – if the Spanish could find treasure in the areas we know as South and Central America, perhaps English navigators could do something similar elsewhere – and the money came not just from London's mercantile community but from wealthy aristocrats and courtiers willing to invest in a speculative venture.

The involvement of these outsiders gave it a new and different character. Private profit and the interests of any single merchant were subordinated to the common interest of the investors as a whole. Stocks of merchandise were to be held jointly. Goods traded on the voyage were to be brought back to London sealed up, and unpacked on arrival under the eyes of senior officials of the company: 'The whole company . . . to have that which by right unto them appertaineth, and no embezzlement shall be used, but the truth of the whole voyage to be opened to the common wealth and benefit of the whole company.'[11] In the event the expedition failed to reach Cathay but did find Russia, and Cabot's 'Mysterie and Companie of the Merchant Adventurers for the Discoverie of Regions, Dominions, Islands and Places Unknown' became the seed of the Muscovy Company, with a monopoly on trade with Russia and the countries beyond.

This notion of 'joint stock' was, for London's merchants, one of the most important discoveries of the age, on a par with that of Russia or America: a New Found Land of almost infinite commercial opportunity. If merchants no longer traded solely on their own account but collectively, and could draw not only on their own capital but that of passive investors, the City of London's combined reach might stretch much further. Schemes, projects and ventures so ambitious that, in the past, only the crown or the church had the resources to undertake them were within the scope of ordinary citizens – though it still helped (as the New River was to find) to have crown backing.

Over the next fifty years, London built steadily on the foundations laid in 1553, until, in September 1599, 101 of the biggest players in the City subscribed over £30,000 to the biggest 'venture' yet, financing a voyage to the East Indies: they petitioned the crown for a charter of incorporation, 'for that the trade of the Indies being so far remote from hence cannot be traded but in a joint and united stock'. The charter was granted in December 1600 and the first ships of the 'Company of Merchants of London Trading with the East Indies' set sail the following February: they returned in June 1603 laden with cargoes that netted the investors a profit of 300 per cent.[12]

Essential for all of these ventures was a royal charter of incorporation, like the one this new East India Company had applied for. Towns had them; medieval guilds had them; the City's own livery companies had them. A corporation was more than just the collection of individuals that made it up: for one thing it enjoyed potential immortality, the ability to outlive its founders, which distinguished it from the alternative model for collaboration in business, a partnership. The crown granted corporations (or their officers or directors, acting on behalf of the body corporate) the right to buy and sell goods and land, and otherwise operate without the need to win the consent of every single member for every transaction. In the late middle ages incorporation usually brought an additional benefit, a grant of monopoly. Today corporations are everywhere, capitalism's ubiquitous agent of delivery, and over the intervening centuries the corporation has taken on many of the characteristics in law of a real person. Tudor lawyers might not have recognised the concept of a corporation as a person, but pragmatic Tudor businessmen could see its practical value.

The incorporated joint-stock form made possible a spectacular widening of geographical horizons: it was ideally suited to the business of long, expensive and risky trading voyages, but it had other uses too. In 1565, Elizabeth I issued patents of incorporation to two mining and metal-working ventures, the Company of Mineral and Battery Works and the Society of the Mines Royal. They too were joint-stock companies, with aristocrats alongside London merchants and tradesmen, but also foreigners (a firm of German merchants and a German ironmaster) among their shareholders; Hugh Myddelton's Welsh silver mines were worked under a licence from the Mines Royal.

There was an important difference between these two mining companies and the trading ventures, however. At the outset, the Muscovy and Levant and East India companies raised new capital for each voyage – the East India Company had no permanent capital until 1657 – and after each voyage the investors were free to take their capital out. But that was impossible with a mine or an ironworks: capital was invested in a manufacturing plant or (literally) sunk into the ground, and it might take years of fruitless digging before a productive seam was struck and a mine began to generate revenue.

The same was true of an aqueduct. Once dug it could not be parcelled up and sold off bit by bit like a ship's cargo. It needed to be kept in being, whole and unbroken. As with the mines, it needed not just joint stock, but *permanent* joint stock. The initial investors were locked in – unless they sold not chunks of the property itself but their paper shares in it to someone else.

The New River Company soon developed into a permanent joint-stock corporation. The Mineral and Battery Works and the Mines Royal eventually faded away, superseded by the Industrial Revolution. The New River Company survived as a water company until 1904 and as a property company for even longer, a triumphant vindication of the strength and solidity of the joint-stock model.

Making a river

Myddelton's project, then, was revolutionary – though its revolutionary character took time to emerge. To begin with there was no company as such, merely a series of personal bargains between Myddelton and his investors, just as the earliest agreements with customers were between the householder and Myddelton. At some point he decided to spread the risk of building the New River across thirty-six shares: the company's 1619 charter of incorporation, issued a decade after building work started and six years after it was completed, says he did this because the cost of construction had turned out to be 'greater and heavier than at first was expected, the successe thereof doubtfull and the opposicons made against it very stronge'. A surviving contract made in May 1612, between him and one of the investors, Sir Henry Neville, reveals that shares cost £100 apiece, plus a contribution to the cost of construction, which eventually amounted to £18,500, or an additional £189 per share.[13]

But not all the shares were equal. Myddelton gave four of them free to Colthurst, as compensation for the loss of his concession. These shares were not liable for any contribution to the costs and, indeed, Colthurst himself was taken on as 'overseer' of the works at a salary of 14 shillings a week (nearly three times the labourers' wage of 5 shillings). He lived to see the work completed, and to take part in the opening ceremony, though not to see his shares pay any kind of dividend.

Myddelton also kept a number of the shares for himself. The 1619 charter lists twenty-nine 'adventurers' holding thirty-six shares between them: two are in Hugh's own name, seven more are held by members of the Myddelton family, and two by trustees for Hugh. Colthurst, by this time, was dead and his shares had either reverted to Myddelton or been sold to other investors. They were an influential line-up: a number were lawyers, seven were knights, fourteen were past, present or future MPs. (The involvement of MPs as directors and shareholders was a feature not just of the New River Company through-out its history but of later London water companies as well: it made enacting legislation to curb water companies' activities a minefield.)

One shareholder, Hugh's brother Sir Thomas, was a former Lord Mayor. Another, Sir Henry Montague, was Lord Chief Justice and a future Earl of Manchester. Sir John Backhouse owned the land on which the New River's reservoir in Islington was built and was proud of his association with the project: when he had his portrait painted years later, his hand rested on a picture showing the reservoir and its accompanying Water House.

Many of the others were not 'in trade' – so were just the kind of investors for whom the joint-stock form was ideal – but a number were drawn from London's mercantile aristocracy, including Peter Vanlore, a 'merchant stranger' born in Utrecht, who held two shares. He was a jeweller and merchant whose immense wealth can be measured by the fact that, in 1604, King James had paid him more than £19,000, a truly enormous sum, for goods supplied.

The economic historian R. H. Tawney called him a 'ubiquitous cosmopolitan, at home wherever he caught the smell of money'.[14] Another, Robert Bateman, was a member of six overseas trading companies and at various times solicitor, auditor and treasurer of a seventh, the East India Company. Many of these men, like the Myddeltons, were connected to one another by marriage or kinship.

To begin with, however, the venture was more like a sprawling partnership than a corporation, and throughout its existence it retained some characteristics of a partnership. For example, all twenty-nine adventurers were on the board, and the number of directors remained at twenty-nine until 1904. There were other idiosyncracies too. Though there is a document clearly setting out the transfer of the City's powers to Myddelton, there is no similar document transferring Myddelton's powers to the company. The company's corporate existence was not recognised by Parliament until 1737, by which time it had been trading for well over a century. The circumstances of its creation led to centuries of debate about whether it was a private or a public body (in practice, it behaved throughout like a thoroughly private enterprise, even if its powers were those of a public corporation).*

---

* Later, when the security of London's water supply was at stake, the company was sometimes treated as if it was a branch of government. During the anti-Catholic Gordon Riots in 1780, troops were sent to protect the river. And in 1803, when a French invasion was threatened, the company compiled a list of all its turncocks, foremen and labourers, most of whom were Irish, with their addresses and family details; this was because the Irish 'have been heard to declare that in case of invasion or insurrection they should use the means in their power to assist the views of the enemies of this

The company owned the land across which the river flowed, although the notion of land 'ownership' was still developing. In its charter of incorporation, the legal basis on which it held the course of the New River was defined in a form of words that one writer (himself a lawyer) described as 'unintelligible except to land lawyers', namely 'as of our manor of East Greenwich . . . in free and common socage by fealty only and not in chiefe nor by knight's service'.[15] That word 'socage' means it held the land free of feudal dues – there was no question of the adventurers having to saddle up and turn out in their armour at the behest of their feudal overlord, the king.

Then there were the shares. Because the idea of the business corporation was still embryonic in the 1610s, these were deemed at the outset to represent not a stake in the business but in the physical course of the river, and so were treated as real property for legal purposes. This meant the adventurers counted as landowners in the two counties through which the river ran, Hertfordshire and Middlesex, entitling them to vote in parliamentary elections. An 1833 agreement transferring ownership of a tiny fraction of a share (some of the original thirty-six had by then been subdivided many times over) refers to 'two undivided twenty-fourth parts of one fourth part of one thirty-sixth part of a moiety of 10 messuages 100 acres of meadow 20 acres of pasture 160 acres of land covered with water and one cut and streame of running water and watercourse . . .' This notion that shareholders actually owned part of the physical watercourse sometimes made

(cont.) country by preventing the supply of water in cases of fire in any part of the capital' (LMA, ACC/2558/MW/C/15/361-2).

for difficulties; it certainly caused remark. In 1857 a judge in a tax case called the company 'quite peculiar ... I believe there is no other corporation in the kingdom similarly circumstanced'. The legal precedents set by cases involving the New River Company held back, until well into the nineteenth century, the development of our modern notion that a company share represents a stake in the capital and profits of an abstract entity, 'the business', rather than in the business's physical assets. The New River was unique, eccentric and gave much doubtless lucrative employment to generations of lawyers.[16]

In the early days it was unquestionably Myddelton who drove the project. Having supplanted Colthurst, he took charge, travelling up and down the river's length during construction and negotiating with landowners, presumably while Colthurst supervised the labourers. Myddelton paid himself £2 6s 8d a week. And when the project ran into difficulties, he pulled off a financial and political masterstroke: he got the king himself to invest.

Work on extending Colthurst's original channel southwards began in March 1609 and, by the end of the year, ten miles had been dug. Then progress stalled for a second time and the project was all but abandoned. A hundred men had been employed; by the middle of 1610, all including Colthurst had been let go. The detailed records show payments only to a man taken on to catch moles, and to Myddelton's clerk, William Lewyn, who was keeping the accounts.

Myddelton's problem was that some of the landowners along the route were refusing to co-operate. They claimed the river would turn their meadows into bogs and quagmires, mangle their farms, cut their fields up into 'quillets' and flood the countryside after heavy rains. Not only that, they had raised sufficient support in the House of Commons to introduce a bill repealing the act that had originally authorised the work: it might have passed if Parliament hadn't been prorogued halfway through the process. These landowners were the source of the 'malice, envy, false suggestions' noted by Thomas Middleton in his poem. The whole scheme and the money so far invested were in jeopardy. The City backed Myddelton, petitioning MPs against the new bill, but Myddelton himself went one better. He appealed to the king.

His timing was good. In 1611, James was desperate to make himself financially independent of Parliament. The prospect of a regular stream of revenue from Myddelton's water was an appealing one. He and his advisers agreed to pay half the costs of construction in return for a half share in the business and half the future profits, and the opposition melted away. Work duly resumed at the end of 1611 and by July 1612 over 300 men were employed.

As with Myddelton's agreements with his other investors, this arrangement with the crown was a personal one between the king and Myddelton. It was a good deal for Myddelton – who was adroit enough to get the king to take on half the project's liabilities without securing any say in its management – and might have been a good one for the Stuarts as well if James's son, Charles I, with his talent for mismanagement, hadn't turned it into a bad one.

That was because the company took time to show a profit. James died in 1626 and, in 1630, Charles, frustrated at the slow rate of return, decided to liquidate this liquid asset. He sold the Crown's half, or 'moiety', in the venture – which by that stage had returned some £4,470 on his father's investment of more than £9,200 – back to Myddelton, just a week before Myddelton died. Charles got £500 down and a further £500 a year in perpetuity: a miserly sum in the context of the company's later enormous profits. Myddelton divided the king's half into a further thirty-six shares, mirroring the original adventurers' shares, and his descendants gradually sold them off. These king's shares were always worth slightly less, because each carried the obligation to pay one thirty-sixth of the £500 every year, a payment known as the Crown Clog, and because they enjoyed no representation on the company's board.

The king's involvement, however, has proved a boon for historians. Almost all the New River Company's early records were lost when a fire destroyed its offices in 1769, but James's advisers insisted that Myddelton rendered detailed accounts of how the royal money was being spent, and a copy was lodged with officials at James's court. Today it's in the National Archives.

Thanks to these records, assiduously compiled by Myddelton's clerk, we know that in March 1612 the workmen on the project were summoned by a drum bought for 14s, and there was also a trumpeter, Davie Gryffethe: in February 1612 he and a fellow Welshman, Rees Uphughes, were paid 12s a week for carrying the surveyor's equipment (this was over twice what a common labourer got, suggesting their job involved a good deal more than simply humping kit). We know that in December 1614 'Wyddoew Tyllstone' was paid £2 9s 4d for a timber log to be sawn into planks. And we know how much the workmen were paid: the labourer's standard day rate was 10d, but they sometimes got an extra 2d if they had to work in water. We also know that an 'Ingen' was used in the work and required frequent repairs, including 7s 4d for 'a legg, plates

& pynnes, mendinge the sullier & for holing the coulter', paid in 1609 to 'Downes of stansteed', presumably a black-smith. The Ingen was described by the diarist John Evelyn as a heavy-duty plough invented by a 'country fellow' and drawn by seventeen horses; it was used for a time to break up the earth.[17]

Taking the levels

Clearly Myddelton himself was proud of his achievement, and with good reason. He had proved himself a canny businessman and a crafty politician, successfully negotiat-ing the shoals of Jacobean high finance. And the river itself was a triumph of the surveyor's art: unlike Morice's water-works, it required no pumping, but harnessed gravity to send fresh water south to the City. It fell just five inches every mile, 'an almost unimaginably gentle slope', as one modern writer calls it.[18]*

The credit for this should go to Edward Wright, the 'mathematician' employed by Myddelton to 'take the levels' or survey the route for the river. Wright was a map-maker and expert on navigation, and has been described as the only fellow of Gonville & Caius College, Cambridge, to be granted sabbatical leave to engage in piracy: in 1589 he had been given leave of absence at royal command to take part in the Goldsmith's Voyage, in which Myddelton

* This degree of accuracy is especially remarkable given that the main instrument for 'taking levels' available was one that went back to ancient Egypt: a frame in the shape of an isosceles triangle with a lead hanging from the apex, known as a 'plummet level'.

had invested, and may have commanded one of the vessels under a *nom de guerre*, Captain Edward Careless.[19] His replacement at the New River (after the rather fiery Wright fell out with Myddelton) was Edward Ponds, another 'practitioner in the mathematicks'.

A mathematician in the sixteenth and seventeenth centuries meant not just someone skilled in calculation or the abstract use of numbers but someone who applied practical scientific knowledge in fields ranging from accountancy to gunnery or navigation or the construction of machines. Wright's actual role at the New River was a cross between what we would call a surveyor, in the sense of one who measures land or property, and a civil engineer, meaning one who designs and builds physical structures, such as bridges or dams. But in Wright and Myddelton's day, there was no such thing as a civil engineer: engineers were military types, who built fortifications or devised ways of undermining them. The word shares a root with 'gin', meaning a trap, and it described someone who contrived or devised things – very often fiendish or murderous things. The character in *Hamlet* 'hoist with his own petard' (a kind of bomb) was an 'enginer' (*sic*); in middle English, 'to engine' had meant to seduce, trick or deceive. In due course the water industry was to play an important role in the development of civil engineering as a profession, and in helping the word acquire its modern association with construction rather than destruction; but to begin with there were no engineers in civilian life.

The word 'surveyor' also had a rather different meaning, or range of meanings. Some men described as surveyors did what we would recognise as surveying. Some had a background in the building trades, some had design skills:

one of the men who drew up early surveys of London and its buildings was a painter-stainer, another doubled as a forger. Some were proto-architects.

But just as often surveyor, like its cognates 'supervisor', 'overseer' and 'inspector', meant one who 'looked over' or managed. Edmund Colthurst was overseer of the New River's construction. The men called surveyors in the river's early days, once it was operational, were actually foremen or middle managers, employed to oversee not just the works but the workmen. In 1700 there was a 'citty surveyour' paid £50 a year with the job of running the staff at New River Head and in the City, and two others earning £30 apiece, one responsible for the river from Islington to Bush Hill and the other from Bush Hill to Ware.

One of them, John White, was subsequently buried in Enfield churchyard in a tomb bearing the inscription: 'I served the New River Company as Surveyor from Lady-day, 1691, to Midsummer 1723', and an epitaph in verse:

> Here lies John White, who day by day,
> On river works did use much clay,
> Is now himself turning that way.
> If not to clay, then dust will come,
> Which to preserve, takes little room,
> Although inclosed in this great tomb.[20]

The Myddelton myth

Myddelton's achievement at the New River impressed his contemporaries. The playwright and author Anthony

Munday, updating John Stow's *Survey of the Cities of London and Westminster*, credited Myddelton as the moving spirit in a matter 'long debated, but never concluded, till courage and resolution lovingly shooke hands together, as it appears it did in the soule of this (no way to bee daunted) well-minded gentleman'. Myddelton, he says, took a great interest in the river's progress and 'did divers times ride to see . . . and diligently observed that admirable art, pains and industry were bestowed for the passage of it'.[21]

Myddelton's undoubted energy and drive, along with his ability to overcome obstacles and his combination of public spiritedness and commercial nous, helped to create a kind of Myddelton myth, elaborated, revisited and reworked by writers and artists over the next three centuries.

Some of the stories that attached to his name were just that, stories. There is no evidence for the legend that he used to sit smoking at the door of his house with Sir Walter Raleigh, who introduced tobacco to England; nor was there any truth in the notion that building the New River bankrupted him and that he died poverty-stricken – he was, and remained, a wealthy man.

The eighteenth-century historian of London Thomas Pennant perpetuated the notion that Myddelton died poor, writing 'he sacrificed private fortune to the public good'. But he also drew on the power of myth when he cast Myddelton as Merlin: 'The dauntless Welshman stept forth and smote the rock, and the waters flowed into the thirsting metropolis', Pennant wrote, adding for good measure: 'No one ought to be ignorant that this unspeakable benefit is owing to a Welshman.'[22]

The river itself was apostrophised in poetry. In 1821 one

verse began in celebratory mode: 'Stream of the Cambrian artist! hail, all hail . . .' Another poet, who preferred doggerel, likened the river to the 'aquaeducts of Rome' but considered it a nobler achievement because New River water was taken into people's homes 'by pipes of lead', and 'of those at Rome the like cannot be said'. A third, John Scott of Amwell, writing in 1776 and deploying what by then had become the familiar metaphor of water pipes as veins and arteries, was more sceptical. Myddelton's water fell short of the Roman aqueducts' splendour, he felt; what's more, Myddelton was in it to make money:

> . . . our mercenary stream
> No grandeur boasting, here obscurely glides
> O'er grassy lawns or under willow shades:
>> As, thro' the human form, arterial tubes
>> Branch'd every way, minute and more minute,
>> The circulating sanguine fluid extend;
>> So, pipes innumerable, to peopled streets
>> Transmit the purchas'd wave.[23]

But the comparison with the Romans and their aqueducts was not easily dismissed. The Victorian apostle of self-help, Samuel Smiles, put the seal on Myddelton's reputation for nineteenth-century readers in his *Lives of the Engineers*, describing the river as 'this great work, more like that of a Roman emperor than of a private London citizen'.[24]

Writers on Myddelton have tended to project on to him the qualities they and their contemporaries admire. For Smiles that was pull-yourself-up-by-your-bootstraps get-up-and-go. For Sir Alexander Houston, the first director of water examination at the New River's successor, the Metropolitan Water Board, it was a particularly twentieth-century concept of public service. Myddelton, he wrote, on the basis of scant historical evidence, was 'an altruist and idealist of the highest distinction'; his creeds were 'health, and the greatest happiness of the greatest number'. And he wrote of the New River:

> Of the million Londoners now drinking New River water there are some who love to dwell in the past. These will picture in their dreams the New River as a silvery stream of crystal purity meandering through the peaceful valleys of Hertfordshire and Middlesex to the City of London to the great glory of a noble knight long since departed to 'the bourne from which no traveller returns'.[25]

Myddelton was a baronet rather than a knight, the New River was rarely if ever a stream of crystal purity, and a businessman like Myddelton was driven as much by the prospect of making money as by philanthropy: as the Victorian journalist John Hollingshead observed, 'There is nothing in the dim fragments of his history to prove that he was particularly disinterested in his dealings, or that, beyond painting his enterprise in colours a little too glaring, he carried on his business upon sentimental principles.' Yet Houston persuaded his employers to devote thirty pages of their annual report in 1926 to this guff, in an essay entitled 'The Romance of the New River'. His aim, he said, was to 'exalt Preventive Medicine, and to surround the subject of the provision of a pure water supply with the attributes of altruism, romanticism and humanitarianism'. Hugh Myddelton, or a distorted version of him, just happened to be a useful vehicle.[26]

One thing most twentieth-century writers agreed on,

taking their cue from Smiles, was that Myddelton was a man who did not give up. Houston calls him an 'indomitable fighter'. Houston's colleague, G. F. Stringer, the clerk to the Metropolitan Water Board, wrote of his 'untiring energy' and 'indomitable will'. And in 1964 Myddelton's biographer, J. W. Gough, praised his 'unusual fortitude and determination'.[27]

But while Myddelton's reputation was secure, Edmund Colthurst was often forgotten: he is not mentioned in H. W. Dickinson's otherwise comprehensive *Water Supply of Greater London*, first published in 1948. It wasn't until a retired doctor and canal enthusiast called Michael Essex-Lopresti wrote a booklet about the river in the 1980s that anyone started agitating for wider recognition. 'In marked contrast to Myddelton, there is no statue, monument, plaque, nor even a road in London named after Colthurst today', Essex-Lopresti wrote. 'This has been drawn to the attention of appropriate councils.' Evidently, they listened. Today there's a Colthurst Drive, a Colthurst Crescent and a Colthurst Gardens close to the New River's route.[28]

As for King James, he had a closer relationship with the river than most of his fellow shareholders. Its course ran through the park of his country house at Theobalds, just south of Cheshunt. He was out riding one morning in January 1622 when his horse threw him and he went head first through the ice into the river. He had to be dragged out by his boots.

3

The River Runs

Once Hugh Myddelton's grand opening ceremony was out of the way, the New River Company began supplying water in 1613, inaugurating London's first modern water supply. It was an epoch-making development, though Myddelton and his colleagues may have been too busy to notice. They had a business to build.[1]

The company's operational base was at New River Head, on the rising ground between Clerkenwell and Islington. Here the river terminated in the Round Pond, adapted from an existing duck pond. Next to the pond was the Water House, the company's network hub, which contained a cistern and the cocks controlling the flow to the mains. A keeper was appointed to live in it and look after the cocks. But it was out in the countryside, so not the right place for a head office.

In fact the company had no proper office, no recognised place of business. Myddelton and his colleagues were men of their time, seeking to achieve what we would see as modern ends but with medieval means. That meant working from home, as virtually all merchants, traders, craftsmen and professionals did. The company was run day-to-day from Myddelton's house. That was where the earliest customers paid their money and signed agreements with Myddelton (not the company) to take the water, and where important documents were kept. But not everything took place there: for the next half century or more, the board (known as the 'court of adventurers') met in one another's houses or in coffee houses and taverns, while money was stored at the treasurer's house.

Myddelton had few precedents to guide him in how to run such a substantial enterprise. Virtually everything had to be invented from scratch, or borrowed from somewhere else and repurposed. The result was a sometimes quirky way of doing business, some aspects of which persisted right through until 1904.

For a start, the agreements with customers broke new ground, and designing them required some agile thinking on the part of lawyers. Today we would say that the New River Company and its customers were entering into a contract to supply water for a certain time in return for payment, with conditions attached. But in early modern England, the notion of contracts extending over a long period did not exist: what we would call the law of contract applied mainly to ordinary bargains for the sale or purchase of goods, and a contract was discharged as soon as the goods were delivered and the money paid.

So Myddelton and his lawyers turned to the law of property, as they had when defining what New River shareholders actually owned. A property lease, which contained standard clauses protecting both tenants and landlords and remained in force over a period of time, provided a handy template. So it was that New River customers signed a 'water lease', and were thenceforth known as 'tenants' who paid 'rent' – even if (unlike with a property lease) there was nothing to hand back at the end. Later water companies followed suit.[2]

Throughout its history the company had no chief executive. The twenty-nine adventurers acting collectively as the 'Governor and Company' took that role. They were served by a full-time salaried clerk or secretary who was appointed for life (to begin with by the monarch, in recognition of the king's shareholding). The clerks were men of substance: one held four adventurers' shares; another, John Grene, was married to one of Hugh Myddelton's granddaughters, who also owned four shares.

As the company grew, the clerk oversaw the collectors, who brought in the money, and the surveyors, who kept an eye on the physical state of the river and the pipe network in town. There were walksmen who patrolled the river in pairs, clearing weeds, looking out for damage and repairing it – the senior took the western bank, his assistant the eastern or downhill bank, which was often built up above the surrounding ground and so needed more attention and involved more work. A circular brick walksman's hut with a conical roof survives in New River Walk in Canonbury, just large enough for some tools and a brew for two out of the rain (once tea had become London's working-class drink of choice). Then there were turncocks, who controlled the supply to householders. And there were paviours too, who laid and maintained the pipes, made good the road surface and connected (and occasionally disconnected) customers.

The pipes were made of elm, which didn't easily rot even when buried in the ground and filled with water. The trunks were bored out and one end was sharpened so it slotted into the end of the next. They were still unearthing old elm pipes from the streets of London well into the twentieth century: gnarled, primitive relics, like something dredged up by fishing nets from Doggerland, the lost land in the North Sea that once joined Britain to the Continent. Fanciful etymologists suggest that it is to this use of wood that we owe the modern term 'trunk line' for long distance pipe and cable networks, and the notion of a telephone 'trunk call', though the derivation is more likely from analogy with a living tree, with its central stem and peripheral branches.*

Early on the company and its imitators developed a distinction between their main or principal pipes – the 'mains' – and the branches, from which most customers actually got their water. The branches were known as 'services', and though also made of wood were usually narrower. Customers were connected in turn to the services by lead pipes.

Because the maximum bore of the elm pipes was only seven inches, more than one was needed in many places – in the mid-eighteenth century there were no fewer than nine mains running parallel in one street, and in time there were fifty-eight leaving New River Head. Normally they were out of sight – detectable only when they sprang a leak, as they frequently did – but later, when the company expanded to

---

* A Board of Works report in 1724 on a shortage of water at Whitehall Palace supports this notion. It refers to one of the New River's 'Main-Trees', and explains that the company had permitted the palace to run a pipe from the main to the fountain in the Privy Garden, but cut off the supply when it discovered it was laying on other 'branches' as well (LMA, ACC/2558/MW/C/15/284). You can see old elm pipes on display at the Museum of London and at the London Museum of Water and Steam, among other places.

serve the West End, some of the pipes ran above ground. In 1773 a diarist wrote of an area in Bloomsbury:

> The whole of the ground north from Capper's Farm, at the back of the British Museum, so often mentioned as being frequented by duellists, was in irregular patches, many fields with turnstiles. The pipes of the New River Company were propped up in several parts to the height of 7 and 8 feet, so that persons walked under them to gather water cresses, which grew in great abundance and perfection.[3]

'Mischievous boys' used to bore holes in these pipes to make fountains, and a man had to go round with a mallet and wooden spigot to stop them up again. The architect Sir John Soane owned a crude drawing of wooden pipes running westwards across open fields towards the newly built Bloomsbury, and another showing them crossing the Fleet, vigorously spurting. There is nothing new about leaking water mains.[4]

Making connections

With his infrastructure in place, Myddelton borrowed Morice's business model, laying mains across the City and charging householders £1 for a connection, plus a quarterly charge based on the size of their premises. By 1629–30 the mains had reached as far as St Paul's to the south, Fleet Street and Gray's Inn to the west and Aldgate and Houndsditch in the east. This was a considerable achievement, if only because London's streets were horribly congested and physically laying the pipes was difficult. When an enterprising engineer of the London Bridge Waterworks decided to map his company's mains in the mid-eighteenth century, he nearly gave up on account of the traffic, and solved the problem only by getting up very early on summer mornings, when the streets were largely empty.

The New River dodged the traffic by laying mains at night. The company spent money for candles, torches and lanterns and men 'to watch nights in the streetes when the trenches ley open'; even so, people and animals frequently fell into holes left open through the hours of darkness and the company and its competitors were forever paying out compensation, right through until the twentieth century.[5]

Still, the scene was set for a resounding success. But after a promising start, London's inhabitants seemed curiously reluctant to sign up. There were 360 customers in 1614 and 1,035 in 1616; after that, growth slowed dramatically. By 1618 almost no new customers were signing on. It took another twenty years for the number to reach 2,150. The City tried to encourage take-up. But when a man called Bancks, in the parish of St Michael Bassishaw, was asked why he did not take New River water, he offered a barrage of reasons. His family was small, he had a pump (presumably connected to his own well) and a cistern that stored rainwater, and he was already paying a water carrier to deliver at the rate of four tankards for a penny. What's more, connecting to the New River company's main would involve him in expensive building work to accommodate the pipe: even if he could have Myddelton's water for free, he wouldn't take it.[6]

He may also have been worried about quality. In theory New River water in its elm pipes should have been fresh and clean, as well as copious in quantity. In practice this

was not necessarily the case. Water-carriers hawking conduit water were said to walk the streets distinguishing their product from the New River's by crying 'Fresh water, fair water! None of your pipe sludge!'[7]* And would-be competitors also rubbished the product. In 1630 a rival scheme to bring water from Hoddesdon in Hertfordshire in a pipe rather than an open trench referred to 'the foulnesse and muddinesse' of the New River and implied that it frequently failed for days at a time. That may well have been because farmers along the route kept damming the stream and cutting holes in the banks, and because they allowed their cattle to wade in to drink the water.

King James I did what he could do help. More than one royal proclamation was issued banning people from throwing dirt and dead dogs into the river or diverting drains into it. There was some royal bullying too: in 1616 the Privy Council wrote to the Lord Mayor and Aldermen regarding New River water and commanding them that 'all such houses within the citty and the liberties, as either out of necessity or conveniencie, may make use of the same'.[8] Successive sovereigns issued proclamations offering the company support and protection. King William and Queen Mary's, in 1689, forbade people from taking

---

* An alternative version, given by Samuel Smiles, has the water-carriers crying 'Fresh and fair New River water! None of your pipe-sludge!' But it was the New River whose water was supplied by pipe direct to households, and the water carriers had lost business since its arrival, so it seems unlikely that they would promote a new competitor in this way, or that the New River should have relied on water-carriers to reach its customers. And a water-carrier filling up at New River Head would have had a long walk down into the City, whereas the conduits were just round the corner from the customers.

water from the river, fishing in it (a proscription widely ignored), watering cattle or keeping ducks and geese on it.[9] This royal backing was further evidence of the company's ambiguous character – both a profit-making private enterprise and an extension of government.

Customers who did sign up, however, enjoyed a service very different from that which modern water users expect. For a start, the supply was only intermittent. In each neighbourhood the cocks would be turned on for two or three hours on alternate days for the company's tenants to fill their butts or cisterns (but never on Sundays). Cisterns, typically made of wood or lead, were once ubiquitous in all but the poorest London houses, in a corner of the backyard or the basement or the kitchen, raised on stone supports with a tap near the bottom.

Company turncocks toured the streets on a regular schedule. They carried iron keys weighing as much as 30lb to open the cocks on 'water day'. Householders had a tap at the end of their quill above the cistern: most kept it open permanently so as not to miss any of the water when it was turned on, and any surplus ran to waste when the cistern overflowed. You couldn't get mains water continuously 'on tap' in London until the decades after 1852, when the companies were, in theory, mandated by law to offer it, though they did all they could to wriggle out of the obligation: the last customers of what had been the Lambeth, Kent, and Southwark & Vauxhall water companies, living on the hills of South London, were only given 'constant supply' in 1910.[10]*

* Some outlying areas got constant supply even later: some of the last houses connected in March 1911 were in the village of Great Amwell, the location of one of the New River's original springs.

Competitors

The New River's business began to take off in the 1650s. And the Great Fire of 1666 left it in a powerful position, as it had destroyed its chief rivals, the London Bridge Waterworks and the conduits. A contemporary account of the disaster by Samuel Rolle singled out the conduits for special mention, in a bravura display of mixed metaphors. It began by likening them to the veins and arteries of the body, 'necessary for the good of London as blood is for the good and health of the body'. This was to become a cliché, but Rolle's version is especially elaborate. And halfway through the City apparently morphs from animal to vegetable:

> If water were, as we may call it, the blood of London, then were its several conduits as it were the liver and spleen of that City; (which are reckoned the fountains of blood in human bodies,) for that the great trunks and veins conveying blood about the body, are seated therein as great roots fixed in the earth, shooting out their branches in divers and sundry ways . . .

Then the body of London is imagined as a battlefield:

> Methinks these several conduits of London stood like so many little, but strong forts, to confront and give check to the great enemy fire, as occasion should be. There, methinks the water was intrenched and ingarrisoned. The several pipes and vehicles of water . . . were as so many soldiers within these forts, with their musquetry charged, ready to keep and defend these places . . .

And all this is given added piquancy in Rolle's telling of the story by the fact that fire and water are, in the classical scheme of things, opposing elements:

> As if the fire had been angry with the poor old tankard-bearers, both men and women, for propagating that element which was contrary to it, and carrying it upon their shoulders, as it were in state and triumph; it had even destroyed their trade, and threatens to make them perish by fire who had wont to live by water.[11]

Both the conduits and the London Bridge works were rebuilt, but not before the New River had benefited by their absence. From then on the process of London's expansion was inexorable, and as the city grew so did demand for water. The New River Company grew with it, until it was, in the words of one historian, 'indisputably the greatest water company in Europe'.[12]

Once it had demonstrated, firstly, that there was a demand for water piped to people's homes, and, secondly, that there was money to be made from it, other entrepreneurs moved in. The company found itself in competition with a series of newcomers. Commercial competition is a commonplace notion to us – indeed, competition on price, quality and service is the bedrock of a market economy. But the economy of seventeenth-century London was rather different. Much import and export business was conducted by regulated companies for whom a patent and a guarantee of monopoly were a necessary condition of success. Domestic trade was controlled by livery companies and guilds, which limited entry. Prices of key goods, such as bread, were set by the authorities.

As new water companies entered the market they had to learn for the first time what competition might involve, and how it should be conducted. They competed on price, but also by using their political muscle. In time they learnt that *not* competing was easier and more lucrative for everyone – except the consumer.

Apart from the London Bridge Waterworks, which was already in the field when the New River arrived, one of the earliest competitors was Edward Ford. In the 1640s Ford tried and failed to build a New River-style canal to bring water from the River Colne, which runs south from Watford past Rickmansworth and Uxbridge to join the Thames at Staines: his scheme, and a rival plan to build a covered aqueduct from Hoddesdon in Hertfordshire to Islington, were killed off by the outbreak of the Civil War.

His prospects improved after this initial failure when in 1655 the Protector, Oliver Cromwell, awarded him a patent under which he set up a works pumping water from the Thames near Somerset House. But after the Restoration, Charles II took the patent away because his mother, Queen Henrietta Maria, complained that Ford's water tower was spoiling her view. The unlucky Ford was allowed to move his business to Durham Yard, east of Charing Cross, and in 1667 his successors were bought out by the New River.

In 1669 the Shadwell Waterworks – the 'Governor & Company of Waterhouses and Waterworks in Shadwell' – was established, east of the Tower of London, to serve an area of partly reclaimed marshland. Its founder, Thomas Neale, a wealthy lawyer and an MP, had leased the land and persuaded Parliament to create a new parish before securing a royal patent to operate the waterworks. As with the Metropolitan Railway stretching out into Middlesex and Buckinghamshire in the twentieth century, Neale was using infrastructure investment as a catalyst for large-scale property development: in a few years the population of the area more than doubled, living in houses built on his land. The company survived until 1807, and eventually became part of the East London Waterworks.

The York Buildings Waterworks – the 'Governor and Company for raising the Thames Water at York Buildings' – was set up in 1675 by what is now Charing Cross station and served Piccadilly, Whitehall and Covent Garden. Its obelisk-shaped water-tower appealed to topographical artists: it features in numerous pleasing views of the Thames shore-line, including one (unfinished for some reason) by Turner. The company had an unusual history for a waterworks. Around 1720 it diversified into insurance, buying up confiscated Jacobite estates in Scotland and using the land as an asset to underpin its new business; later it tried forestry, coal-mining, ironworks and glass-making. It was hair-raisingly incompetent and most of its leading lights were as blatantly dishonest as their investors were gullible. The company lost a fortune at everything it tried, resorting to financial chicanery, fraud and embezzlement in its efforts to stay afloat. At its last gasp it raised new capital in 1810 to invest heavily in its water business, only for that to turn out as disastrously as all its other speculations. Its water assets were eventually taken over by the New River in 1818.[13]

The Hampstead Water Company was another rival. It was set up in 1692 to supply water from the ponds on the Heath at Hampstead and Highgate, and in 1701 it was actively poaching disgruntled customers from the New

River in the smart new streets springing up north of Piccadilly, which were too far from New River Head for water
to arrive in more than a trickle. A letter to the New River's
governor warned him that his customers in this area were
'so uneasie at the ill servitude that they are inviting the
Hampstead Waterworks to lay in pipes in those Streets,
which if not speedily prevented will be some hundreds of
pounds per annum out of the Company's present Income
in those parts only'.[14] But the Hampstead company had
nowhere near as much water to distribute and was ultimately bought by the New River in 1856, by which time its
product was fit only for railway engines and the Metropolitan Cattle Market.

And then, in 1694, a man called Hugh Marchant had
the bright (if slightly unsavoury) idea of using the flow of
water in the city's sewers to drive a waterwheel. Marchant's Waterworks began life with a patent from the City
and had waterwheels in St Martin's Lane and Hartshorn
Lane off the Strand. One story says it survived until the
1770s, when it shut down because the authorities discovered it was no longer pumping water (which may have
been just as well, given the source) but was instead using its
waterwheel to drive a corn mill.

The New River enjoyed a bulwark against competition
thanks to its history. From time to time its rivals – including
Ford and the York Buildings company – went to the Privy
Council to try to carve out some exclusive area of supply in
which the New River was not allowed to compete, but they
never succeeded. Probably the main reason – as the Privy
Council pointed out on one occasion – was that the rivals,
unlike the New River, weren't paying the king £500 a year.

Making money

In time the company became synonymous with money as much as with water. In 1667 the playwright John Dryden, in his comedy *Sir Martin Mar-all*, slipped in a gag about the price of New River water, 'dearer by sixpence the pound than ever God Almighty made it . . .' The play had them rolling in the Restoration aisles; Pepys saw it several times and, on the first occasion, remarked, 'I never laughed so in all my life'.[15] The shareholders were laughing too. By the 1680s the company had an income of £21,000 a year and expenditure of less than £8,800, leaving a huge profit. In 1683 over £12,000, or £168 per £100 share, was distributed in dividends at a time when a London schoolteacher might hope to earn £50 a year and a pub landlord turn a profit of £100.[16]

*

On the basis of the New River's experience, plenty of people came to believe there was big money to be made in water supply, but the reality was that none of its competitors ever enjoyed the sort of profits that became routine at the New River. The reason was straightforward. The New River delivered water to customers throughout the City by gravity alone; only when it decided to expand into the West End did it need to install a pump, and then only to serve part of its area. All the other companies were dependent on a supply from the Thames; all had to install machinery to push water uphill from the river to their customers; and pumps – whether powered by unreliable wind, intermittent tides, hungry horses or steam engines, which burned coal at a ferocious rate – were expensive.

The New River continued to make large profits throughout its history, apart from a blip in the early nineteenth century: profits so large as to be almost absurd. Its share price reflected the fact. In 1985 Bernard Rudden, professor of comparative law at Oxford and one of several writers seduced by the river and its idiosyncrasies, published *The New River: A Legal History*. In it he compiled a table of the dividends per share and the price from 1633 to 1903. What had started out as a £100 share was selling for £15,200 in 1827 and £95,000 in 1883. The average dividend in the eighteenth century was £265, an income that would by itself have put the shareholder in the top 3 per cent of London's wealthiest residents. By 1827 the dividend was over £500, and it reached £2,560 in 1883. The last share transaction noted by Rudden took place in 1901, when an undivided King's share sold for £120,000 and the dividend was £2,703.

Whoever spent that £120,000 overpaid, however, because when the company was finally bought out in 1904, the holders of each original share got just £67,800 (though they also got a stake worth £1,365 in a new company set up to manage the New River's property portfolio, and the purchase price was paid in government-backed 'water stock', which paid a dividend of 3 per cent a year). Nonetheless, the majority of the shareholders had done extraordinarily well. Had one of the original Adventurers survived, by some miracle, until the buy-out, Rudden estimated that he would have enjoyed on his initial £289 investment (£100 plus £189 towards construction costs) an *annual* return, across 292 years, including dividends and the final redemption value, of 267 per cent. The figure is simply staggering.[17]

4

Froth and Bubble

On Monday, 26 October 1663, Samuel Pepys woke around one o'clock in the morning, and in turn roused his wife. 'My wife being waked rung her bell, and the mayds rose and went to washing, we to sleep again till 7 o'clock, and then up, and I abroad . . .' While his sleep-deprived household did the laundry, Pepys himself spent the whole day out. A later diary entry in April 1666 gives a clue as to why: 'Home, and being washing-day, dined upon cold meat'.[1]

As Pepys knew (though only at second hand, unlike his wife and servants), washing clothes used more water in the home than any other activity – and it was an exhausting, time-consuming and intensely disruptive business.

Washing days (or 'washing weeks' in some larger and wealthier households) were a bracing, even brutal challenge, which is why Pepys's servants got up at two in the morning to get started. It was a challenge to which generations of women were likewise forced to rise. And while washday was in progress, it displaced everything else in the domestic life around it.

Water for washing first needed to be heated, because pre-modern soap would not lather in cold water: the first thing Pepys's maids would have done when they got up so early was revive the kitchen fire. The need to have hot water throughout the day meant too little time and too little space on the fire to cook as well, and the large containers used to hold the water for laundry often doubled as cooking vessels in any case, which is why Pepys was forced to dine on 'cold meat'. Monday became a popular day for washing because the household could eat the leftovers from a Sunday roast.

Once the day had got underway, clothes were washed in relays and the water reused where possible, the most delicate items going first in the cleanest water. They might first be rubbed with soap, though other cleaning agents were available, including wood ash and stale urine. Stored urine turns into ammonia, an effective bleach; wood ash (or 'pot ash', if it had come from a kitchen cooking fire) contains potassium hydroxide, an alkali which combines well with fatty acids. The resulting compound was known as lye and readily cut through dirt and grease; it was made by pouring water a number of times through the ash. Especially dirty clothes, such as nappies, might be soaked in a cold solution of lye for a day or two to loosen the dirt.[2]

As coal superseded wood in London's fires, wood ash became an expensive luxury and, with nothing in their fireplaces from which to make their own cleaning agents, Londoners bought commercially-manufactured 'black soap'. John Stow, in 1598, thought soap boiling a relatively recent addition to the city's manufactures. It was made by boiling ashes to create lye, which was then mixed with whale oil or with the tallow produced by rendering down butchers' waste. Rendering was a notoriously smelly business, which made the soap itself smelly as well. But a Parisian visitor remarked in 1698 that 'the Stink of the Black Soap is almost all clear'd away' if the clothes were subsequently rinsed in large amounts of water: note that 'almost'.[3]

Higher quality and more expensive soaps were also available, including 'grey soap', made chiefly in Bristol, and a white soap known as 'castle soap', imported from the Mediterranean (including from Castile – hence the name) and made with olive oil and the ashes of native Mediterranean saltmarsh plants. A tax was imposed on soap under Cromwell's Commonwealth, lifted at the Restoration, reimposed in 1712 and not finally abolished until 1853, three-quarters of a century after John Wesley had coined the phrase 'cleanliness is next to godliness'. Godliness was often priced a little high for poorer folk.

Laundry was synonymous with physical exertion. Heating water involved lifting large, full containers on to and off the fire; rinsing clothes involved much fetching of clean water and the carrying away of used, scummy water after it had been emptied from the washtub scoop by scoop. And then there was the washing itself. If soaked in lye, clothes needed to be pounded and pummelled to remove the dirt: this might be done on a flat surface, such as a wooden block, with a bat-like implement known as a battledore or beetle. If soap (which was milder) was used instead of lye, the clothes required considerably more agitation to work the dirt loose in the tub, as well as several changes of water for the rinsing. The historian Ruth Goodman calls all this 'monstrously hard work – long and slow and very damaging to the hands'.[4]

She quotes from a poem written in 1739 by Mary Collier, a washerwoman in Petersfield, Hampshire, who spent her life labouring as a domestic servant in the houses of rich folk, one of whom spotted her talent for verse and urged her to publish. Collier describes a typical washday, rising early while her husband still sleeps, standing freezing outside her employer's house because the maid has over-slept and isn't there to let her in, then being confronted with a pile of delicate fabrics to launder while the mistress of the house comes down occasionally to issue instructions:

> Now we drive on, and resolv'd our Strength to try,
> And what we can, we do most willingly;
> Until with Heat and Work, 'tis often known,
> Not only Sweat, but Blood runs trickling down
> Our Wrists and Fingers; still our Work demands,
> The constant Action of our lab'ring hands.

Mary's day would end long after her husband had returned home from work; and her wages were just six or eight pence a day:

> For all our Pains, no Prospect can we see
> Attend us, but *Old Age* and *Poverty*.[5]

Not surprisingly, people valued types of water that were good for washing. One of the most frequent complaints about the stuff supplied by the London water companies was not that it was dirty or smelt but that it was too hard, which made it difficult if not impossible to work up a lather on washday. It *was* dirty, though: a mid-eighteenth-century Londoner's book on housekeeping advised the laundress against using water 'when it first comes in, which being always thick, and very often yellow, gives the linen a muddy cast'. Best to give it time for the impurities to settle in the household cistern and the water to clear.[6]

More water companies of course meant that more water was more readily available, which perhaps made doing the laundry fractionally easier. But it didn't seem to make people any more eager to wash themselves. In his illuminating book *The Making of the English Middle Class 1660–1730*, the historian Peter Earle noted that Samuel Pepys often complained about dirtiness in other people, but Earle doubts that he normally washed much of himself beyond his hands and face. Seventy years later another diarist, Stephen Monteage, records his feet being washed about once a month, normally by his maid. 'Whether either of them were in the habit of washing those parts of their bodies which lay between face and feet one cannot tell since they never tell one,' wrote Earle, 'which in the circumstances would suggest that they rarely did.' And he observed that there was not a single bath-tub in the 375 inventories of middle-class Londoners he studied.[7]

Doing business

The arrival of the London Bridge Waterworks and the New River may have had little impact on personal hygiene, but the New River Company had helped to change notions of what it meant to be 'in business'. Its success contributed to a financial and commercial revolution and an entrepreneurial frenzy – until, that is, a backlash taught Londoners about the dark side of the modern commercial world.

In the late seventeenth century, most London businesses were still in the hands of traditional sole traders, whose place of business was their home and who didn't distinguish between their business and their household accounts. The successful ones invested any spare cash in property or in loans to family, friends or spendthrift aristocrats, not in shares. Joint-stock companies, such as the New River, were rare – there were only a handful of any consequence – and most London businessmen had nothing to do with them: investing in company shares, like investing in government debt, was something only the very rich did.[8]

But London's middle classes were growing wealthier. Their taste for home comforts, such as piped water, was growing in parallel with their wealth: new water companies found a ready market both for their product and their shares. At the same time, new scientific and technological developments were throwing up new business opportunities in many other fields. Projectors, promoters and improvers were everywhere, many seeking to raise money by issuing shares. By the start of the eighteenth century, the London business world was awash with new ideas, and a joint-stock boom had developed. Investment in company shares ceased for a time to be the preserve only of the wealthy.

The permanent joint-stock form pioneered by the New River Company had finally come of age, but the novelty of it all meant that unwary investors were easy prey. The projects on offer ranged from the hare-brained and fraudulent to the inspired and the perfectly sensible. There were agricultural improvement schemes, companies making products from glass to fabrics to china, as well as insurance, fisheries, mines, canals – and, of course, water companies. But there were also schemes for trading in hair, in woad, and in broomsticks from Germany, for paving the streets of London, for turning salt water into fresh and for manufacturing a flintlock machine-gun that fired nine shots a minute – with round bullets for Christians, square ones for Muslims. Famously (if apocryphally), there was a scheme 'for carrying on an undertaking of Great Advantage but no one to know what it is', whose shares were reputedly snapped up at £2 a pop. The origin of the story may be a newspaper hoax, which was explained at the time as an attempt not to exploit but to expose the gullibility of investors: to 'convince the public, with what Facility designing people, under Colour of an Advantageous Undertaking, may at any time impose upon a credulous Multitude'. The promoters of the hoax offered to return their victims' money. But the biggest project of them all became a byword for 'extraordinary popular delusions and the madness of crowds', to quote the title of an 1841 book by the financial journalist Charles Mackay.

*

The South Sea Company was originally floated in September 1711, to trade with Latin America – though it never made a profit from the cargoes of English cloth and African slaves that it sent across the Atlantic. So it diversified. The Bank of England, a joint-stock company founded in 1694, was already lending money to the government; the South Sea went one better and determined to buy up the country's entire national debt – much of it in the form of loans, which individuals had made to the government in return for annuities – and then float it by selling dividend-bearing shares.

The idea was that the government would save money by paying the South Sea Company less in interest than it was paying its annuitants, while the lenders would swap their annuities – for which there was no market and which tied up their money for years – for South Sea shares, which they could sell for cash.

But it was all a scam, masterminded by a handful of clever fellows who made fortunes from insider trading. The company's revenue from its voyages to South America was negligible, and the interest payments from the government nowhere near enough to meet the handsome dividend payments the company promised. It could afford to continue in business only if it kept issuing new shares, which brought in cash to meet its liabilities. And it depended on a constantly rising share price to entice investors.

To begin with it worked. Government ministers and MPs were persuaded to back the scheme with massive bribes. The public were persuaded to buy by a combination of hype and the prospect of making a quick killing by selling their newly acquired shares in a rising market. The company lent money freely so investors could buy its shares, and if it thought the price needed propping up, it bought shares itself. In May 1720, they were selling for five times their value at the start of the year, in June for eight times, and in August for almost ten times.

That people (including some highly sophisticated people) fell for it seems at first glance astonishing. Isaac Newton bought shares, then sold them at a handsome profit; only to buy more. But Newton and his contemporaries, faced as they were by a completely new phenomenon, had more excuse than those swept up in later speculative frenzies, such as the railway mania of the 1840s and the modern dotcom bubbles.

In late summer the bubble burst, as it was bound to. By September, South Sea stock was down to little more than its original face value, and many of the company's investors had been ruined. Ironically, one reason for the collapse was a measure intended to protect the company.

*

Most of the new joint-stock ventures had no charter of incorporation. They were, in effect, unregulated; anyone could start one at any time. And there were too many of them. As interest in South Sea stock grew, it also generated increased interest in other shares and other projects: other bubbles. The danger was that all these other ventures would suck in too much of the nation's available cash, and might leave too little available for the South Sea Company, with its gargantuan craving for capital. So strings were pulled, and in June 1720 Parliament passed what became known as the Bubble Act, which banned the formation of unincorporated joint-stock companies. Many of the new companies seeking funding in the markets were effectively strangled at birth. Which was fine, except that many South Sea shareholders also had shares in these new ventures, which were now worthless. Many of those who had sub-scribed in advance for more South Sea shares had to sell their existing South Sea holdings to find the money to buy the new South Sea shares, driving down the price in the process.

The ban, which meant that any joint-stock venture needed an act of Parliament to get started, remained in force until 1825. For the next 200 years, investment in shares was often referred to as 'speculation', and specula-tion was a dirty word, implying dishonesty and sharp practice and the dangerous recklessness of the gambler. Only infrastructure companies, dealing in canals, docks and waterworks, and later gasworks and railways, went to the trouble and expense of forming joint-stock companies and getting an act of Parliament, if only because they needed powers to acquire land and other rights.

Owning shares went back to being the preserve of the rich, the moneyed men – as it remained, with occasional exceptions, until well into the Victorian era. A surprising and unlooked for consequence of this was that the Industrial Revolution was for the most part financed not by harnessing the country's vast reserves of capital through share issues but by individual entrepreneurs, trading on their own account or in partnership with a handful of others. The capital that might have gone into manufacturing, ship-owning or exporting went instead into government debt, bonds and banking – laying the foundation for what ultimately became 'the City' – and into water and canal companies.

The South Sea bubble was the background against which, two years later, the Chelsea Waterworks was launched. Surprisingly, despite the whirlwind unleashed by the South Sea collapse, confidence had returned to the markets, or at least to the market for waterworks shares: the Chelsea company successfully raised £40,000.*

* A list of Chelsea shareholders in March 1741 gives an idea of the kind of people who took shares in joint-stock companies. It lists 138 investors. Most have addresses in west London; a few live further away – in Cheshire, Dorchester and Cobham, for instance. One, Lewis Schrader, lives in Germany: he is one of the two largest investors, with 160 shares, alongside another man with a German name, Augustus Schutz of Brook Street. The shareholders included twenty-eight women, four baronets, five knights, eleven military officers, seven with aristocratic titles of one sort or another, and thirty-seven men who styled themselves 'esquire', indicating pretensions

In the archive

To research the history of London's water, the place to go is the London Metropolitan Archives, just behind the old Finsbury Town Hall in Clerkenwell. It is housed in a former printworks, and from the first-floor reading room you can just see New River Head. One of the LMA's many excellent qualities, for me, is that to get there involves a 45-minute walk from my home along the old route of the New River through Islington.

Like all well-run archives the LMA is a place of rigour and precision: much depends on the accuracy with which everything is catalogued and labelled, and the care with which it is returned to the correct place after use. I can't now remember why I called up ACC/2558/MW/C/15/195. I must have found the reference number in some other author's footnotes. It was a printed memorandum 'On the origins and present conditions of the Southwark & Vauxhall Water Company', and I wanted to look at it as part of the detailed research I was doing on the Southwark & Vauxhall and its sister company, the Grand Junction Waterworks, in the 1870s (see Chapter 18). But the catalogue number was unfamiliar. The LMA has

---

(cont.) to gentility (LMA, ACC/2558/MW/C/15/135, Chelsea Waterworks list of members). But not all shareholders were so posh. A printed list of London Bridge Waterworks proprietors in the same year contains eighty-four names (twenty of them said to be 'deceased'), of whom eleven are women, one a baronet and thirteen esquires: all the rest are plain 'Mr', perhaps reflecting the more workaday, less genteel character of the City (LMA, ACC/2558/MW/C/15/305 List of the names of the proprietors).

nearly three centuries of documents accumulated by London's water companies, all preserved when they and their corporate records were taken over in 1904. When the Metropolitan Water Board in turn was transformed into Thames Water and privatised in the 1980s, the documents were handed over wholesale to the LMA. They were catalogued by company: ACC/2558 refers to the whole collection, and each of the nineteenth-century water companies has a two letter designation: NR for New River, GJ for Grand Junction and so on. But what did MW/C mean? And why was a Southwark & Vauxhall document not filed under SV?

What I had (luckily) stumbled upon, it transpired, was a collection of 'items abstracted from the archives of the Metropolitan Water Board and its predecessors for exhibition purposes' and then never returned to their original places. ACC/2558/MW/C stood for Metropolitan Water Board clerk's department. Many of the visually most arresting and historically most interesting items in the LMA's water industry collection had ended up under ACC/2558/MW/C. And this particular storage box was a revelation: what caught my eye when I opened it was less the nine-page survey of the Southwark & Vauxhall's history that I was supposed to be looking at; nor the New River's eighteenth-century correspondence with Thomas Coram's Foundling Hospital; nor the *Illustrated London News*' article on London's water supply from 1884 – one of many written by Victorian journalists, for whom water infrastructure and its history was a source of recurrent fascination.

What elicited a raised eyebrow of astonishment and a suppressed whoop of excitement was a series of impressive documents issued and signed by eighteenth-century kings and queens. They dated from an era when monarchs were concerned with both important affairs of state and trivial matters of what amounted to housekeeping – and treated both with the same prolix solemnity.

The earliest document dated from July 1725 and was addressed, like the others, to 'The Governour and Company of Chelsea Water Works'. It was a warrant giving the company permission to use as reservoirs a pond and a 'Canal or Bason lately made . . . over against Devonshire House' in what was then part of St James's Park but which we now know as Green Park; they were to supply 'our Palace of St James's and the lower part of Westminster' and the company was given permission to lay pipes from them. The Surveyor-General had reported that the reservoirs would produce enough water for a fountain in the Palace gardens. The company was to supply the Palace at 'low and moderate rates'.

Another warrant, dated June 1729, gave permission to enlarge the 'upper canal' in St James's Park and was signed Caroline R, 'By the Queen's Most Excellent Majesty Guardian of the Kingdom etc' – Caroline was married to George II and acted as regent during his visits to Hanover, where he was also the Elector. In 1736 the company obtained the Queen's warrant to enlarge another reservoir in Hyde Park and to install a waterwheel on the 'Serpentine River' to drive a pump. The company's pitch had obviously been made on aesthetic as well as on utilitarian grounds: accompanying the warrant was a charming watercolour plan showing the existing round basin and its enlargement, surrounded by avenues of stylised trees. Curling round inside the circular basin and down a long straight extension is the legend 'This is propos'd to hold a Large Quantity of Water, and will be Beautyfull to the Parke'.[9]

The New River was a creature of the City, but the Chelsea Waterworks served Westminster – and Westminster was the Crown's territory. Royal permission was obviously required for reservoirs in the royal parks, but royal goodwill, to put it no higher, was useful if you wanted to operate in Westminster at all. And many of those who lived in the new streets and squares of St James's and the West End – such as Hanover Square and Cavendish Square – had connections at court: good relations with the Palace were good for business.

In fact, to start a waterworks anywhere in London, it helped to have connections – the political sort. A water company needed the right to buy land and dig up the roads to lay pipes, and for that it needed an act of Parliament or a patent from the Crown or permission from the City. Starting a waterworks was as much a political challenge as a technical or financial one, and it is striking how many of the early water companies numbered MPs among their founders, or their founders' friends and relations. One of those who set up the Chelsea company, for instance, was Richard Molesworth. He was a member of the Irish parliament in Dublin, which wasn't much help in starting a London waterworks, but his father was a member of the Parliament at Westminster – and of the committee that scrutinised and approved the Chelsea company's bill.

Influential friends could be useful in heading off potential competitors as well. At least twice during the eighteenth century, the idea of an aqueduct to bring water from the Colne was revived, in 1718 and 1764. Both schemes failed to get the necessary act of Parliament thanks to opposition from landowners and mill owners and the New River, all of whom were well represented in both the Commons and the Lords. The bills' failure meant that, although the Colne scheme was revived at least three times more in 1830, 1855 and 1872, from the mid-eighteenth century on the Thames and the Lea were the only practical sources for water in the quantities London needed – a significant problem in the nineteenth century, when both rivers became horribly polluted.

The Chelsea company, incorporated in 1723, was one of the most successful of the early water companies, surviving right through to 1904. Though it served Westminster, it got its name because it took its water from the Thames at Chelsea. A channel took the water up to a reservoir on the site of what is now Victoria station – the railway simply took over and filled in the channel and the basin after the waterworks had moved upriver. The basin filled up at high tide. Some of the water was then released into another channel that led back into the Thames and turned a water-wheel, which in its turn powered a pump that sent water to the reservoirs in St James's Park and Hyde Park.

The first engineers

Seventeenth- and eighteenth-century London was booming. The population expanded from around 200,000 in 1600 to 500,000 in the 1670s, and 740,000 in 1760. A brick tide crept across the landscape, especially to the east and west, like obliterating lava. New streets sprang up among the fields and market gardens, and keeping their inhabitants watered posed a series of technical challenges; tackling them prompted the emergence of a new profession.

George Sorocold was described as many things – an architect, an expert on hydraulics, a mathematician – but he was also the first English civilian to be called an engineer. He was one of a number of knowledgeable outsiders on whom the New River relied in its early years for high-level technical expertise. Christopher Wren, no less – architect, astronomer and polymath (as well as 'Surveyor' of the King's Works) – had been asked, around 1700, to suggest ways to improve the company's inadequate supply to Soho Square in the rapidly growing West End. He was defeated by the ramshackle way in which the company's network had developed, concluding, in effect, with the engineer's equivalent of 'I wouldn't start from here'.

Sorocold had more success: he correctly diagnosed the problem and how to solve it. Unhappily, the practical measures he took to implement his own plan fell short and may have contributed to the end of his career as an expert on waterworks.

Sorocold had married young, just seven months after being admitted to Emmanuel College, Cambridge, in 1684. His formal education thus finished abruptly and he went on to have at least thirteen children. No one seems to know where he acquired his engineering expertise, but neither a lack of training nor his wife's incessant pregnancies prevented him building up a busy practice in England and Scotland from the mid-1680s onwards, specialising in waterworks. In London he worked on improvements not only for the New River but for London Bridge Waterworks, for whom he designed a waterwheel that rose and fell with the tide. He was acknowledged to be 'ingenious', and he built (water-driven) 'engines', so we shouldn't be surprised that in 1708 a contemporary coined a new term and called him 'that great English engineer'.[10]

At the New River, Sorocold constructed a second reservoir just up the hill from New River Head, known as the Upper Pond, which is still in use in Claremont Square, beside the buses toiling up Pentonville Road. It features – along with the rest of New River Head – in several artists' prospects of eighteenth-century London from the north, though Canaletto thought the view needed improving and casually moved it 200 yards to the west.[11] The reservoir's purpose was to provide sufficient pressure to supply the West End and Islington with something more than a weak and apologetic dribble. This was a good plan, and it worked; where Sorocold failed was in devising ways to push water up the hill to the new reservoir from New River Head. He designed a pump powered, uniquely and unsuccessfully, by a combined six-sail windmill and horse-mill. The windmill was one of the earliest tower mills built in Britain, but was twice in twenty years deprived of its sails in high winds and had to be abandoned. Unfortunately the building also proved too narrow at the bottom for the horse to exert its full force to work the machinery, as it walked round and round inside. Much of the pumping power was in fact supplied by a waterwheel driven by the overflow from the reservoir at New River Head, and Sorocold's structure was later supplanted by a steam engine.[12]

This may have been Sorocold's last project, because after 1711 he virtually disappears from the historical record: he was described in 1717 as the 'ingenious, unfortunate mathematician'. Perhaps the failed experiment at

the New River precipitated a breakdown; perhaps all
those children simply got too much for him?[13]

An operation of the New River's complexity really
required a chief technical officer on the staff – something
the directors evidently realised after their experiences with
Sorocold. So around 1718 they appointed a rising young
man called Henry Mill, then in his thirties. Mill was an
inventor with two patents to his name, one for an improved
type of carriage spring and the other for what may have
been the world's first typewriter, though no clues have survived as to how it actually worked. He was taken on as the
New River's 'surveyor' but reported directly to the board,
so was more than just a middle-ranking overseer. By 1725,
he was being referred to for the first time in the company's
history as 'engineer and surveyor of the works'.

He designed other waterworks, at Northampton and at
Sir Robert Walpole's Norfolk estate, Houghton Hall, but
he sounds a rather lazy man. In the winter of 1741–2 a
group of New River shareholders surveyed the state of the
river and wrote a series of damning reports on the work
Mill was doing on a site near Ware. They clearly didn't
think much of him. He failed to get out of bed at his inn
until late morning, having sprained his ankle, employed a
great many labourers to little or no purpose, left them
unsupervised, and produced designs either 'in so grand a
manner as if for a Cathedral' or simply baffling. 'There is
a piece of brickwork. Wee inquir'd the use of it, but it was
a mistery to everyone there, as well as to us . . . Some persons suppos'd to understand such work, are of Opinion,
that Mr Mill is out of his Element, and knows not what he
is about.' In his defence, it was bitterly cold and the workmen were 'so bennum'd as scarce to be able to handle their

tooles'. 'On our Return from this Survey,' the shareholders wrote, 'wee met Mr Mill going to his workmen & could not forbear blaming his so scandalously dilatory method of acting, but the weather being so severely cold, would not wait his tedious apologies . . .'[14]

Despite this, he remained in post for more than fifty years, until his death at the age of eighty-seven in 1770, becoming the first, if not the most distinguished, in a long line of long-serving and long-lived London water engineers.

5

Here Be Dragons

On Valentine's Day 1726 a pair of dragons appeared just off the Strand. 'A Lancashire wizzard, with green matted locks and grim visage, will for some hours feed the eldest dragon with live coals', a pamphlet published a few weeks earlier had predicted. 'And a Welshman, bred on the top of Penmanmaur . . . will lay hold of the bridle to direct the motion of the creature.' The dragon, readers were told, lived on Newcastle and Scotch coal, and would produce so much smoke from its nostrils that it risked blotting out the sun.[1]

London's first proper steam engine was a sensation. Its construction at the York Buildings Waterworks at the foot of Villiers Street provoked intense interest and some concern – all of which the pamphlet satirised. The author was probably Dr John Arbuthnot, doctor, mathematician and good friend of some of the greatest literary luminaries of the age, including Jonathan Swift and Alexander Pope. He was also a close associate of the Duke of Chandos, a leading shareholder in the York Buildings company and the developer of an estate of expensive new housing around what is now Cavendish Square, just off Oxford Street. York Buildings had constructed a reservoir 100 yards north of the square and laid a pipe to it from the river to supply the new houses: the steam engine was needed to force the water up and along the pipe.

Its arrival caused alarm among the waterworks' neighbours. They feared not only the smoke but the noise and the risk of an explosion. The pamphlet mocks those fears: the idea that the engine might be so forceful that it risked sucking the Thames dry seems, shall we say, an exaggeration. The text was an elaborate joke, even if Chandos himself dismissed it as 'a very stupid performance'.[2]

Whoever wrote the pamphlet had almost certainly watched the new engine in action (it took weeks to get it working properly). But even a sophisticated observer such as Arbuthnot struggled to convey the true strangeness of this new mechanical beast, as did a Swiss traveller who found the whole contraption 'curious'. 'Smoke issuing with force through a little tube,' he wrote, with the hesitant command of technical detail of a man faced with an outlandish novelty, 'and corresponding with a large and tightly covered boiler full of boiling water, sets in motion a large piece of machinery, composed of wheels, counterpoise, and pendulum, which in their turn cause two large pumps to work continually.'[3]

The man in Arbuthnot's account, feeding the dragon with coals, was what we would call a stoker. Over the next two centuries stokers became ubiquitous: anything powered by steam, whether an industrial engine, a railway locomotive or a ship, depended on the brawn of stokers or firemen shovelling coal, their faces reddened by the heat from their fireboxes. It was a skilled job, requiring not just the muscle to move up to two tons of coal a shift but the ability to distribute the stuff evenly across the grate. Here was London's first stoker.

The Welshman with his 'bridle' was the engine minder or driver. To the pamphlet's author, his movements must have looked like those of a man riding or driving a horse. A better analogy might have been the helmsman of a small sailing boat, constantly trimming the vessel, making small adjustments to keep on course while making the most of the wind and the tide. His job, too, was a new one, requiring new knowledge and new skills.

The York Buildings dragon had been designed by Thomas Newcomen, who called it an 'atmospheric engine'. It didn't last. It was taken out of commission in 1731 because the cost of the coal to run it made it too expensive. Newcomen had developed his engine to pump water from mines and for that it proved both effective and economic: either they were coal mines, with an abundance of fuel on the spot, or they were tin mines or lead mines where the value of the end product justified the expense. But York Buildings was pumping water not to get at something much more valuable but for its own sake, and water was a decidedly low-value commodity. The extravagance of a steam engine could not be justified. The company went back to using horses to power its pumps, trudging in an endless circle; its unpaid coal bill totalled £660 15s. And it was still unpaid sixty years later in 1794, by which time the sum outstanding had risen to £840 15s with interest.[4]

Discovering steam

Newcomen was not, in fact, the first to harness steam power to pump water, nor the first to employ it at York Buildings. Steam's moment had first arrived some thirty or forty years earlier. Just as the idea of the carbon filament lamp occurred to both Edison and Swan in 1879, so the idea of using steam as a source of energy dawned on several experimenters and theoreticians in a similar lightbulb moment in the closing decades of the seventeenth century.

Credit is usually given to Thomas Savery for getting there first. In 1698 he patented a 'fire engine', exploiting the fact that water heated to steam occupies a much greater space than in its liquid state – 1,670 times greater, in fact. If the steam is not released into the atmosphere but retained in a closed vessel, the pressure it exerts is enormous; conversely, if the steam is allowed to condense in the vessel, it creates a partial vacuum which will suck in air – or water – to fill it.

A Savery fire engine has no piston and no moving parts, except taps to operate valves. It works by releasing steam from the boiler into a cylinder. The steam cools and condenses and a valve is then opened, which sucks in the water to be lifted. More steam from the boiler is then allowed into the vessel and the pressure forces the water up and out through another valve.

Savery installed small versions of his machine in large private houses, and then the York Buildings company installed one in 1713 or 1714. But it was not a success. A major disadvantage, by comparison with later steam engines, was that the valves had to be opened and shut by hand. But there were other problems as well: the engine was double the size of those Savery had installed elsewhere, and he discovered what many inventors and developers have since found, that scaling up is not as straightforward as it sounds. He also taxed the manufacturing techniques of the day to breaking point and beyond.[5]

'I have known Captain Savery at York Buildings make steam eight or ten times stronger than common air,' a contemporary wrote, 'and then its heat was so great that it would melt common soft solder; and its strength so great as to blow open several of the joints of his machine.' Another observer wrote that the engine was too big for one man to work: 'And it was liable to so many disorders, if a single mistake happen'd in the working of it, that at length it was look'd upon as a useless piece of work and rejected.'[6]

Newcomen's 'dragon' was a considerable improvement on Savery's engine. It was the first to use steam to drive a piston, and thus the first that most of us would recognise as a steam engine, with enough moving parts to mesmerise onlookers like John Arbuthnot and the Swiss observer. It was called an atmospheric engine because it used atmospheric pressure at 14.7lb per square inch (psi) to force a piston down into a cylinder in which steam was condensing and creating a partial vacuum. The piston was attached at the top to one end of a wooden beam, which rocked on a central fulcrum (hence 'beam engine', another name for these devices). The other end of the beam was connected by a chain to a pump below the engine, and the weight of the pumping mechanism at the end of the chain pulled the beam down and the piston up again at the end of each stroke, while the cylinder filled with fresh steam, ready to condense and start the next cycle. Newcomen marketed his invention under Savery's patent, but it worked on a quite different principle.

Over time a good many improvements were made to Newcomen's design, and, by 1740 – a decade after York Buildings scrapped its engine – London's water engineers were ready to have another go. A frost in the hard winter of 1739–40, followed by a prolonged dry spell that was to last years, disrupted supplies of water and made customers restless. The problem was especially acute for the Chelsea company, which was expanding fastest in order to supply the emerging West End and needed a way to force more water from its intake in Chelsea to its reservoir in Hyde Park. In October 1741 the directors resolved to investigate buying a 'fire engine' and sent a deputation to Bristol to look at steam engines employed in the coal mines there. In December 1741, they ordered the first of two Newcomen engines. It became a tourist attraction. A print from 1752 depicts a group of well-dressed saunterers come to see this strange machine, standing at the water's edge while a man poles a raft made of elm pipes past them, and black smoke streams from the new engine house: the Dukes of Buckingham, in what would become Buckingham Palace, did not appreciate the smoke.[7]

Next the Shadwell waterworks installed a Newcomen engine, and York Buildings tried again with more success in 1752. In 1760 the London Bridge Waterworks installed one on the riverside at Broken Wharf. Then, in 1766, the design was improved still further in a machine built for the New River by the great eighteenth-century engineer John Smeaton; it replaced George Sorocold's horse mill for pumping water from New River Head to the company's upper reservoir. By 1775 there were ten engines operating in total, and London had become an important market for steam: the Industrial Revolution had arrived in the metropolis.

Erasmus Darwin celebrated the new technology in verse in his long poem of 1792, *The Economy of Vegetation*. He discerned in the coal mined from 'earth's remotest caves' a 'giant-power', which was transforming urban life, not least in its application to waterworks:

Here high in air the rising stream he pours
To clay-built cisterns, or to lead-lined towers;
Fresh through a thousand pipes the wave distils,
And thirsty cities drink the exuberant rills.

He predicted a bright future now that mankind had found a
way to harness nature's power:

Soon shall thy arm, unconquered steam, afar
Drag the slow barge, or drive the rapid car;
Or on wide waving winds expanded bear
The flying chariot through the fields of air.[8]

It was a shrewd forecast, though no one yet has succeeded
in building a steam-powered aeroplane.

The envy of Europe

By the mid-eighteenth century London had become dependent on the man-made water networks that kept it alive.
Cities had long been talked of as living organisms: now London's water supply made the metaphor a reality. An author
in 1756 listed eighty-eight large water mains across the
city – including the fifty-eight belonging to the New River –
which, he wrote, 'like the veins and arteries in the body
natural, are branched out into a vast number of smaller
pipes which convey the water through all parts of the City
and suburbs; into the houses of which it is carried by small
leaden pipes, to the great convenience of the citizens who
(I think it is not to be doubted) are better supplied with this
precious element than the inhabitants of any other city.'[9]

It became a commonplace, uttered by admiring visitors and self-satisfied locals alike, that London's water supply was the envy of Europe. European visitors were astonished and impressed by London's networks of pipes and the fact that water was delivered to 'every house', when even the most advanced European cities could manage little more than piped water to public fountains.

Englishmen, too, enthused. An updated edition of Stow's *Survey of London* in 1720 wrote of the New River and the other London water companies:

> There is not a street in London, but one or other of these waters runs through it in pipes, conveyed under ground: and from those pipes there is scarce a house, whose rent is £15 or £20 per annum, but hath the convenience of water brought into it, by small leaden pipes laid into the great ones. And for the smaller tenements, such as are in courts and alleys, there is generally a cock or pump common to the inhabitants; so that I may boldly say, that there is never a city in the world that is so well served with water.[10]

Nonetheless, there were grounds for complaint. One was that, increasingly, people had no alternative but to pay for water, and the burden fell especially heavily on the poor – even the inhabitants of courts and alleys probably paid their landlord, who in turn paid one of the water companies for the supply to the common tap.

The piped supply, once a luxury, had become a necessity as the city grew and alternative sources of water vanished. Most of the surface water that was once abundant in London had disappeared into culverts or was too polluted to drink safely. By the end of the century some

80 per cent of the houses north of the river were supplied with commercial water.

There were still alternatives. You could dig your own private well, though that was itself expensive and increasing abstraction of groundwater by breweries meant wells sometimes failed because someone else was taking the water. You could use the parish pump, which was free – but only if you could afford the time you might have to spend in the queue. Or you could dip a bucket into the Thames, and for those living close this was evidently a popular option. The Lambeth Waterworks, when it launched in 1782, deliberately chose not to lay pipes in streets close to the river because it assumed people there wouldn't be willing to pay.

Another cause of complaint was that the companies couldn't keep up with the demand they had created. They resorted to a number of strategies to cope, not all of them customer-friendly. The Chelsea company supplied water at the outset for seven hours a day on three days a week; but in 1729 it switched to delivering six days a week for just three hours – a crafty saving of three hours of water a week. In 1730 it did something similar, reducing supply to four hours a day on four days a week: manoeuvres that, between them, reduced the total hours from twenty-one to sixteen a week. But shortages and the need to ration delivery persisted, which was how the company came to take the brave step of buying a steam engine. Elsewhere companies flatly refused to lay pipes to newly built streets, ostensibly because they didn't think it would pay (in which case, owners or builders often paid to put in services themselves), or they disconnected customers in distant parts of their service area to save on water.

The consumer finds a voice

One result of all this was the first stirrings of a consumer consciousness that was to find fuller expression at the beginning of the next century. It first emerged in a series of pseudonymous letters to the newspapers in 1766 and 1767, identified by the historical geographer Carry van Lieshout in her study of London's eighteenth century water industry; the letters were perhaps written by supporters of one of the periodic schemes to bring water from the Colne, in competition with the New River. They introduced readers to the idea, novel to many of them, that monopolies might not work in the public interest; this was cutting-edge economic thinking, a decade before Adam Smith published *The Wealth of Nations*. 'When we have but one shop to go to,' wrote someone who signed himself DL, 'we must take the commodity at the seller's own price; and in many parts of Westminster, where the water is alone supplied from the New River, individuals have suffered great inconveniences. But it is to be hoped the Parliament will, by opening fresh shops, prevent an almost absolute monopoly.'[11]

Competition was not forthcoming in the 1760s – the Colne scheme failed to win parliamentary backing – and events during the first two decades of the nineteenth century demonstrated that, in the water industry at any rate, it can be disastrous, which is one reason why today we think of water as a 'natural monopoly'. But the seed planted in the 1760s bore fruit over the next few decades. Two correspondents to the *Morning Post* in 1775, who signed themselves *Curtius* and *Aquae Vindex*, attacked the water company directors as 'covetous, mercenary men', described the supply to lower Westminster as a 'matter of acquatic tyranny' and attacked the arbitrary charges and take-it-or-leave-it attitude of the Chelsea company.[12]

A year later John Scott of Amwell wrote his poem, quoted in Chapter 2, describing the New River as a 'mercenary stream'. Scott knew what his contemporaries were saying and echoed them. Like others, he compared the company's pipe network with the 'arterial tubes' of the human body, but one in which nature and commerce were entwined. And he lamented that the company's product was a 'purchas'd wave'.

Then in east London in 1785, a man called John Robins, living in Ratcliffe, finally lost patience with his supplier, the Shadwell Waterworks, after his water rates had gone up from 10s a year in 1772 to 15s in 1778 and then 18s. At that point he refused to pay the new charge, though he offered to continue paying at the old rate. The company cut him off and summonsed him to court and he resorted to fetching water from the Thames. He argued his case in 1790 in a pamphlet, 'A Bone to Pick—recommended to the several water companies of this metropolis; or a check to Avarice, Tyranny and Oppression'. The company, he maintained, was guilty of 'arbitrary and insolent behaviour to their customers' and 'unreasonable and unjustifiable demands'. It was able to get away with it, he said, because it had entered into a 'diabolical combination' with the neighbouring West Ham Waterworks, founded in 1743: 'This is the blessed effect of monopoly,' he concluded.[13]

Robins was right. There *was* a 'diabolical combination' at work in the London water industry; in fact there were several, as the companies colluded rather than competed with one another. The Shadwell and West Ham companies had, as Robins suspected, reached an agreement not to undercut one another on price: the deed setting it out is dated 1785, the year Robins decided enough was enough, but the arrangement had apparently been in place for some years. In the City, the New River and the London Bridge Waterworks had agreed not to poach each other's customers or offer them cheaper water way back in 1738,[14] and in 1799 the London Bridge Company came to an arrangement with the Borough Waterworks in Southwark to raise prices simultaneously in order to maintain the 'harmony between the companies'. There were plenty of examples of companies helping one another out when they experienced difficulties with supply, and sometimes tipping their notional rivals off when disgruntled customers sought to switch. In the 1720s and 30s, it is true, the New River and Chelsea companies competed vigorously for customers in the West End, but in time they concluded – without anybody writing the fact down – that competing on price was a mug's game. What looked on paper like a competitive business, with multiple overlaps between the companies' service areas, was in fact a comfortable oligopoly – a market dominated by a small number of large sellers. One consequence of oligopoly is that the suppliers usually collude in keeping prices high, and that's what they did in London's eighteenth-century water business.

The standard bearers for this early consumer movement were not wholly in agreement about what needed to be done to improve things. The Colne scheme proxies in the 1760s thought competition was the answer. So did John Robins and *Curtius* – 'who wished there were twenty more waterworks and that all by a reasonable charge might prosper'. *Aquae Vindex* thought there should be a free municipal supply available to anyone who didn't want to pay the companies' charges.[15]

In truth, they were the only possible solutions, at a time when the resources of the British state weren't powerful or organised enough to apply a third solution: government regulation. In the eighteenth century, none of the campaigners got what they wanted. In the early nineteenth century, competition was tried – and found wanting. Public ownership and regulation had to wait a good deal longer.

Engineering dynasties

Henry Mill at the New River had been the first employee of a London water company with 'engineer' in his job title. By the mid-eighteenth century, most of London's growing fleet of water companies were employing someone on the staff to act as their chief engineer, though he might well be styled 'inspector' or 'surveyor'. They included some talented and distinguished men.

Mill's successor at the New River was Robert Mylne, an energetic Scottish wunderkind, descended from generations of Edinburgh masons, who himself trained as both a mason and a carpenter before taking himself off to Paris and then Rome to learn architecture.[16] There he was tutored by Piranesi, studied the Roman system of aqueducts, visited Pompeii, Herculaneum and Sicily, and earned the grudging respect of his much wealthier contemporary and potential rival, Robert Adam, who is today much better known. Adam, another Scotsman, was also studying in Rome and acknowledged Mylne's talent, but feared that, because he was poor, he might poach jobs by being willing to work more cheaply.

In 1758 Mylne won first prize for architecture at Rome's Academy of St Luke – the first Briton ever to do so.* He arrived back in London aged twenty-six, planning to travel home to Edinburgh by ship, when he learned of a competition to build a new bridge over the river at Blackfriars. The deadline gave him two months to prepare drawings. There were sixty-nine entries, a vigorous pamphlet war (in which Mylne pseudonymously rubbished his rivals), and then he got the job. It may have helped that the secretary of the committee running the competition was a fellow Scot.

Mylne's bridge took almost a decade to build but was widely admired and made his reputation. He fared better as a bridge-builder than his elder brother, William, whose North Bridge linking Edinburgh with its New Town across the Nor' Loch collapsed when almost complete, killing five people. Robert's bridge lasted just under a century but had to be replaced when the removal of old London Bridge just downstream increased the speed of the river's flow and undermined it. He went on to have a distinguished career as a designer of public buildings and country houses, and as clerk of the works at the Royal

* There was a grand prize-giving with three specially written 'symphonies', attended by ambassadors, nobility, monsignors, artists and dilettanti and sixteen cardinals. The Old Pretender, son of James II, and the Stuart claimant to the British throne, was also there, though that was tactfully not mentioned in Mylne's letters home. Robert Adam, still wary and still jealous, went to see his winning designs and (perhaps predictably) didn't think much of them (Ward, *The Man Who Buried Nelson*, p. 36).

Hospital in Greenwich and surveyor of the fabric at St Paul's Cathedral.

*

The New River's offices, and the company's wharf, at which elm logs were landed and bored out to make pipes, were right next to Blackfriars bridge, and Mylne succeeded Henry Mill as the New River's 'surveyor and engineer' in 1767. He stayed in the job until his own death in 1811, when he was succeeded by his son, William, who served until *his* death in 1863, father and son between them occupying the post for an astonishing ninety-six years. Robert's attachment to the venture can be judged from the fact that he gave William the middle name Chadwell, after one of the River's two original springs, and for much of his time with the company he and his family lived in the Water House at New River Head. The Mylnes are buried in a neo-classical mausoleum in the churchyard at Great Amwell, looking down through the trees on the pool in the river that marks the site of the second original spring.

Mylne also helped establish engineering as a profession. In 1771 he was a founder member, with John Smeaton, builder of bridges, harbours and lighthouses and pioneering improver of steam engine technology, of the Society of Civil Engineers, which met weekly in London coffee houses and taverns. Until its establishment, Mylne later recalled, engineers rarely met one another unless it was when they gave evidence in court cases. He and Smeaton thought it might be helpful to have a less adversarial forum – with no point-scoring lawyers present – in which engineers could exchange ideas and where 'the sharp edges of their minds might be rubbed off'.[17]

Another founder member was John Rennie, like Smeaton a builder of canals, docks and bridges, and a man who also worked in the London water business as the first engineer of the Grand Junction Waterworks. His son, another John and also a distinguished engineer, later remarked that, until the society's foundation, the profession of civil engineer was unknown. 'Previous to that time we were simply known as "vulgar mechanics" – men who toiled with their hands, as masons, bricklayers, carpenters, blacksmiths etc.'[18]

The society (later renamed the 'Smeatonian Society' after Smeaton's death) was essentially a dining club. The first professional organisation, the Institution of Civil Engineers, did not arrive until 1818. But Smeaton and Mylne's club was an early acknowledgement that such a thing as civil engineering existed and that its practitioners might benefit from sharing their experiences and expertise.

*

Many eighteenth-century engineers were, to varying degrees, self-taught. Mylne was exceptional in having both a craftsman's technical training and a professional education as an architect. Samuel Hearne at the London Bridge Waterworks had no technical training or theoretical understanding of hydraulics at all: he had previously been the company's secretary. Another engineer, Thomas Simpson (whom we first met in the Introduction), began his career, like Mylne, as a craftsman, in his case a millwright near Carlisle. He arrived at the Chelsea Waterworks in 1778 and first came to the notice of the Chelsea directors in 1781. They had commissioned another millwright on their staff to recommend improvements to their waterwheel: along with the company's steam engines, it drove the pumps that sent water from the waterworks' tidal basin at Pimlico to the reservoirs in Green Park and Hyde Park. Simpson put in alternative proposals of his own. An outside expert endorsed Simpson's suggestions and the directors adopted them. His new wheel raised more water, and the board gave him a thirty guinea bonus, then another bonus when he installed a second new wheel shortly afterwards.[19]

In February 1784 Simpson was appointed the company's 'inspector'. As a practical engineer, he made one enormous contribution to the water supply not just of London but of towns and cities everywhere. He devised a method for joining iron pipes by inserting them into one another via a socket and sealing the joint with hemp or flax and soldered lead: previously they had been joined with flanges, which left no room for expansion, and the pipes cracked as the temperature changed. Simpson's innovation made the early nineteenth-century switch from wood to iron pipes feasible.

Even before becoming Chelsea's de facto chief engineer, Simpson had been appointed engineer to the Lambeth Waterworks as well, and when he died he was succeeded in both roles by his son, James, one of the most impressive and influential of nineteenth-century water engineers. James was still in post at both Chelsea and Lambeth at his death in 1869, which meant father and son between them served for eighty-five years, almost rivalling the Mylnes for longevity.

6

Water Wars

Ralph Dodd was a visionary. He was also an exceptionally difficult man. He started out as a painter before becoming a self-styled engineer, and tried and failed to dig the first tunnel under the Thames, from Gravesend to Tilbury: work started in 1799 but was abandoned in 1802 after more than £15,000 had been spent. Throughout his life his fertile imagination threw up ingenious plans for projects of all sorts, most of which never came to fruition, or if they did, were implemented by sounder men.

Among his better ideas was the creation of new water companies for London. In 1805 he published *Observations on Water*, an eccentric mix of science, history and self-justification (the failure of the Gravesend tunnel was not his fault, according to a footnote stretching over several pages), which also pointed out the unmet need for a piped supply to London's expanding suburbs and promoted two new water companies, the South London and the East London Waterworks.[1]

Both companies were duly launched and received acts of Parliament, but Dodd's connection with them was short lived. In August 1805, the South London Waterworks fired him as its engineer, for reasons unspecified: the directors felt they could not share them with their shareholders.

Then, in August 1807, he was dismissed by the East London Waterworks as well. A few years later he was convicted of assaulting the clerk to the Colchester Waterworks, where he was also briefly engineer: his lawyer described him as 'irritable'. The problem, whatever it was, ran in the family: in 1806, his son, Barrodale Dodd, was sacked by the board of the newly created West Middlesex Waterworks after quarrelling with the directors; their secretary later described him as 'refractory'.[2]*

All three companies survived the departure of the argumentative – and very probably incompetent – Dodd and his son, and went on to inaugurate a period of intense, even destructive competition in water supply: a real-world test of the new-fangled ideas about the benefits of free markets and competition put about by Adam Smith. The economist had a low opinion of most joint-stock companies, but believed that 'bringing water for the supply of a great city' was one of only four types of business other than overseas trade to which the joint-stock form was suited. The others were banking, insurance and canals. Why? Because most of what they did was routine, so there was little opportunity, he felt, for the companies to mess up.[3] London's 'water wars' between 1810 and 1817, however,

* Ralph Dodd eventually gave up on waterworks and switched to steamboats. He died in 1822 at the age of sixty-seven, after being injured when the boiler of a boat burst at Gloucester; he was advised to go to Cheltenham for treatment, but being penniless, and despite his injuries, he walked there in mid-winter. It killed him. His worldly wealth amounted to just £2 5s. The editor of the *Mechanic's Magazine* called him 'a very ingenious schemer without any practical talent whatever' (John Graham-Leigh, *London's Water Wars*, pp. 84–5).

show that Smith got water comprehensively wrong. 'Messing up' turned out to be ridiculously easy, and unregulated competition proved to be a disaster. The companies were only rescued by the creation of a monopoly or cartel that aimed to restrict competition in the interests of the suppliers (but not, of course, the consumers). That would not have surprised Smith, whose many penetrating insights included the observation that 'People of the same trade seldom meet together, even for merriment and diversion, but the conversation ends in a conspiracy against the public or in some contrivance to raise prices'.

The story of the ensuing shambles is told in a little book by John Graham-Leigh, *London's Water Wars*, which is essential reading for anyone interested in London's water history. This chapter, in fact, is indebted to his work.

Monopoly under attack

The eighteenth century had seen a steady flow of new water companies. They included, besides the Chelsea Waterworks, the Bankside Waterworks established in the 1730s, the Borough company in 1771 and the Lambeth company in 1785. The latter's works were in the gardens of Belvedere House, now the site of the Royal Festival Hall, and its intake was where the Hungerford railway bridge into Charing Cross now stands.

Dodd's South London Waterworks joined them, serving an area stretching from Camberwell to Clapham, with water drawn from Vauxhall Creek at the mouth of the River Effra. The Effra itself meandered in bucolic fashion down from the hills of Norwood; the river mouth was overlooked by the Cumberland Tea Gardens, which have today been supplanted by the post-modern ziggurat housing MI6, and the Effra is a storm sewer. The company pumped its water to a pair of circular reservoirs near what is now the Oval cricket ground.

The South London company's relations with its main competitor were good. When it suffered an early disaster – its works were destroyed by fire in August 1807, six weeks after its launch – the Lambeth stepped in and offered to keep the supply going to its fifty-six customers until the South London could rebuild. The new company was prevented by its act of Parliament from competing in areas already served by the Lambeth company, and Lambeth voluntarily reciprocated, taking up pipes it had laid in the South London's district, 'being of the opinion that a competition would not be to the advantage of either company'.[4] This was sensible, and indeed the Lambeth's directors seem to have been unusually far-sighted and self-sacrificing for capitalists of the era: they had refrained from paying themselves (or their shareholders) a dividend in sixteen of the company's first thirty-five years, choosing instead to reinvest their profits. The policy paid off: between 1818 and 1833 the company paid annual dividends ranging from £50 to £250 per £300 share.

Things were less harmonious north of the river. The West Middlesex Waterworks was authorised to serve the area westward from Kensington through Hammersmith to Ealing and Hounslow. West Middlesex at this date was still largely agricultural, with scattered settlements and the occasional gentleman's villa: no one was likely to get rich supplying it with water. The new company was effectively forbidden from supplying the existing built-up area in

Westminster – if it took on any Chelsea Waterworks customers, it would have to pay its rival £10 per house.

The West Middlesex intake was at Hammersmith, just upstream from the Old Ship, a riverside pub, which was already old even then. The company's original building was replaced in 1909 by a new pumping station, which was in turn decommissioned in 1997 and converted into housing next to the Great West Road. Ninety thousand vehicles a day surge past it, oblivious to its history.

No sooner was the works at Hammersmith under construction than the company decided its ambitions were too modest – or perhaps that it would never make money unless it found a more populous district to supply. In May 1808 the directors minuted their view that 'the well-known extortion and limited power as to supply of the New River Company and the bad water and injudicious management of the Chelsea company render a competition against them, even in the lower or long established part of Marylebone, likely to be very gainful'. Unfortunately, the £20,000-worth of engines and reservoirs at Hammersmith were not up to the task of serving this much larger area, and so had to be expensively scrapped and replaced even before they had gone into service.[5]

The company purchased a tract of land in Kensington and constructed a reservoir on Campden Hill near Notting Hill Gate. In 1810 it got a second act of Parliament authorising it to supply a whole series of parishes in the burgeoning West End. It had widespread support from local residents, who were delighted at the prospect of competition if they thought it would give them a better service, and plenty signed a petition in favour of the company.

The West Middlesex directors believed – or pretended to believe – that they were on a crusade against monopoly: 'The struggle against an attempt at monopoly,' they told their shareholders in November 1809, when they announced that they were 'determined to possess the North Western District', including Marylebone and Paddington (and that the shareholders were going to have to cough up more money to pay for it), 'will add additional lustre to the patriotic exertions of the individuals who have so liberally advanced their capital in this most important public undertaking.' Monopoly – which in the seventeenth century had been the businessman's friend, a necessary guarantee of commercial success – had become a dirty word.[6]

The West Middlesex duly pressed ahead, laying mains in areas served by the New River and/or the Chelsea companies. Central to the directors' offer to customers was 'high service' to cisterns on floors above ground level in order to supply upstairs WCs and bedrooms, thanks to 'the power of their engines' and 'the matchless elevation of their grand reservoir'.[7]

Across town the East London Waterworks got its act of Parliament in August 1807 and quickly bought the two existing companies serving the area, the Shadwell Waterworks and the West Ham. Its intake was at Old Ford on the River Lea and to begin with it confined itself to laying pipes through the tract of open fields awaiting development east of Whitechapel. But then the East London directors decided to go on the offensive as well, and started laying mains into the New River's area in the City and northwards past Hackney. In June 1809 the company's committee of works submitted a report to the directors suggesting 'it was

material to the interest of this company to omit no opportunity of creating a competition in favour of the company'.[8]

A fourth important new player also entered the market,
the only one not connected with the Dodds. The Grand
Junction Waterworks was initially an offshoot of the Grand
Junction canal, which had powers it wasn't using to supply
water to households in the Paddington area. In 1811 those
powers were leased to a group of investors connected with
a venture called the Stone Pipe Company, which manufactured pipes by boring through limestone blocks quarried
near the village of Guiting Power in the Cotswolds.
The company had tried and failed to persuade first the
West Middlesex and then the East London to adopt its
product, so the Stone Pipe directors decided to set up their
own water companies instead, one in Manchester, one in
Dublin and one in London. They recruited the leading
engineer, John Rennie, obtained an act of Parliament in
1811, and set out to supply water pumped out of the canal
into reservoirs at Paddington.[9] The reservoirs – there were
eventually three – sat hard by what was to become Paddington station: one became Talbot Square, one Norfolk
Square, both of them traces of a manmade waterscape still
imprinted on the modern streetscape. The site of the third
lies underneath what is now St Mary's Hospital.

The Grand Junction competed directly with the New
River, the Chelsea and the West Middlesex. Its publicity
materials, as with those of the West Middlesex, promised
much – and it was also offering something no other
London water company had even contemplated: 'constant
supply'. For the first time customers would not have to wait
for the local turncock on his rounds every two or three
days to turn on their water. The Grand Junction's works,

the company boasted, were 'ten feet above the highest street in Marylebone, and (what has never before been effected) they give a supply so copious and regular, that the water is always on . . . This abundant supply of water is always pure in the pipes. It is constantly fresh, because it is always coming in.'[10] But within months the company was in trouble because the stone pipes turned out to leak, and leak badly: in July 1812, Rennie conceded that they weren't fit for purpose and, in March the following year, the company formally resolved 'to have nothing further to do with the stone pipes'. The ones already laid were dug up, and iron ordered for their replacements.[11]

The company's early history was haphazard. Board meetings often had to be abandoned because too few directors had bothered to turn up. In December 1812 the manager was let go because the company couldn't afford him: a tiny staff of just six men and a boy remained. John Rennie was furious when he heard the chairman had accused him of taking bribes from the Stone Pipe Company (the board seemed more concerned about who'd leaked the remark than in whether there was any truth in it).[12] And the directors made extravagant promises they couldn't keep. With such an inauspicious start, it's astonishing the company survived, let alone went on to flourish.

Speculators and spivs

The Grand Junction's first directors gave every impression of being a bunch of chancers, but in that they merely reflected the times. The Regency business world was an often corrupt place, and the new water companies and their managements were among the progeny that swam up from its murky depths.

Take the example of George Boulton Mainwaring. Mainwaring was the first chairman of the East London Waterworks, and a founding director of the Grand Junction, as well as a director of the Stone Pipe Company and, briefly, an MP. He was also an out-and-out crook. His father, William, had been MP for Middlesex and chairman of the Middlesex justices. William and his son ran a bank – which went bust in 1814 – and William also got his son on to the Middlesex bench and into the post of county treasurer, responsible for collecting a rate to pay for things such as prisons, court houses and bridges. In this post, it later emerged, George had successfully embezzled at least £18,000.

At the East London, he masterminded a scam in which he and a crony sold shares they weren't entitled to (and which they pretended had been taken by rich City bankers) at a considerable premium, inflating the price despite an express agreement that no shares would be sold on the open market for fear of encouraging speculation. He and the crony were thought to have made profits of between £10,000 and £12,000. Mainwaring had to resign as a director. He remained as Middlesex county treasurer, however, until his fraud there was unmasked in 1822 and he fled to the continent, never to be heard of again.

Among the East London's other directors were Joseph Merceron, Thomas Lumley and George Watts. Merceron was a profoundly unpleasant character, dubbed by his modern biographer 'the Boss of Bethnal Green'. He was a slum landlord, a corrupt Justice of the Peace and colleague of Mainwaring's on the bench, and the dominant if malign power in the Bethnal Green vestry. Metropolitan vestries were often corrupt, notorious for what the Victorians called 'jobbery': the practice of handing out building and supply contracts to one's mates. Bethnal Green was one of the worst and Merceron ran it as his personal fief through a combination of manipulation, intimidation and bribery, awarding lucrative contracts to his friends and siphoning large sums out of the vestry coffers into his own pocket. He was clever, energetic and evidently charismatic, as well as utterly unscrupulous: the original East End criminal godfather, a Mack the Knife in magistrate's garb.[13]

Lumley, a merchant in Gutter Lane, and Watts, a chemist in the Strand, were also directors of the West Middlesex (Lumley was its chairman) until they were forced to resign in December 1810: they had been part of a committee negotiating on behalf of the company to buy the York Buildings waterworks, but when the deal collapsed they promptly stepped in and completed the purchase as individuals, setting themselves up in competition with the West Middlesex. Their fellow directors took a dim view of this.

Lumley also had to resign from the East London after an inquiry into unusual movements in the company's share price: as with Mainwaring, he was suspected of having enriched himself by speculating in the shares allotted to him. (But then, so were the rest of the board.) The East London directors were accused of driving up the share price partly by paying dividends out of capital – that is, money raised from new shares – a questionable and unsustainable practice, which was nonetheless widespread in the early nineteenth century. Lumley and his chums had been able to make quick profits from share sales even before the company had started trading.

Similar charges of speculation were later made about the founders of the West Middlesex as well, where a £100 share was selling for £225 in June 1810 (the price later collapsed to £12). Critics accused them of having fraudulently gone on raising funds and laying pipes even though they knew their concern couldn't possibly make money, purely for the purpose of issuing shares that they could then sell at a profit. In 1821, the company's secretary, M. K. Knight, called all this an 'unfounded assertion', arguing that the founders were themselves victims. They had been 'duped' by their engineer into believing the capital investment required would be far less and the revenue far larger than turned out to be the case, just as all the new companies had been misled into thinking they could match the profitability of the New River Company: 'The fact simply appears to be this; that in 1810 the engineers and proprietors of the new companies were theorists, who laughed at the practical men, the old companies, and suspected them of unfair practices: in 1820 the theorists of 1810, though they have now become the practical men, have found to their cost the difference between reality and illusion.'

But in rejecting the charges, Knight was strategically vague. Between April and June 1810, when the West Middlesex share price was rising most sharply, he identified only three individuals who bought low and sold high and might therefore be defined as speculators. But he also identified twenty-eight original shareholders – whom he does not name – who sold their shares in this period, netting sometimes significant profits: Thomas Lumley would have been one of them. Were they not speculators too? Apparently not.[14]

Cast iron and dirty tricks

The collapse in share prices followed an outbreak of frenzied competition, made manifest by an epidemic of holes in the road – which, with their accompanying clutter and congestion, became a fact of London life. Cast-iron water pipes had arrived. They were the new companies' not-so-secret weapon, enabling them to offer the high service to upper floors that more affluent customers were starting to demand. They leaked much less than the old wooden pipes and could withstand higher pressures. And they had become cheaper: British iron production quadrupled between 1791 and 1810, and prices fell as a result. But they were still costly, especially for the old companies which had to dig up their existing wooden mains and replace them with iron to keep up with the newcomers.

A watercolour of 1834 by George Scharf depicts the laying of an iron water main in Tottenham Court Road, with tools and material strewn about, two men carefully drilling a hole in a large pipe in the background and, in the foreground, another workman, bent like some necromancer's assistant over a cauldron emitting black smoke and sparks; he is watched by a handful of wary children as he conjures the veins and sinews of the modern city into being.[15]

Scharf's picture is unusual only in making the business of laying pipes its central subject. Street excavations appear constantly in the work of nineteenth-century topographical artists, irritating and inconvenient in real life but adding incidental interest for the armchair viewer. In Thomas Shotter Boys' 1842 set of lithographs, *Original Views of London*, four of the sixteen street scenes feature roadworks or excavations of some kind, including a fine array of massive iron pipes waiting to be dropped into a trench in *Piccadilly, Eastwards*.[16] And one of the most famous of all Victorian paintings, Ford Madox Brown's *Work*, completed in 1865, depicts a gang of navvies in the bright morning sunshine in Heath Street, Hampstead, at work on a sewer. They are being observed by two middle-class intellectuals, Frederick Maurice (the founder of Christian socialism) and the historian Thomas Carlyle. The pair look like loafers but are, Brown tells us, really hard at work too . . . thinking.[17]

The vicious battle for market share among the water companies was fought partly on price, partly in more underhand ways. Consumers were inundated with a blizzard of paper – handbills and printed notices and special offers. On one Grand Junction handbill offering water 'at moderate rates', someone, presumably the collector, has scrawled '25 per cent less than the present price and 50 per cent where you have been over rated'. In 1811, the New River's collectors were authorised to cut customers' rates where the East London had made them an offer: in many cases prices came down by 20, sometimes 30 per cent. A New River handbill urged customers not to switch supplier until they had heard the New River's counter-offer: 'the New River Company,' it said, 'are determined to make a sacrifice, and meet their opponents on any terms they may offer.'[18]

Dirty tricks abounded. The commonest abuse seems to have been workmen from one company 'accidentally' damaging the lead pipes of a competitor's customers: sometimes they refused to repair the damage unless the customer agreed to switch suppliers. The West Middlesex made a habit of changing the supply to houses served by its competitors without the owners' consent, though often with the connivance of the household servants. The York Buildings company got in on the act, deploying its workmen by night to change New River customers over to its service without their knowledge. Rivals' employees were bribed. One of the New River's collectors put about a rumour that the West Middlesex was insolvent. One of its turncocks harassed West Middlesex employees as they canvassed for customers, 'shouting and using gross and insulting language'. Things got so bad that rival gangs of pipe-layers apparently had pitched battles in the trenches.[19]

Forty years later, *The Times* looked back with astonishment on what it called this 'war of extermination':

> The combatants sought (and openly avowed it), not their own profit but their rivals' ruin. Tenants were taken on almost any terms. Plumbers were bribed to tout like omnibus cads for custom. Such was the rage for mere numerical conquest that a line of pipes would be often driven down a long street to serve one new customer at the end. Arrears remained uncollected lest offence should be given and influence impaired. Capricious tenants amused themselves by changing from one main to another, as they might taste this or that tap of beer . . . In many streets there were three lines of water pipes laid down, involving triple leakage, triple pumping and storage costs, and a triple army of turncocks . . .[20]

The same streets were being dug up continually to lay mains and connect and disconnect customers. There was an inevitable backlash: residents and local authorities hated the mess and the expense of putting the road surface back, however much they enjoyed the prospect of different suppliers undercutting one another.

Monopoly triumphant

The financial pressure on the New River in particular was enormous. In February 1814, the board set up a committee to consider the company's position. In a sign that a truce might be imminent, it suggested no longer laying expensive iron pipes outside its core area. It also felt the New River was losing out for what seems to the modern observer to be an unlikely reason: its rivals had more shareholders.

The New River's seventy-two shares (some divided) were held by just 120 individuals, and they liked to think of themselves as a classy bunch. The new companies' thousands of shares were held by 'tradesmen and shopkeepers, who are continually canvassing and going from door to door, soliciting your tenants to change, and with a degree of activity and perseverance which can alone attach to principals in the concern'. Owning shares, once the preserve of the elite, was once more being democratised, as it had been during the South Sea Bubble, and even when they didn't break the rules, the new companies and their shareholders were playing the game with a vigour and commitment that the upper-crust types running the New River found hard to match. 'A board of gentlemen meeting once a week,' the New River directors decided, 'is perhaps not the best calculated successfully to contend in a warfare of this description . . . and who cannot and will not descend to some of the practices countenanced by their opponents.' The gentlemen amateurs of the New River feared they were being trounced by middle-class player-professionals with greater energy and fewer scruples.[21]

*

The New River may have struggled; the York Buildings company gave up completely. After its takeover by Lumley and his fellow-conspirators, it had raised a fortune in new capital, which it put into iron pipes and a new steam engine, only to find it simply couldn't get enough business to justify the investment. The company was ruined and York Buildings' water assets were bought by the New River. The London Bridge Waterworks also struggled. The New River laid pipes right through its district, poached many of its customers and was deaf to pleas from its smaller rival to be treated kindly. It did not survive the rebuilding of London Bridge, selling out to the New River when John Rennie's plans for a new bridge were approved.

The newcomers weren't making any money either. They all had to raise large amounts of extra capital – in the case of the West Middlesex, more than three times the amount originally authorised. And all three companies were unable to pay the dividends they had promised shareholders – even the East London, which briefly paid 7 per cent in 1810 out of capital, was paying no dividend by 1814, while the Grand Junction didn't manage a dividend until 1819. As for the New River, it lost 5,000 customers in four years and its rental income fell by 21 per cent. Its dividends fell too, from an average of £450 per share in the years up to 1810 to just £23 in 1814.

The East London was the first to call for a truce. In May 1813 it wrote to the New River. The two companies agreed not to poach customers who still owed their previous supplier money. Later they went further and drew a line on the map fixing a boundary between them; each took over the other's pipes and customers on their side of the line. The boundary ran down the old Roman road (now the A10) from Stamford Hill to Shoreditch, then through Spitalfields to the modern St Katherine's Dock, just east of the Tower of London. A formal deed was drawn up and signed by both companies on 9 November 1815.

*

Earlier in 1815 it had been the New River's turn to sue for peace, this time with the West Middlesex. There was talk of a merger, but they decided on a boundary agreement and, in January 1817, settled on a line running roughly down Hampstead Road and Tottenham Court Road.

Then, on 3 July 1817, representatives from all four companies in the west – the New River, West Middlesex, Chelsea and Grand Junction – met at New River Head and came to a 'general arrangement'. London was carved up between them. The New River had given up the West End but kept the City, Bloomsbury and Holborn and was soon to add Soho and Covent Garden with its takeover of York Buildings. The Chelsea got Westminster and St James's south of Piccadilly, plus Kensington and Chelsea. The West Middlesex took Marylebone north of Oxford Street between Tottenham Court Road and Edgware Road. The Grand Junction occupied an irregular wedge of territory covering Mayfair and Bayswater: it was a small patch but a wealthy one, where demand for water was high.

Most saw the arrangement for what it was. Despite all the rousing rhetoric of the past few years about smashing

monopolies, the companies had ditched cut-throat competition and created a new, even bigger and more powerful
monopoly, or oligopoly: a cosy arrangement that kept costs
down and prices up.

Cynically and indefensibly, the companies opted to
keep their 'general arrangement' largely a secret. Some of
the companies' acts of Parliament expressly forbade them
from selling or assigning any of their rights of supply –
which the carve up inevitably involved, and which meant
it was against the law. But they also knew the deal would
not be popular with the public. Many people had welcomed competition, despite the holes in the road, because
it meant they paid less. Now they were once more at the
mercy of a single supplier. Many had no inkling of what
had been done until their water company withdrew from
their street and cut them off, and some had to wait weeks
to be reconnected by whichever company now had exclusive rights in their district. The companies' standing with
the public sank rapidly. And it sank even lower when,
within months of the general arrangement, they put their
prices up by 25 per cent or more.

Blaming Parliament

It's hard to blame anyone but the companies for this
state of affairs – both the chaotic and financially ruinous competition and the subsequent cynical carve-up.
Yet rather than blame their own misjudgement, the companies chose to blame Parliament instead. The view got
about that Parliament had deliberately legislated to
encourage competition – that there was a visible hand

guiding the process – and that this had been a mistake. Politicians, pamphleteers and people giving evidence to public inquiries subsequently took it as a truism.[22] I am not so sure. For one thing, the new companies' initial acts of Parliament all explicitly restricted them from competing with the existing companies. And the ramshackle way Parliament worked, particularly when it came to private legislation, made the development of a consistent policy on competition (or anything else) deeply improbable.

Parliament was deluged with private bills, which took up a huge amount of both houses' time. Between 1801 and 1884 it passed 18,500 private acts, an average of more than 220 a year, and that figure does not include those introduced as bills that failed to pass (today around two private bills are introduced each parliamentary session). At the start of the century, a private act was necessary for everything from getting a divorce to enclosing agricultural land to digging a canal. Joint-stock companies needed an act to establish themselves, and further acts whenever they wanted to raise extra capital or extend their powers. Much of the detailed scrutiny of these bills was conducted by committees, but until reforms in the middle of the century forced on Parliament by the torrent of legislation involved in setting up new railway companies, the committees were huge: in some cases any member who chose could attend and vote, in other cases the committee was a 'select' one, but that didn't mean it was objectively small. The select committee that sat to consider the original Chelsea Waterworks bill had seventy-one nominated members, and all the members for London, Westminster and Middlesex were allowed to attend as well.

Pre-reform committees were, according to Frederick Clifford, the historian of private legislation, 'to a great extent partisan assemblies, composed of friends of a bill or members pledged to oppose it'. Members frequently had an interest – sometimes a very direct one, as shareholders or landowners or competitors – in the project under scrutiny. Among the bill's 'friends' was the committee chairman, who was usually the member promoting it. Committees were a forum not for debating issues of principle but for horse-trading, as the promoters of a scheme sought to buy off opposition and opponents sought to throw a spanner in the works. The procedure was slow, cumbersome and enormously expensive and not easily reformed – not least because officials of both houses of Parliament, up to and including the Lord Chancellor, got a significant part of their income from the fees for private bills. When reform did eventually come – in the House of Lords in the 1840s and the House of Commons in the 1850s – committees were limited to four or five members with no direct interest in the subject under debate, and serving under an impartial chairman. At that point they were expressly enjoined to consider not just the interests of the parties involved but the wider public interest as well.

But under the system prevailing in the first decade of the nineteenth century, it's hard to see how Parliament could have pursued a consistent policy on anything that involved private legislation. If Parliament did legislate to create competition through a series of poorly co-ordinated private bills it happened more or less by accident: a reflection of the thoroughness with which *laissez-faire* economic ideas had imbued almost the entire body politic.

7

Heavy Duty

In 1778 the Shadwell waterworks in east London had bought one of a new generation of steam engines manufactured by the Birmingham firm of Boulton & Watt. Soon, the Chelsea, London Bridge, New River, Lambeth and Borough water companies had them too, and as new companies were formed, they adopted large Boulton & Watt engines for pumping almost as a matter of course. The days of windmills, watermills, tide mills and horse mills were numbered, though it took decades for the old technologies to disappear completely: the East London Waterworks was still using waterwheels for some of its pumping in the 1860s.

Boulton & Watt engines were up to five times more powerful and efficient than the previous generation of engines based on Thomas Newcomen's designs. Until they appeared on the market, there was always a question mark over whether the performance of a steam engine pumping water really justified its considerable price and equally enormous running costs. James Watt, the engineering genius who patented his improved design in partnership with Matthew Boulton, removed all doubt.

Steam pumping engines were heavy industry: water, the simplest cleaning agent known, was delivered to Londoners by one of the dirtiest technologies, whose boilers produced a stream of black smoke. Pictures of vanished eighteenth- and nineteenth-century waterworks all include at least one smoking chimney, making the lives of neighbours (such as the Dukes of Buckingham) a torment with its daily harvest of soot, along with the juddering and vibrations of the engine itself.

Children of my generation were taught that Watt invented the steam engine after watching the lid of his mother's kettle lifting as it boiled – a eureka moment to sit, in the popular mind, alongside Archimedes' bath or Newton's apple. Evidently, since Watt did not in fact invent the steam engine, this story is not true. But the popularity of the myth says something about the impact of Watt's design both on industry and in the popular imagination. The Age of Steam, one could argue, really began with Watt.

Watt realised that Newcomen's device had a significant drawback: a good deal of time and energy was wasted by alternately heating the cylinder, then cooling it by injecting cold water to bring about condensation, then heating it again. So he connected the system to a separate chamber in which to condense the steam, allowing the cylinder holding the piston to remain at a constant temperature. The result was a huge improvement in efficiency.

To compare different machines, steam pumping engineers developed the concept of 'duty': the weight of water an engine could raise one foot by burning one bushel of coal. The improved Newcomen engine installed by John Smeaton at New River Head recorded a duty of 7.22 million lb per bushel. An engine at a mine in Cornwall, meanwhile, recorded a duty of nearly 10 million. But, in 1777, a Watt engine was erected at the same mine and achieved almost double the efficiency. In tests carried out in 1788 a Watt engine installed at New River Head raised almost three times the amount of water and used around one-third the amount of coal as the Smeaton engine.[1]*

As with Newcomen's, Boulton & Watt machines were beam engines, and as with Newcomen's, they operated with the steam at very low pressure – which was sensible, given the crude manufacturing techniques available and the potentially lethal danger of a bursting high-pressure metal container. Before long the London water industry developed into an important market for their machines.

Cornish power

Though London bought plenty of steam engines, the development work was mostly done elsewhere, especially in Cornwall. The next big breakthrough was made by Richard Trevithick – most famous today as the builder of the first practical steam locomotive. Trevithick was the son of a Cornish tin mine 'captain' and became engineer at the Ding Dong mine near Penwith, in the far west of Cornwall. Trevithick decided he could improve on the

---

* Comparisons of different engines' efficiency are complicated by the fact that early nineteenth-century weights and measures were not standardised. The bushel is a measure of volume, not weight – because it was easier to estimate the volume of bulky commodities, such as grain or coal, than it was to weigh them. But the bushel meant different things in different parts of the country: a Cornish bushel was usually taken to represent 94lbs of coal, a London bushel 82½lb, a standard bushel 86lb, and a Winchester bushel 79 to 82lb. Thank heaven for the metric system (https://www.muse-umsassociation.org/download?id=77607).

Newcomen-Watt atmospheric approach by using steam at high pressure to *push* the piston.

The stationary 'Cornish engine', which he and others developed in the years up to 1820, was a beam engine that worked by using steam 'expansively', in the jargon. At the start of the engine's cycle, high pressure steam from the boiler at up to 50 psi forces the piston down into the cylinder. Once it's moving, the inlet from the boiler is shut and the steam already in the chamber expands, cooling and losing pressure as it does so. At the bottom of the stroke an 'equilibrium valve' is opened, linking the top and bottom of the cylinder. The weight of the pump gear pulls the piston up again and the expanded steam migrates through the equilibrium valve to the bottom of the cylinder and out into the condenser, creating a partial vacuum that helps pull the piston downwards even as fresh steam at high pressure is pushing it from the other end.

Trevithick also developed a 'Cornish boiler' to deliver the necessary high pressure steam: unlike the upright boilers of earlier engines, which heated the water from below, these were horizontal cylinders with a flue running through the middle from the fire at one end to an exhaust chimney at the other. There was more metal in contact with the hot exhaust gases, and a larger surface of hot metal in contact with the water.

Cornish engines weren't much good for anything except pumping water – but for pumping water they were unrivalled, a near-perfect fit of form and function. While the best of Watt's engines might achieve a duty of 30 million or so, Cornish engines could achieve three times that – and more. The highest duty ever recorded, by an engine at the Fowey Consols mine in 1835, was over 125 million.[2]

Cornish engines were big, with massive beams and cylinders that dwarf the onlooker. They were also costly: as *The Engineer* observed in 1866, 'Say what we may of the excellent wearing qualities of the Cornish engine and of its economy of fuel, it is a most expensive machine.'[3] It is impossible to resist the statistics – not least because the men who built and operated these machines, and those who cherish them today, were themselves fascinated by their specifications and took pride in what the figures said about their size and power. The largest survivor, at the London Museum of Water and Steam at Kew Bridge, was built in 1869 for the Grand Junction Waterworks. It has a cylinder 100 inches across (that's more than eight feet or 2.5 metres); its beam weighs 54 tons. It was still in use in the 1940s and worked occasionally up until 1958, nearly a century after it was built. It could shift 7.5 million gallons of water every twenty-four hours. Its slightly smaller stablemate, the 'Kew Bridge 90 inch', is the largest beam engine in the world still working. It had an output of 6.4 million gallons, was built in 1846 and operated more or less continuously for almost a century, until 1943, and is still brought out of the engineering equivalent of mothballs from time to time and put through its paces. Both engines are still in their original building.[4]

To watch one of these leviathans at work inspires awe. They rise up several storeys, filling the spaces created for them: it's impossible to take them all in with a single glance; they surround the onlooker, who must assimilate them component by gleaming component. They move to a ponderous rhythm, and produce surprisingly little noise. The 90-inch makes one stroke every 10 seconds or so, gathering its strength for each almighty heave then releasing it with a sudden and disconcerting spurt. At one end of the beam a slim greased shaft descends rapidly and then ascends slowly from the pump housing: attached to the shaft out of sight is the pump plunger, which weighs 32 tons. At the other end of the beam is the massive piston head in the shape of a corrugated drum, which descends 11 feet with each stroke. As Erasmus Darwin put it, after watching one of James Watt's engines at work:

> Quick moves the balanc'd beam, of giant birth,
> Wields his large limbs, and nodding shakes the earth.[5]

For decades, these monsters supplied the thirsting metropolis year in, year out, reliably and relentlessly. They are potent symbols of the forces unleashed and then successfully harnessed by a technological revolution.

A murky deal

It took a while for the first of these Cornish engines to reach London. When it did it was in one of those questionable deals that abounded in early nineteenth-century business, involving a talented young engineer, a sometimes shady businessman and a failed mining speculation.

The engineer was Thomas Wicksteed, who had already, in his teens, shown 'that energy of character for which he was remarkable through life', according to his obituary, and who in 1829, at the age of just twenty-three, had been appointed engineer to the East London Waterworks. In his new job he was responsible for a pumping station at Old Ford on the River Lea, which was equipped with Boulton & Watt steam engines.

In 1835, as Wicksteed later recounted, the company was thinking of making major alterations to one of its engines at Old Ford. 'It was then suggested by Mr Grout, one of the directors, that instead of altering the engine in question, it should be taken down, and a Cornish engine erected in its place; and he stated that the saving in fuel that would be effected by adopting his suggestion would amply repay the company for the increased outlay consequent upon the erection of a new engine.'[6]

At this stage Wicksteed had never seen a Cornish engine, but he did know how they worked and he endorsed Grout's opinion. In August of that year he was despatched to Cornwall 'for the purpose of obtaining information respecting the engines in use there' and carrying letters of introduction, one of them to the engine-builders Harvey's of Hayle. In Cornwall he looked at twenty-four different engines and came back with a highly favourable report.[7]

William West, the engineer at Fowey Consols, was invited to look over the works at Old Ford and say if he thought a Cornish engine was suitable: he confirmed it would be, and made a good impression on the two East London directors deputed to meet him.[8] But the board as a whole was divided: a Cornish engine was expensive; many engineers thought the reputed improvements in efficiency were overstated. It took Wicksteed over a year to overcome the scepticism of some of his directors.*

---

* This was not the only subject on which the directors were divided. Their minutes show that, at a number of meetings in September, October and November 1835, they squabbled over who should serve on the board's committees and over a replacement for their chief clerk, who had just died. First they appointed his son, who had

Then Grout intervened again. He had 'learnt that a good second-hand engine was to be disposed of at a comparatively low price', and Wicksteed was sent off once more to Cornwall to buy it. On 2 June 1837 he wrote excitedly to his directors announcing he had closed the deal: 'It is one of the handsomest engines in the county and performs as good duty as the best.' And for the benefit of the sceptics, he added: 'I expect to be able to put one of the Cornish engines to a complete test before I leave, which will I hope have the effect of satisfying the doubts of those who do not think as I do on this subject.'[9]

H. W. Dickinson, the engineering historian who told this story in a 1946 lecture to the Newcomen Society, remarked, 'We should like to know more about Mr Grout, whose foresight and caution had such a happy outcome.'[10] Joseph Grout, we now know, may not have been quite the disinterested party that Wicksteed implies or Dickinson probably assumed, because he was not only a director of the East London Waterworks but also chairman of the company that had originally commissioned the engine and was now selling it, the East Cornwall Silver Mining Company.

Grout was fifty-nine in 1835, and very wealthy. He and his older brother, George, had made their fortune with a silk manufacturing company in Norwich: they were the first in Britain to make crepe, which became an essential purchase for anyone in mourning. But, in the 1830s, Grout

---

(cont.) been serving as his deputy; then they rescinded the appointment but gave the young man a pay increase 'out of respect for his late father'; then they decided to appoint him after all 'during the pleasure of the court' (LMA, ACC/2558/EL/A/01/027).

retired from the business and decided to diversify, into mining among other things.*

The East Cornwall company had raised £20,000 in 1835 to reopen five disused silver mines just west of the River Tamar, and the engine had been bought to pump out the flooded seams. As with so many nineteenth-century mining ventures, it proved to be wildly over-optimistic, if not actively fraudulent, and one Cornish mining historian, Rick Stewart, describes it as a 'mares nest of corruption and double dealing'.[11] It went out of business in 1837 and one investor wrote ruefully on his now-worthless share certificates: 'Kept as a warning to avoid ever speculating again.'[12] According to Stewart's unpublished history of the mine, Joseph Grout was not only chairman of the East Cornwall but a director of the Tamar Smelting Company, which was buying the mine's ore at well below its real value. The East Cornwall's first manager was dismissed because he flouted Grout's wishes by insisting on selling some of the ore to a smelter in Sheffield who offered a better price. The East London and Wicksteed may have been victims of Grout's rather cut-throat approach to business:

* Grout later resided at Tring Park in Hertfordshire. In 1851 he was living there with his nephew and his family and a substantial household of nineteen servants, and describing himself as a 'proprietor of mines, waterworks, landed proprietor'. There is a portrait of him in Great Yarmouth Museum, a portly gentleman dressed in sober black and white with a full head of greying hair and an open, slightly startled expression (UK Census Online; Hertfordshire Genealogy, http://www.hertfordshire-genealogy.co.uk/tring-local-history/brown-ac-book/notes/brown-grout-tring-park.htm; Art UK https://artuk.org/discover/artworks/joseph-grout-founder-of-grout-and-co-partner-18071852-2079).

having been promised the nearly new East Cornwall engine for a 'comparatively low price', they ended up paying over £7,000 for something that had cost the mining company just £4,000.

The engineer of the Grand Junction may have been warier than the much younger Wicksteed. He too visited Cornwall in November 1835, 'in accordance with Mr Grout's wish', examined a number of engines and estimated his company could save between a half and two-thirds of its coal bill by adopting a Cornish engine. But the following year negotiations with suppliers in Cornwall broke down and the Grand Junction sought tenders instead for new engines from Boulton & Watt and another firm.[13]

To begin with, the East London's engine behaved alarmingly in its new home. The pump was fitted with 'clack' valves – simple hinged flaps that permitted water to flow only in the direction in which the flap opened. In London the machine was pumping more water and operating at a higher speed than in Cornwall, and working against a lower head of pressure than a pump that had to force water up from the bottom of a deep mine. In these circumstances, the opening and shutting of the valves was so violent that it shook the building. Wicksteed installed a standpipe up which the water was forced in order to increase the head, and then, in 1839, a new and improved type of valve was patented.

But it was all worth it. Wicksteed ran trials to compare the performance of the new machine with one supplied by Boulton & Watt in 1826. The Cornish engine recorded a duty of almost 91 million; the Boulton & Watt just 40 million. The engine was so successful that the company soon bought a second, naming it 'Wicksteed' in their engineer's honour.* News evidently spread of this remarkable improvement in efficiency, and soon the other London water companies were queuing up to buy Cornish engines as well, and turned to Wicksteed to help them. He became a kind of Cornish engine guru – though he had first to persuade the reluctant East London directors to let him undertake outside work.[14] Alongside his day job he acted as a consultant engineer to the Grand Junction, Vauxhall, Southwark, and Kent Waterworks. When the Grand Junction was thinking of installing a Cornish engine in 1844, he compared the coal consumption of their existing engines with the East London's Cornish at Old Ford and concluded that the Old Ford engine was up to two-thirds more efficient. But employing Wicksteed did not guarantee success: the Grand Junction's first Cornish engine at Kew Bridge, installed in June 1846, didn't work properly to begin with. Not until November of that year (by which time an experienced Cornish engine driver from Liskeard, Stephen Luke, had been employed) was it fully operational.[15]

* The East London made a habit of giving its engines evocative names. In 1866, a visiting American water engineer recorded that the four engines at Old Ford were called Hercules, Ajax, Cornish and Wicksteed; in 1900, by which time the main pumping station had moved to Lea Bridge, the engines were named Victoria, Prince, Princess, Duke, Duchess, Prince Consort and, er, Horizontal. (James P. Kirkwood, *Report on the Filtration of River Waters for the Supply of Cities* (St Louis, 1869); Institution of Mechanical Engineers: Visits to Works 1900 via *Grace's Guide*.)

Industrial might

All this extra business was excellent news for the companies that built the engines. Three foundries between them produced an estimated 1,250 of the 1,550 pumping engines made in Cornwall. Two were in Hayle: Harvey's and its great rival, the Cornish Copper Company Foundry, later known as Sandys, Carne & Vivian, eventually taken over by Harvey's in 1875. The third of the trio was in the south of the county between Truro and Falmouth: Fox & Co's Perran Foundry. As London's water companies invested in Cornish engines, the impact was felt more than 250 miles away in a county that today we think of as a backwater, reliant on tourism, but which was once a crucible of heavy industry.

Some of the components of a Cornish engine were enormous, and the Cornish foundries developed impressive techniques for casting them, though it sometimes took more than one attempt. The massive pumping engine cylinders, which could stand up to 12 feet high, were cast in a pit sunk in the foundry floor. The process was evidently spectacular, and impressed even the foundry-owners themselves: 'Such an impetuous torrent of white-hot fiery flop rushing from the lips of two furnaces through two channels to opposite sides of the mould,' wrote Barclay Fox of the Perran foundry, in 1842. His sister Caroline recorded in 1840 that the casting of a 14-ton beam attracted almost the entire population of Perran to watch, 'who looked highly picturesque by the light of the liquid iron'. She regretted not having brought any chestnuts to roast to make use of so much waste heat.[16]

The biggest cylinder ever made for a Cornish engine – installed at the Cruquius pumping station in the Netherlands, for this was a flourishing export industry too – was supplied by Harvey's in 1849 and measured 144 inches in diameter. An abandoned 'miscast' of the cylinder features in a striking photograph apparently taken some years later in the works' yard. The cylinder is lying on its side. Inside it, leaning on a thin cane, stands a white-bearded and well-dressed member of the management in overcoat, fur collar and regulation-issue Victorian top hat. To one side stands a moustachioed middle-aged man in three-piece tweed suit and bowler hat, no doubt a middle manager. On the other side, holding upright a huge plank marked in feet as a scale, stands a workman in a jacket and sailor's peaked hat.* It is a picture that projects self-confidence, industrial might and class distinction: Victorian Britain distilled into a single image. Harvey's became the dominant supplier of engines to London's waterworks, with contracts to maintain and sometimes to operate them as well. It had a workshop on the Southwark & Vauxhall Waterworks site by the Thames at Nine Elms in Battersea, and a flying squad of fitters ready to go should any breakdowns occur.

*

* I had originally assumed the photograph was contemporary with the casting, which made identifying the three men difficult. But the quality of the picture is much too good for a photograph from 1849. One website identifies the top-hatted gent as Francis Harvey, presumably head of the firm at the time, with Jebus Bickle, 'an important figure at Harvey's who came from a family of engineers', and the foreman, Billy Gilbert. (http://angarrack.info/content/144-inch-diameter-cylinder-powering-eight-beams-used-drain-haarlemmermeer-netherlands-cruqui and *Grace's Guide*).

As London money flowed into Cornwall, machinery and men flowed in the other direction. Many of the companies' 'engine drivers' had Cornish (or sometimes Irish) names. Take the Loam family: the Cornish-born Mathew Loam erected engines for Harvey's at waterworks around England and in Holland. One of Mathew's sons, Michael, was resident engineer at the Grand Junction waterworks in Hampton; another son, Stephen did the same job at the Southwark & Vauxhall works next door – bright lads from the provinces wafted to the capital on a tide of pumping engines.[17]

In time the Cornish engine itself gave way to improved machines. Though ideally suited to pumping water, it had its drawbacks: tremendously efficient under a steady load, it lacked flexibility. When there was less water to be pumped, it could be paused between strokes, but the decision to pause had to be the driver's. The high pressure 'rotative' engines that superseded it, and transmitted their power to a revolving driveshaft rather than a beam, storing energy in a flywheel, could respond much more rapidly to sudden variations in pressure and speed. By the 1880s leading London water engineers considered the Cornish engine had had its day. Gradually the centre of manufacturing gravity shifted from Cornwall as the county's mining industry itself faded away. The Perran foundry closed in 1879. Harvey's closed its own foundry and shipyard in 1903.

8

Consumer Affairs

In 1819 a young caricaturist called Lewis Marks produced a satirical print entitled 'John Bull's Water Works! or unfeeling Speculators threatening to cut off one of the Necessaries of LIFE!!' It's a riot of cock jokes, exhibiting all the gleeful vulgarity of the finest Regency satire. Four beefy axe-wielding turncocks represent London water companies, the New River and West Middlesex prominent among them. Each threatens a hapless customer standing in front of a cistern or water butt and suggestively straddling its tap. One is a buxom woman who tells the man from the West Middlesex, 'I'm determined to protect my husband's Cock.' As she bestrides the tap her skirt has ridden up to reveal an expanse of leg: perhaps some special favour is hinted at should the turn-cock show mercy. Two of the customers are small boys: one, his face anguished, has already lost his cock. And John Bull himself, with empty pockets, is trying to fend off the New River man. 'We're all combined to raise the price of this Necessary Article,' one turncock says. 'So down with your Cash, or I'll cut your Water off!'[1]

By 1819 the sporadic eighteenth-century trickle of consumer complaints about the evils of the water monopoly had become a torrent, thanks to the price increases that followed the 'general arrangement' and the water companies' arrogant and arbitrary behaviour. They found themselves under attack not only from individual customers but also from some MPs, from the Marylebone vestry – a well-connected and influential body made up by law of ninety-two 'gentlemen and peers' and thirty tradesmen – and from a new phenomenon: a single-issue consumer pressure group. In creating a modern market for water, the companies had also created the first modern consumers and a new kind of consumer activism.

Marylebone was one of the wealthiest parts of the capital, and it had been the scene of some of the fiercest competition. In February 1818, the vestry realised that, with the end of competition, it was now at 'the mercy and discretion of perpetually fluctuating boards [of directors], who may make such exorbitant demands that will materially deteriorate the property of this parish.'[2] With house prices under threat, it was time to act. The vestry decided to start its own parochial waterworks and, in May, petitioned Parliament for a bill (the first of two) authorising it to proceed: there's a reference to it in Lewis Marks's print, which includes a piece of paper on which is written: 'Bill in Parlt to authorize certain parishes to supply themselves with Water to check the Extortions of the monopolizing Companies.'

*

Over the next seventy years the question of whether London's water should be in municipal hands became one of the most hotly contested political issues in the capital. The Marylebone initiative signalled the first serious attempt to get a local authority involved in water supply since the

City had ceded control to Peter Morice and Hugh Myddelton. The gentlemen and tradesmen of Marylebone hoped to get one of the companies to provide water under contract on terms laid down by the parish, to protect their parishioners from arbitrary price rises.

The attempt failed. The companies persuaded enough local residents to sign a petition against the proposal, on the grounds that it might lead to an increase in the parish rates – the property tax levied to cover poor relief and other parish expenses. Vestries, and the local tradesmen who served on them, were notorious for parsimony, and a vestry could be defined as an assembly whose principal object was to keep the rates as low as possible: raising the spectre of a rate increase was an effective tactic, and the bill was killed.

But one Marylebone resident didn't give up. A man called James Weale had become convinced that all water companies – but the West Middlesex in particular – were speculative swindles intent on plundering their customers. Weale was evidently a talented political agitator and, after the companies put up their prices in late 1818, he persuaded others to back his cause. He and the vestry began a campaign against the water interest, with handbills, placards and public meetings. The West Middlesex was alarmed. A public meeting called to protest 'the recent combination of the water companies and the increased water rates' in February 1820 was met by a threatening circular from the company warning residents against 'incautiously joining any association tending improperly to injure the company', and suggesting the companies were being asked to supply water on terms so low that it might 'endanger the supply itself'.[3] The company thought the campaigners' literature inflammatory. Their documents, its secretary later complained, 'would make a very great impression on the parish', coming as they did from a vestry 'composed of noblemen and gentlemen'.[4]

Weale also founded the Anti-Water Monopoly Association, which stirred up opposition to the companies in neighbouring parishes, such as St George's Hanover Square and St Pancras. Lewis Marks's print neatly encapsulates the main plank of its platform – the rapacity of the companies and their outrageous price rises – though two of the butts are labelled Ditch Water and Dirty Canal Water, hinting at a subsidiary concern that was to become more important as the century wore on, that of water quality.

The majority of water company customers acquiesced, however reluctantly, in the price rises and paid up. But a hard core, perhaps 10 per cent, resisted. The association's principal tactic was to refuse to pay increases in water charges, and instead to go on paying the old rate. Weale hoped that one or more of the companies would go to court to recover the full charge and that the resulting case might set a precedent. In the event, the companies did not rise to the bait, but simply disconnected the customer.

As it became increasingly clear that resistance was futile and only resulted in losing your cock, the association's influence waned. At that point it played its last card and sought a parliamentary inquiry. The association's chairman, William Fremantle MP, moved the proposal in the House of Commons – and took the chair of the committee conducting the investigation.

Fumbling and bumbling

In the minutes of evidence to the 1821 committee, we hear the authentic voice of early nineteenth-century consumers – albeit exclusively middle class. They also tell us a lot about the companies and the men who ran them: virtually all the engineers and secretaries gave evidence, and a poor job some of them made of it. During the course of the century the London water companies got used to giving evidence to public inquiries, which were launched into their activities with relentless frequency, and they became quite adept at it: but in 1821 they were fumbling and bumbling in the face of such public scrutiny.

The first to give evidence was the New River's engineer, W. C. Mylne. He was then aged forty and had been in the job since 1810, so was no tyro. Yet he seemed hopelessly ill-prepared. He was quickly obliged to admit that he had no idea how much water his employer actually supplied to customers west of the City. 'Do you mean to say that the company are ignorant of the quantity of water supplied by the works?' his questioner asked incredulously. 'They know nothing more than what the river produces,' he replied. His most recent precise figures dated from 1790. Nor did he know the quantity of water supplied per household, because the company only counted its 'tenants', and some of the tenants were themselves landlords with multiple slum properties who 'farmed' the water rates, turning a profit on the difference between the New River's discounted charges to them and their own charges to the hapless folk who rented their properties.[5]

Those weren't the only questions he couldn't answer. He could not say what the difference in cost was between wood and iron pipes. He could not say how much water his steam engines raised per chaldron of coal burned.* He could not say how many houses the New River had supplied in 1811. He had to be summoned back a few days later for another go.

The New River's secretary, who followed Mylne on the first day, was not much better. He couldn't answer the questions Mylne had dodged – not his province, he said – but nor could he answer questions that *were* within his province, such as the number of houses the company currently supplied: he was compiling figures but they were not yet ready. The veteran Thomas Simpson, Chelsea's engineer, was more impressive, particularly when it came to the advantages and disadvantages of wooden versus iron pipes. 'The expense of wood is in the repairing them,' he told the inquiry authoritatively – only to be contradicted by his colleague, the Chelsea secretary, who claimed that laying down iron pipes had not in fact reduced the company's repair bill.[6]

Three days elapsed between the first day's evidence and the second, and most subsequent witnesses did better – perhaps word had spread of Mylne's blundering and they had taken care to do their homework – but still their

---

* A chaldron, like a bushel, was a measure of dry volume, and as with the bushel meant different things in different parts of the country. A London chaldron was defined as '36 bushels heaped up, each bushel to contain a Winchester bushel and 1 imperial quart and to be 19½ inches in diameter' – basically a cartful. Coal was customarily sold to large users by the chaldron.

performances sometimes fell short. The company witnesses were all asked about the general arrangement. Many of the answers sound fudged; they were certainly inconsistent. With the exception of Simpson, who claimed the deal 'was done between the boards' – 'I was called upon but I had no concern in making the arrangement,' he said – they at least agreed that it had been worked out between the officers of the various companies, not the directors, that it was not in writing and that nothing had been signed – perhaps to make it easier to disown it if it were challenged.[7]

Mylne and Simpson disagreed about whether the arrangement involved companies selling the pipes left in the ground in areas from which they had withdrawn: Mylne said it had, Simpson said it hadn't. Joseph Steevens, the engineer of the East London, said each company took over the pipes left on its side of the line: 'I am not aware that a shilling of money passed between either party,' he said. This was simply untrue: the New River's abandoned wooden pipes to the east of the line were worth much less than the new iron pipes given up by the East London to the west, and so the New River paid its rival £700 a year for ten years in compensation.[8]

The West Middlesex secretary, M. K. Knight, had the effrontery to argue that customers were now better off because their rentals no longer had to reflect the costs of two or more pipe networks in each area – conveniently ignoring the enormous price rises the companies had introduced nonetheless.

The companies justified the increases by arguing that, if they had gone on as before, they would have gone bust: the old rates, said Knight of the West Middlesex, never paid enough for an adequate profit. They pointed to the significant investments they had made in iron pipes and new pumping engines. The mains were now full at night, which made more water available more quickly for fire-fighting, and the companies were able to offer 'high service' to upper floors to customers willing to pay extra.[9]

They also pointed out that demand had increased. There had been a vast rise in the number of WCs since 1810, said the Grand Junction's engineer – in many houses even servants now had a downstairs WC – while water was also piped into gentlemen's stables, where it was used for washing carriages. In general, in fact, water was used more lavishly. 'There is hardly a door that you pass in which water is not applied to the pavements in front of the house, which was not done formerly,' he told the inquiry.[10]

Customer complaints

James Weale, leading the charge for the consumers, got the best part of two days in which to make his case. Central to it was a modern restatement of an old argument, that something so essential as water should not be left in the hands of private commercial interests. 'The supply of a large town with water cannot be assimilated, I conceive, to a trade in grain or other commodities,' he said:

> Water must be considered as one of the elements necessary to existence, the same as light and air, and not merely as an article of subsistence like corn, nor of convenience like coal; and therefore its artificial sup-ply to a great city ought not to be the subject of free trade, nor any kind of trade.[11]

'The supply,' he went on, 'should be profuse, rather than sufficient, and gratuitous to the poor.' The costs of water-works and delivery should come out of the rates, just like the costs of paving, drains and police. And the system should be controlled by local commissioners not by 'trading joint-stock companies', which were out to make a profit. The mistake, Weale said, was for the City to have put the supply of water in the hands of private business in the first place, way back in Sir Hugh Myddelton's day.

He was followed by a succession of aggrieved customers. For the most part they were respectable tradesmen and professionals: an auctioneer and appraiser, a grocer, an artist, two surgeons, a 'mourning coach master', a 'superfine colourman'. One was an antiquarian, scientist and baronet, who wrote to the committee 'from his sick bed', another was 'a private gentleman' living in Hoxton. This last also described himself as a water campaigner and was the only witness to suggest that the price of water might be of concern to the working classes, not just the well-to-do. He cited two adjoining houses where the East London company had put up the rates by 50 per cent, but said in one case that might be justified because it was occupied by a laundress: he had brought her receipts as evidence, 'because it is clear an old laundress or washerwoman could give no satisfactory evidence to this committee'.[12]

The witnesses all told similar tales: of charges reduced then suddenly increased; of customers being transferred between companies without notice; of being obliged to pay off a previous tenant's unpaid bill on moving into a property; of loyalty to one company being betrayed when it abandoned the area.

A few witnesses complained about quality. John Richardson, the mourning coach master in Tichborne Street, had been persuaded to switch from the New River to the Grand Junction, who told him it was high time someone put an end to the New River's monopoly. 'After being supplied a very short time by the Grand Junction, my family complained that the water was very dirty, and were much dissatisfied with it; they produced me a mug which had been filled with water overnight, and there was a heavy sediment at the bottom.'[13]

Some witnesses had taken their complaints to the company secretaries. Not all these interviews went well. James Day, a hatter, claimed to have been treated 'cavalierly' by the West Middlesex secretary.[14] William Newton, an artist, had gone to the office of the Grand Junction company after they cut him off and spoke to the secretary. The conversation was 'bad-tempered' and he had now installed his own pump and a rainwater tank: 'I shall not take any water of them at all.'[15]* John Thorowgood, a plasterer in South Molton Street, took matters into his own hands when the Grand Junction cut him off, and dug up the street to reconnect himself.[16]

Sometimes the ill-temper became public. One witness had chaired a meeting at which the chairman of the East London company was apparently shouted down. 'I think the defenders of the company had a very fair hearing,' he told the inquiry, 'as far as it was possible to keep silence where there was a great public feeling.' But had there not

* Newton went on to become 'miniature-painter in ordinary' to William IV and Queen Victoria. He was eventually knighted.

been considerable tumult at the meeting? 'There was tumult, but not disturbance,' he said blithely. The East London chairman in question (the only director of any of the water companies to give evidence), told the inquiry that he had been 'very much interrupted in the course of my address', and that he had eventually walked out.[17]

Throughout the evidence from consumers, the company representatives were given opportunities to respond. It's clear that the decisions they took on pricing were often arbitrary, depending as they did on a necessarily subjective assessment of a property's rateable value. Sir Harry Englefield's rate was cut by a guinea a year when the Grand Junction's collector asked the butler to let him look around the house, from which he concluded that it was smaller than it looked from the outside and that since Sir Harry's WC was in the basement he should not be paying for high service.[18] The company representatives themselves admitted that the rates charged often varied wildly: the Grand Junction's secretary cited Berkeley Square, where one house was rated at 30s, another at 40s, two others at £5 apiece. He and the engineer had done a re-rating in 1819 designed to 'equalize' the charges – they had of course been equalized upwards.[19]

Sometimes the companies' responses reveal evidence of strain. The West Middlesex secretary, M. K. Knight, found it difficult to keep his temper when talking about James Weale and his campaign: a meeting would be called by Weale, said Knight, 'and all the malcontents of the parish would naturally flock to that meeting'; minds had been 'poisoned'; the campaign had been 'fomented by party, kept up by party, and still maintained by party'. To Knight and the other water company officers, what they faced were a series of individual complaints, all of which they believed could be resolved individually. It was essentially a private matter between the companies and their customers. They did not accept and could not see that the matter raised the wider political issues articulated by Weale. 'I deny that it is a public grievance,' Knight asserted flatly.[20]

Nevertheless it is possible to sympathise with Knight and Mylne and their colleagues, for they were perhaps the first executives of commercial companies providing a public service to be forced to submit to this kind of public inquisition. Eighteenth-century water companies – like canal companies or dock companies – might face a committee of the House of Commons or the House of Lords when seeking a private bill, and objections to their plans might then be aired by interested parties, but that was a formal process in which the rules were reasonably clear and the purpose of the exercise was evident. Fremantle's water inquiry of 1821 was much closer to a free-for-all. The companies were obliged to attend and participate when Parliament summoned them, because they operated for the most part on the basis of powers granted to them by Parliament. But there was nothing in it for them.

A failed experiment

The 1821 inquiry heard copious evidence of the companies' high-handedness, so the outcome was remarkable. The committee concluded that the 'old companies' had indeed enjoyed an effective monopoly, so the arrival of competition had been, in principle, a good thing. But because of the 'peculiar nature of these undertakings', involving as they did heavy capital investment and a product that went to waste if it wasn't sold as soon as it was made available, unbridled competition risked bankrupting them. The general arrangement might look like 'a combination against the public' but was, in fact, necessary for the companies' self-preservation because the only alternative was 'mutual destruction'.[21]

The 'experiment of competition had failed', the committee concluded. But it was not prepared to recommend any kind of government intervention – which to us might look like an obvious solution. One phrase in their report hints at the underlying problem: it would need stronger evidence 'to justify an interference of the legislature affecting private property'. Private property was sacrosanct. What an Englishman did with his own property was his own affair, or a matter to be worked out between him and his customer, not something to be dictated by Parliament.

The one measure the committee was prepared to recommend was a curb on the companies' ability to fix their own charges – so a bill was proposed to limit what they could charge to 25 per cent above the 1810 level for ordinary service, plus extras. Fremantle duly introduced such a bill, but it failed to get a second reading.

The political establishment's first attempt at tackling the perceived abuses of the London water companies had apparently ended in complete failure. But though the campaigners' crusade sputtered and died on this occasion, they were to get many more opportunities to put their case in the coming decades. Fremantle's was the first of at least sixteen major inquiries into London's water supply by royal commissions and Parliamentary committees between 1821 and 1899. They are evidence of widespread and continuing public dissatisfaction. But they also show the 1821 campaigners had chalked up one important success. However much the committee might regret it, a precedent had been set: henceforth it became increasingly clear that 'an interference of the Legislature affecting private property' *was* justified when something as vital as the water supply of London was concerned.

9

The Dolphin

By modern standards the water which the early nineteenth-century water companies supplied from the Thames and the Lea was filthy, and for a time grew ever filthier. Not surprisingly, people noticed: in fact, London's decidedly iffy water had been matter for satirical invective for years.

In 'A Description of a City Shower' in 1710, Jonathan Swift had identified the contents of the sewers feeding the Thames:

> Sweepings from butchers' stalls, dung, guts, and blood,
>   Drowned puppies, stinking sprats, all drenched in mud,
>   Dead cats, and turnip tops, come tumbling down the flood.[1]

In 1726 his friend, Dr John Arbuthnot, borrowed some of Swift's imagery in his pamphlet on the York Buildings dragons, where he described Thames water as 'foetido-cabbageous, dead-dogitious, dead-catitious, Fish-street-bilious' and 'excrementitious'.[2] Later, the splenetic country gentleman Matthew Bramble described 'the agreeable potation extolled by the Londoners as the finest water in the universe' in 1769 in Tobias Smollett's *Humphrey Clinker*:

If I would drink water, I must quaff the mawkish contents of an open aqueduct exposed to all manner of defilement; or swallow that which comes from the river Thames, impregnated with all the filth of London and Westminster – human excrement is the least offensive part of the concrete, which is composed of all the drugs, minerals and poisons used in mechanics and manufacture, enriched with the putrefying carcases of beasts and men, and mixed with the scourings of all the wash tubs, kennels and common sewers within the bills of mortality.[3]

Despite this, dirty water had been only a minor issue at the time of the 1821 inquiry. A few years later, the water campaigners regrouped and tried again. Quality now joined their list of complaints.

The centrepiece of this new campaign was a pamphlet, *The Dolphin, or the Grand Junction Nuisance*, published anonymously in March 1827. The word 'dolphin' is a nautical term; it means a structure of wooden piles driven into the bed of a river or dock to act as protection or as a mooring. Several of the London water companies had dolphins guarding their intake pipes in the middle of the river, but the author of the pamphlet, later revealed to be a journalist called John Wright, editor of *Hansard*, took aim at one in particular belonging to the Grand Junction Waterworks at Chelsea.

Wright began his pamphlet as the 1821 campaigners had begun, by attacking the monopoly that now controlled the 'daily supply of an article as necessary to existence as light and air', and the 1817 general arrangement that had brought the monopoly into being. As a result, he wrote provocatively, the water company customers had been 'counted out, and handed over . . . from one set of monopolists to another, like so many negroes on a West Indian estate, or so many head of cattle at a fair'. It was an apt analogy in one respect at least: the popular campaign to abolish slavery had forged many of the tools – petitions, pamphlets, public meetings – now being deployed by the water campaigners.[4]

Wright sketched out the history of all the water companies, heaping praise on Hugh Myddelton and the New River as he did so; but the Grand Junction could do nothing right. 'In price – in quantity – in quality, they will be found to have broken every engagement they have made with the public', he wrote.[5]

Wright's main beef had to do with quality. The Grand Junction had initially promised a supply of water from 'the pure ethereal streams' of the rivers Colne and Brent to the west of the metropolis, brought to London via the Grand Junction canal; but when the canal company found there wasn't enough water for both householders and boats, and customers complained about the quality, the intake had been switched to the Thames next to Chelsea Hospital at a cost of nearly £50,000. But, in its new position, the Grand Junction's dolphin sat opposite the outlet of the Ranelagh sewer, which had started life as the River Westbourne but which by the 1820s had become polluted – badly, according to Wright, but just a little according to the company. A 'modern Fleet Ditch' Wright called it, quoting Ben Jonson's *On the Famous Voyage*, before conjuring his own nightmare vision of the company's product drawn from near the sewer's mouth, in a memorable rhetorical onslaught: 'A fluid, saturated with the impurities of fifty thousand houses – a dilute solution of animal and vegetable substances in a state of putrefaction – alike offensive to the sight, disgusting to the imagination, and destructive to health.'[6]

Though Wright didn't know it, the Grand Junction was aware that it was distributing sewage to its customers, because its former consulting engineer John Rennie had told it as much. Rennie had been asked back to cast an eye over the company's new intake on the Chelsea embankment in December 1820. The steam engines, he reported, were working well; but he identified a problem with the sewer, which rendered the water pumped up by the engines 'at times very foul', especially when the incoming tide carried the sewer water directly into the mouth of the company's intake pipe. Eight years later the medical officer at Chelsea Hospital substantiated this, describing 'the foul and blackish stream' from the Ranelagh sewer on which floated 'no small portion of undivided filth from the privies'; he concluded that 'a considerable quantity of human excrement' was sucked into the Dolphin by the steam engine.[7]

The company kept quiet, hoping the new reservoirs it was building at Paddington would allow any impurities to settle out of the water before it was distributed, and threatened in an advertisement in *The Times* to sue Wright for libel. 'They were ready to allow,' the company wrote years later, still protesting innocence, 'that the site whence their supply was drawn at Chelsea was ill chosen, inasmuch as being near the mouth of the Ranelagh sewer it might have the appearance of being – although in reality it certainly was not – influenced by the drainage water.'[8] But in the fevered climate of the 1820s and 30s, when the water companies seemed to be everyone's favourite whipping boy, it was appearances that counted.

Offensive and destructive to health

Wright's pamphlet prompted an outcry, as it was meant to. There were newspaper articles attacking 'the Grand Junctioneers' and petitions, culminating in a public meeting at Willis's Rooms in St James's. Willis's had started life as a spin-off from Almack's Club, where aristocratic young men with more money than sense gambled fortunes every night. The assembly rooms were used for society balls and political gatherings and occupied a building specially designed, as it happened, by the New River's engineer and surveyor Robert Mylne.

Willis's selection as the venue for the meeting reflected the type of people the organisers hoped to sign up to the campaign: rich, titled, influential. They succeeded: the Marquess of Salisbury was there, along with six earls, a future governor-general of India, several MPs and the publisher John Murray. The chairman (who turned up late) was Sir Francis Burdett, the country's leading parliamentary radical, to whom Wright had addressed his pamphlet. Burdett was a quixotic politician whose support for reform had frequently brought him into dramatic conflict with the authorities – on one occasion he was gaoled for seditious libel; on another he was imprisoned in the Tower of London by order of the House of Commons. In the course of his long career he fought many battles and lost most of them, only for history to conclude he'd been on the right side: the fight over London's water was no exception.

The meeting passed a series of resolutions, probably drafted by Wright. One, echoing the language and sentiments of Swift, Smollett, and Wright's *Dolphin*, condemned the water supplied by the Grand Junction as 'charged with the contents of the great common sewers, the drainings from dunghills and laystalls, the refuse of hospitals, slaughter-houses, colour, lead and soap works, drug mills and manufactories, and with all sorts of decomposed animal and vegetable substances, rendering the said water offensive and destructive to health.' An ex-director of the Grand Junction – who preferred not to give his name – was hissed when he tried to defend the company.[9]

A hostile witness, William Matthews, who had slipped in at the back, was later rather dismissive. 'The meeting amounted to about sixty persons, consisting of a few noble-men, gentlemen – and not a small proportion of medical practitioners,' he wrote, claiming the whole exercise was merely a ploy to launch a rival water company.[10] Matthews was an apologist for the water companies, who, in 1835, published *Hydraulia*, at once a compendious history of water engineering from classical times onwards, and a vig-orously written polemic attacking the water companies' critics – a kind of anti-*Dolphin*. He had published a book about the nascent gas lighting industry in the same year that Wright's pamphlet appeared, and was a gas enthusi-ast. His motive for defending the water companies seems to have been fury at the way water pollution was being blamed on toxic run-off from gasworks.

The meeting in Willis's Rooms launched a new anti-water company campaign, with Wright as secretary and Burdett as the figurehead, and in June 1827 Burdett success-fully pressed in Parliament for a royal commission to investigate the London water supply. Royal commissions later became notorious as exercises in procrastination: if a government wanted to bury a difficult or controversial issue, it set up a commission to look into it. But in the nineteenth century they were instruments of real change. They were not a new idea – the first was set up in 1085 by William the Conqueror to oversee compilation of the Domesday Book – but they had gone out of fashion in the eighteenth century. In the nineteenth century, they came back into vogue, as powerful tools for establishing facts, identifying problems and bringing about improvement. The reformer Edwin Chadwick is usually said to have pioneered the use of commissions in this way, but the 1827–8 commission on the water supply predated Chadwick: it was an early harbinger of the formidable movement that developed in the ensuing decades to promote and improve public health.

There were three commissioners, all technical experts – a chemist, William Brande, a doctor, Peter Mark Roget, and the distinguished engineer Thomas Telford. And some of the evidence they heard was stomach-churning. One witness, whose home overlooked the tidal Thames from which several of the companies took their water, told of watching the carcasses of dead dogs float up and down with the tide for ten or twelve days at a stretch. Others told of the 'entire destruction of the fisherman's trade between Putney Bridge and Greenwich' because the water had become so foul and the fish had all died. Dutch eel fishermen coming to London to sell their produce told of meeting the 'bad water' as they came up the river – they knew it by the shining scum on the surface, and it killed up to two-thirds of their cargoes, which they kept alive in wells on board filled with sea water. Witnesses claimed to have found leeches, 'shrimp-like, skipping animalcules', lively red insects, 'oily scum', a 'stinking black deposit' and 'little round black things, like juniper berries' in their cisterns. They described water that was 'thick and not fit for tea or grogs', 'not fit for a Christian to drink' or 'like pea soup in wet weather'. The landlord of the Blue Posts in Burlington Gardens complained of a spoonful of black mud per gallon of water and testified that 'boiling in such water spoiled the best of vegetables'. A fishmonger claimed his fish turned yellow and died after just six or eight hours in a cistern of Grand Junction water.[11]

Despite this, the commissioners' report in April 1828 was a tepid affair – for reasons I will discuss in Chapter 13. Its principal recommendation was a vague one: that London's water supply ought to be derived from other sources than the Thames and Lea. Nonetheless, Burdett made the best of it. The commissioners had found the complaints about London's water to be well-founded, he claimed, and he urged the appointment of a select committee to examine alternative sources. And he went further, arguing that 'it was the bounden duty of government, who ought to watch over the health of the people, to see that the town was plentifully supplied with good water'.[12]

To begin with Burdett got nowhere. He was proposing a dramatic widening of the role of government to include responsibility for public health, and the Tory Home Secretary, Robert Peel, was aghast at the implications: government might end up responsible not just for water but for the gas and the lighting and the paving of streets, and not just in London but everywhere else. If there were ills that needed tackling, Peel thought, the remedy should be left to private enterprise. It was three months before he relented and sanctioned the committee, after first trying and failing to get three of the companies – the West Middlesex, Chelsea and Grand Junction – to pay for a survey of possible alternatives to the Thames as a source.[13]

Among those who gave evidence to the committee was the Grand Junction's chairman, William Clay, who tried to rebut any suggestion that the company was motivated purely by a desire to make profits. The company had been working to improve its supply for a long time, Clay said, because it felt 'our duty to the public coincided with our own interest in making our supply exceptionally good'. It was an early appearance of an argument much used in our own day by companies trying to fight off external regulation: it's in commercial organisations' own interests to supply a good quality product or service and not to cut corners, the argument runs, so they can safely be left to get on with it untrammelled by rules imposed from outside. Publicly Clay defended the dolphin intake, whose water he said was perfectly satisfactory provided it was taken 'at such a period of ebb [tide] as to have allowed the whole of the drainage water of London to have flowed back past our works'. But privately the company decided it would have to do more and, at a general meeting in September 1828, Clay told shareholders the directors were giving their 'unremitting attention' to securing a supply 'to which the most fastidious cannot justly object'.[14]

Going upriver

The Grand Junction was not the only company persuaded, as *The Times* put it in 1849, to make 'such alterations in their service as might silence what they regarded as the captious clamour of the public'.[15] All those pamphlets and public meetings, all that evidence to inquiries, all those letters of complaint and confrontations with water company staff weren't wasted: a new force, public opinion, had been mobilised, and it proved to be powerful.

The first company to take action was the Chelsea Waterworks, whose intake was a short distance downriver from the Grand Junction's. In January 1829 it began operating a pioneering filter bed to remove impurities from the water it distributed. While the Roget-Brande-Telford royal commission was hearing all that evidence about the disgusting state of the Thames, the Chelsea company was already doing something about it, and may justly have felt rather smug. But the other London water companies were slow to pick up on filtration, relying instead on 'subsiding reservoirs' in which the water sat for several days to clarify and (hopefully) purify it.

The East London Waterworks responded to the pressure by moving its intake. It had begun life at Old Ford on the River Lea, filling its reservoirs there at every high tide. But as with the Thames, the tidal Lea had filled up with sewage. Following the 1828 commission, the company went three miles upriver to Lea Bridge, at the river's tidal limit. An open channel was dug to take this cleaner water downstream to the existing works at Old Ford, where it went into subsiding reservoirs before being pumped into the mains. The work was completed in 1833.*

The Grand Junction's move from its dolphin intake at Chelsea took longer to achieve, though that wasn't really

---

* The grand opening had to be put back from 22 May because the building work wasn't quite finished: a passing clergyman wrote an angry letter after spotting the contractors' men at work on a Sunday (LMA, ACC/2558/EL/A/01/025, East London court minutes, 8 May, 15 May, 29 May 1833).

the company's fault. It was an indication of the intensely political nature of the water business and the difficulties involved even then in large projects: there is nothing new about 'nimbys'. Over the years the company drew up several different plans for a new source. One involved going to Richmond and bringing water in a pipeline alongside Kew Gardens, part of the Crown estate, to a new waterworks at Kew Bridge – it was abandoned when the government withheld permission, apparently because of fears it might 'interfere with the enjoyment and privacy of the gardens and [royal] pleasure grounds'.

After an ambitious but abortive plan to take water from the River Colne (*The Times* called it 'a scheme of almost Roman grandeur'[16]), in 1833 the company introduced a bill to take water from the Thames by Kew Bridge. It passed the Commons smoothly but, at the last minute, ran into opposition in the House of Lords; an objection was raised by none other than the Duke of Cumberland, brother of King William IV, who lived just across the river on Kew Green. Cumberland and his neighbours weren't happy at the prospect of a waterworks and its smoke within sight of their homes. The company was forced to give the residents the right to approve its plans as a condition of getting its bill. That was in August 1835, seven years after the Grand Junction first set out in search of a new intake.

Even then the saga wasn't over. Detailed plans were drawn up and sent off to the Kew Green residents. But the Duke of Cumberland had just gone to Hanover, of which he was to become ruler in 1837, and in his absence his neighbours didn't dare give their approval. With the clock ticking – the company's act gave a deadline by which the new works were to be completed – it went looking for yet another site and found one a short distance away from the river, where it no longer needed the approval of the Kew residents.[17]

Anyone might think the project was jinxed – a suspicion reinforced by the problems once construction actually started in 1836. A conduit pipe was laid on the bed of the river using a diving bell, but in August 1838 the bell's air pipe became tangled and nearly cost two men their lives.[18] Building work supposed to be completed by July 1837 was not actually finished until a year later. Many of the iron pipes for the company's new 30-inch main to the reservoirs at Paddington were found to be defective: once laid and in use, they cracked with tedious frequency. Even the railings for the fence around the site turned out wrong: for some reason every other panel had to be recast.[19] The delays and escalating costs led the company to put off building the filter beds it had originally intended. The works were enlarged in the 1840s (when filter beds were installed) and again in the 1860s, and the site remained operational right up until the 1970s, when it became what is now the London Museum of Water and Steam.

The West Middlesex, too, invested in subsiding reservoirs – in Barnes, across the river from its original Hammersmith intake – and the New River built two at Stoke Newington: one was lined with stone from old London Bridge after its demolition. But despite the improvements, the companies' reputation remained poor. In 1849, William Clay professed surprise that the public were ignorant of all the improvements they had made. But that, as he conceded, was because they hadn't told anyone about them: to the companies' other failings must be added a neglect of public relations.[20]

Rotten borough

Some other companies seemed utterly indifferent to the outcry, particularly the Southwark Waterworks. In 1832, the year the cholera first came to London, George Cruikshank published a savage satirical cartoon. Entitled '*Salus Populi Suprema Lex*' (it comes from Cicero and means 'the health of the people is the supreme law'), the coloured print depicts a monarchical figure crowned with an upturned chamber pot sitting atop a domed structure in the middle of the Thames, labelled 'Source of the Southwark Water Works'. The figure holds up a goblet overflowing with black liquid and in the other hand has a trident from which hang strands of equally black and unnameable filth. From either side streams of effluent flow into the river from a succession of sewer outfalls. One is labelled Walbrook, and at its mouth three washerwomen are at work. A well-dressed gentleman standing above them makes ironical reference to the 'march of cleanliness'. The opposite bank is thronged with people, presumably Southwark Waterworks customers. 'Give us clean water!' they cry, and 'We shall all have the cholera'. Doctors and scientists took thirty years to agree that cholera was a waterborne disease; Cruikshank's ordinary Southwark residents had already decided, apparently, that it was.

Beneath the caricature is a satirical poem, a royal address to his 'subjects in the Borough' from 'Cadwallader ap-Tudor ap-Edwards ap-Vaughan, Water-King of Southwark', whose other honorifics include 'sovereign of the scented streams, autocrat of the slushes, raining prince of the golden showers . . . agitator-in-chief of the intestinal canals . . . warden of the sink ports, receiver general and distributor of sewers'.[21]

The Southwark company was unique among London water companies during this period in being owned and run not by a joint-stock company but by a single proprietor, John Edwards Vaughan. Edwards Vaughan was a public figure and not an especially popular one, one of those Regency characters who combined business with politics, and pursued each with comparable vigour and disregard for ethics. He was born in London, but after his father bought an estate near Neath, he decided he was also Welsh (hence the 'Cadwallader ap-Tudor . . .' etc) and was MP for Glamorgan for two years from 1818, until the local Tory squirearchy ensured he was thrown out as a dangerous radical. He found a new billet as MP for Wells in Somerset, which seems apt for a man in the water business. His radicalism was only skin deep; the *History of Parliament* calls him 'an ambitious opportunist, radical in his election tactics, but not in his politics'. He was rich, having married two heiresses in succession, and had added Vaughan to his surname in 1829 when a wealthy lawyer of that name left him his property. The architect John Nash was a cousin and Edwards Vaughan managed his business affairs.[22]

Cruikshank's squib actually had two targets – not only Edwards Vaughan's Southwark waterworks, but also his opposition to the Great Reform Bills of 1831–2, which aimed to provide parliamentary representation to the new manufacturing towns, and abolish the old corrupt 'rotten boroughs' with just a handful of voters in the pocket of some local grandee. Part of the poem's conceit is that Southwark, also known as the Borough, remains rotten on account of its dreadful water supply. The poem also suggests Southwark residents should be grateful for the nutritious solids served up with their water, which was pumped unfiltered, straight from the river into people's houses:

> Oh! how could you dream there was any thing vicious
> In matter putrescent, or excrementitious,
> Or refuse of gas-works, that poisons the fishes,
>   Which rot in the water you drink? . . .
> For a wholesomer fluid can't be, to my thinking,
> Since it serves you at once both for eating and drinking:
> Then gobble it down, my good Folk! without shrinking.
>   Why es-chew what has chew'd been before?[23]

The poem owes much to the report of the 1828 royal commission, and even has footnotes quoting some of the witnesses' criticisms of Thames water – among them Dr John Paris, who told the inquiry that, unless something were done, 'the ravages of some fatal epidemic may be fairly anticipated'. Paris was prescient.

South of the river

Edwards Vaughan died in 1833, leaving behind a business with the worst water in London and no money. His heirs formed a new joint-stock company and moved the intake to Battersea. By 1839 this new company had, in effect, become part of a family utility business that played a central role in London's water industry up until 1876. Its head was William Clay, who had become chairman of the Grand Junction in 1825 at the age of thirty-three. Clay's father-in-law had been a Grand Junction director and its largest shareholder; when young William married his daughter in 1822, the old man gave him 120 shares, and two years later got him on to the board. William came from a business background – the Clay family was in shipping – and in 1832 became the Liberal MP for Tower Hamlets. When the Southwark waterworks became available, the energetic Clay saw an opportunity: south London was poor, but it was also poorly served by its existing water companies. There was enormous scope for growth, and money to be made. But his descendant and biographer, the distinguished business historian Christopher Clay, believes there was more to William's interest in the Southwark company than that:

> He was also a convinced reformer with a sincere concern for the well-being of ordinary people ... The possibility of providing an improved water supply to such deprived parishes as Southwark, Bermondsey and Rotherhithe, which would improve sanitary conditions and make it easier to combat the many fires which afflicted the area, must therefore have appealed strongly to his humanitarian instincts. However there is no need to regard these as alternative explanations for his take-over of the Southwark Company. Almost certainly he was motivated by both profit and philanthropy, for it was very much in the spirit of the age to believe, as he certainly did believe, that profitable ventures could spread social benefits whilst philanthropic ones could (indeed should) be profitable.[24]

Clay's consortium included several of his relatives and two of his associates at the Grand Junction, the company secretary and the engineer. Among the other ten directors were the Cornish steam-engine maker Henry Harvey and two sons of the engineer John Rennie. There was also John Stewart, the illegitimate son of a West Indian sugar planter, who may have been Britain's first mixed-race MP. Stewart's money came from slavery: he was awarded almost £25,000 compensation in 1833 for 546 freed slaves in British Guiana and Grenada; the produce from his plantations was brought to England in Clay-owned ships. Between them these men owned a third of the company's shares and William Clay alone owned more than £52,000-worth by 1841.

At Battersea the company built a pumping station, a seven-acre subsiding reservoir and two-and-a-half acres of filter beds. A century later one of London's most distinctive landmarks, Giles Gilbert Scott's Battersea power station, was built on the site, the upturned table legs of its four chimneys dwarfing even the Southwark & Vauxhall's vanished standpipe.

When the Clays bought the Southwark company, there were two other water companies in the built-up area south of the river, the Lambeth and what had been the South London but had since changed its name to the Vauxhall Waterworks. To begin with they had avoided competing, but, by the 1830s, any gentleman's agreement had been abandoned and they were both laying mains in one another's territory and attempting to poach each other's customers.

The Lambeth claimed the Vauxhall started it: in 1834 it was offering to provide a service to higher floors at 10 per cent less than the Vauxhall 'in consequence of the ruinous competition which has been commenced by the rival company'.[25] The Vauxhall played the plucky underdog, congratulating itself in its publicity on refusing to do a deal with its competitors at the expense of customers, on the lines of the 'general arrangement' north of the river. The Southwark inevitably became embroiled in the conflict. Contemporary accounts suggest an affair of sharp practice, dirty tricks and ruinous price-cutting exactly like the water war of 1811–17 on the other side of the Thames – right down to rival gangs of workmen fighting in the streets.[26]

Eventually the Vauxhall, the weakest of the three, admitted defeat. In 1843 it decided on a merger with the Southwark as the only way out of the difficulty. It approached Clay, who was by now a baronet after a brief stint as a government minister. By September 1845 the hatchet had been completely buried and the Southwark & Vauxhall Waterworks had come into being. The Vauxhall's old works, next to what is now the Oval, were sold off, and the Phoenix gas company took it over, building gasholders on the footprint of the old circular reservoirs – hence the Gasworks End, familiar to spectators at the Oval cricket ground. The Southwark's works at Battersea were extended, Sir William Clay became chairman of the combined operation, and the Southwark's secretary got the equivalent job in the new company.

*

There was one other company south of the Thames. The Kent Waterworks had been established in 1809 to serve Deptford, Greenwich, Lewisham and Rotherhithe; its first engineer was the same Barrodale Dodd, son of Ralph, who had fallen out so abruptly with his directors at the West Middlesex company.* The Kent got its water from the River Ravensbourne, but in 1859 it sank the first of a series of deep wells that produced large quantities of pure water and soon replaced entirely the trickle from the Ravensbourne. By the late 1860s, the stuff Kent Waterworks pumped straight up from the chalk was viewed as the unpolluted gold standard for London water.[27]

The Southwark & Vauxhall, by contrast, became notorious for poor quality. Its Battersea intake, originally well clear of the built-up area, soon found itself downriver from the sewers carrying the waste of burgeoning districts such as Clapham. The microscopist Arthur Hassall, who published a book on London's waters in 1850, looked at two samples of the S&V's. The first, he said, 'as regards its animalcular contents, [is] in a worse state even than the Thames water itself, taken from the bed of the river'. The second, he said simply, was 'the most disgusting I have ever examined'.[28]

---

* Before the company launched, his surviving 'day journal' shows he spent 206 days on surveys, meetings, lobbying and selling shares to the locals in 1807, 222 days in 1808 and eighty-one days in 1809 (LMA ACC/2558/MW/C/15/207).

10

Boiling, Toiling and Baths

In 1855 Charles Dickens wrote a letter of complaint to his water company. 'I beg to represent to you that my supply of water is often absurdly insufficient,' he wrote, 'and that although I pay the extra service rate for a bath cistern, I am usually left on a Monday morning as if there were no such body as a New River Company in existence – which I sometimes devoutly wish were the case.' Complaints in the past had produced a temporary improvement, he wrote, 'and for a few days or a few weeks I have had what I pay for; and then I have subsided into my old condition and the water has been turned off before my tanks are filled'. The letter was signed with a flamboyant flourish bordering on the belligerent.[1]

Dickens was not alone. Water was often in short supply and the service erratic, and the companies and their customers alike had perforce grown used to the idea. The customers had to lump it; the companies braced themselves for frequent complaints and developed strategies for managing them. A printed receipt left with the architect John Soane in Lincoln's Inn Fields in 1810 and signed by the New River's collector, C. Hinde, records payment of £1 10s for two quarters' water rent, but most of the text is taken up with instructions on what to do should something go wrong. 'For want of water,' it says along the top, 'Attendance is given at Peel's Coffee-House, Fleet Street, on Tuesdays and Fridays, from 12 till 1 o'clock, where complaints are desired to be sent in writing.' And then at the bottom a further rubric, instructing the customer 'In case of fire, or want of water', to send to the local paviours or turncocks, who are listed by name with their addresses.[2]

The water was needed for cooking and cleaning, and of course for doing the laundry, but for all the campaigners' rhetorical insistence on water as a 'necessity of life', people were still deeply reluctant to drink the stuff neat. Many in the eighteenth and nineteenth centuries preferred tea or, to the horror of the moralists, beer. Much of the pressure to clean up London's water came from those who saw making it fit to drink as a way of keeping the labouring classes out of the pub and free from the dangers of intoxication; it might have disconcerted them to learn that beer was a good deal more nutritious than tea and an important supplement in people's diets.

Occasionally men of science or water company engineers boasted that they were 'water drinkers'. W. C. Mylne of the New River had a pipe from his cistern directly into his dressing room, 'and there I drink a glass of water every day of my life'. It was, he said, a very good thing to take a glass of water every morning. But water for drinking at table, he confessed, he first filtered, because otherwise it was too cloudy. 'It does not agree with [your family] unfiltered, though it agrees with you?' he was asked. 'You must please the eye as well as the palate,' he replied. 'It has a brighter appearance, decidedly, when filtered.'[3]

Domestic filters – typically ceramic drums with a tap at the bottom – were kept in the kitchen or dining room and passed the water through charcoal to remove impurities. Though brighter to the eye, filtered water was said to be 'flat' and lacking the sparkle of water that came from the mains – even if the sparkle was frequently the result of impurities. When it *was* drunk, water was often added to something else to disguise the taste. Servants might drink gin and water; the mistress of the house might use water to dilute her wine.

Dollies, peggies and possers

As in previous centuries, the biggest demand for water in the nineteenth-century home came from doing the laundry. The technology available had improved, though not by much, and some 'labour saving' devices had been introduced, but washing clothes still required enormous physical effort.

Many homes by now had back- or side- or saddle-boilers in the chimney of the kitchen fire: they provided hot water on tap, but in nothing like the quantities needed for a full day's laundry. Other homes had a copper, a large metal cauldron for washing dishes and boiling laundry, mounted on a brick plinth and heated by a firebox underneath. Coppers could be huge. In 1795 Parson Woodforde of Weston Longville in Norfolk took delivery of a new one, almost two feet wide, nearly 20 inches deep and weighing more than 45lb. When completely filled, bucket by bucket, it would have held around 9,000 cubic inches of water, weighing 325lb – or 147 litres.

From the eighteenth century onwards, soapy clothes might be churned in the tub with a 'dolly' or a 'posser' – the one resembling a small three-legged wooden stool with a long handle, the other a copper plunger. They saved the washerwoman's bleeding hands, and in time supplying laundry paraphernalia became a significant business. A nineteenth-century advertisement for washing dollies offered a bewildering variety, from 'peggy dollies' with five legs and a 6-inch head to 'Preston peggies' with morticed handles and 7-inch heads; they cost 33s 6d a dozen.[4]

The social historian Ruth Goodman says the work was made marginally easier by the support women's corsets gave their backs, but testifies from personal experience to the labour involved:

> It is no surprise that so many women from the period mentioned in their diaries tempers fraying on wash day. It is difficult to say what was more tiring, the dollying or the carrying of all the water back and forth, but together these tasks left a woman fit to drop.[5]

Laundry was expensive. In 1844, a weekly wash for a labouring couple with four children was reckoned to take at least two days and cost 2s 6d in soap, coals and the woman's time (priced at 5s a week at a time when a male labourer might earn 15s). In 'first class private families' in London, washing bills could amount to £400 a year.[6]

Despite the heavy lifting involved, doing the washing was almost always women's work. The historian Amanda Vickery says that, outside the 'sealed world' of the army and navy – where men were prepared and in some cases expected to do their own laundry, just as they were expected to do their own sewing – there was 'a real taboo' against men getting involved. 'A man who had to wash for himself was a pitiful spectacle – hands in the tub was a feature of the widower's desperation.'[7]

Laundry used a lot of water, sometimes all the household had available. Nelly Weeton, a governess at a house in the Lake District, told the dreadful story of her ten-year-old pupil Mary's death in 1810 after her skirts caught fire.

> Without the loss of a moment, I flew into the servants' hall for the ironing blanket – it was washing week and I recollected seeing it there . . . I threw the blanket to the nurse, who was trying to extinguish the flames with her apron. While she was rolling her in the blanket, I ran again into the butler's pantry and servants' hall, to find some water to throw upon her, and cool the burning flesh. I could find no liquid of any kind.[8]

Given the punishing nature of the washerwoman's job, some took a drop of something to help the process along. It was a calumny to allege, as the *Acton Gazette* did in 1945, that laundry historically involved three things, 'a woman, a washtub and a bottle of gin', but it was not entirely untrue.[9]* A mid-nineteenth-century song celebrated, if that's the right word, the life of the itinerant washerwoman (a Cockney, to judge by the rhyme):

> Toiling, boiling all the day,
> Rubbing, slushing, sloshing,
> Firsting, bursting everyway,
> Going out a-washing.

---

* The *Acton Gazette* would have had a particular interest in the subject: by the end of the nineteenth century, Acton was home to many of London's commercial laundries.

I gets my eighteen pence a day
(with grub and gin however),
As much as I can put away
To keep my strength together.
Weak folks say it's all a sin
And at us get reviling,
But – there's nothing like a drop of gin
To keep the copper boiling![10]

Taking in washing was an exhausting but reliable way to make money for a working-class woman, though the sums were often meagre. Owning a mangle or wringer as well gave her precious economic agency. Women who lost husbands in industrial accidents might be given a mangle by the man's employer in lieu of financial compensation, so that they had some way of earning a living. In Dickens's *Our Mutual Friend*, Betty Higden, desperately poor but too proud and too independent for the workhouse, gets by through a combination of child-minding and taking in laundry at her tiny cottage in Brentford; she has a mangle, which is worked for her by the orphan Sloppy.*

The word 'mangle' comes from the Dutch and is itself derived from a Greek word, meaning 'an engine of war'. Early 'box' mangles were indeed pretty fearsome, full of stones to weigh down the rollers that pressed the water out of the wet clothes; operating them was heavy work. The writer Dorothy Hartley quotes a song:

* Sloppy's talents extend, unlike Mrs Higden's, to reading the newspaper: 'He do the police in different voices,' as she proudly remarks – a phrase appropriated by T. S. Eliot in the first draft of one of the great twentieth-century poems about water, *The Waste Land*.

Cheer boys cheer!
My mother bought a mangle.
Cheer boys cheer!
She filled it full of stones.
Cheer boys cheer!
She makes me turn the handle.
Cheer boys cheer!
It nearly breaks my bones![11]*

Washing clothes could also be a sociable affair. A nineteenth-century photograph sentimentalised the business: it shows five women with voluminous aprons in a court or alley, standing around a pair of wash tubs with dollies in them, and next to a tap from which they are filling metal buckets. Wet clothes are hanging from lines over their heads, and one has paused in her work to take a drink from what looks like a flagon. They look jolly enough. Someone has given the picture a title: 'The Gossips'.

But given the work involved in laundering clothes, some just didn't bother. There are stories of people – and not just the very poor but respectable tradesmen and artisans' families – sleeping in unwashed sheets and wearing unwashed underclothes until they fell to pieces. Or if they did wash their clothes, they never managed to get them clean. As a result, they stank. Whitechapel's medical officer of health in the mid-century wrote of watching women

---

* You can see a mangle at Audley End near Saffron Walden in the 'dry laundry', next to the stove for heating smoothing irons and beneath the drying racks hanging from the ceiling, and it is indeed an imposing piece of kit. The 'wet laundry' round the corner contains two coppers, a row of six sinks with washboards, and a pump. Country house laundry was carried out on an industrial scale.

'merely pass dirty linen through very dirty water' (which may in fact have been stored urine, known as 'wash') and said he always left the door of his surgery open when he had poor patients: 'When I am coming downstairs from the parlour I know at a distance of a flight of stairs whether there are any poor patients in the surgery.'[12]

In 1830 Edward Bulwer-Lytton popularised a new term describing the working classes, 'the great unwashed' – a term that had real and powerful meaning for middle-class folk, who by that stage mostly did wash but had to encounter those who didn't.

Cleanliness and godliness

The sixteenth-century notion that bathing and the application of water to the body might be harmful persisted for a very long time. A manual of etiquette from 1782 advised wiping the face every morning with a linen cloth but not washing it in water, because that made the skin too sensitive to cold and sunburn. And the fact remains that many people, not just the poor, seem to have had an active aversion to water. A physician, Robert Willan, observed in 1801 that 'by a strange thoughtlessness, most men resident in London, and very many ladies, though accustomed to wash their hands and face daily, neglect washing their bodies from year to year'.[13] The historians Roy and Lesley Adkins, writing about Regency England, say: 'Everyone would have smelled, even genteel women like Jane Austen, who in mid-September 1796 admitted to Cassandra [her sister]: "What dreadful hot weather we have! It keeps one in a continual state of inelegance."'[14] If the Adkins are right, there had been a terrible falling-off since the time of Ruth Goodman's Tudors.

But attitudes were starting to change. By the 1820s, there was a widespread view among the middle classes not only that cleanliness and moral uprightness were connected but that a clean body was a healthy body. Perhaps the shift had something to do with the fashion for sea-bathing, which accustomed affluent trend-setters to the idea of immersion. Perhaps John Wesley's notion that cleanliness was next to godliness had simply gained wider currency. Perhaps it had something to do with the wider availability of water in the home.

This enthusiasm for bathing had its limits. Respectable folk had no tolerance for the working-class boys and men – 'idle and disorderly persons' – who took to swimming in the New River from its earliest days, and the company did all it could to stop them, though with little success. In 1809 a man called John Tyre got two months in Newgate Prison after bathing in the river, then running naked round Highbury Fields within sight of the rather grand properties in Highbury Terrace; his stiff sentence didn't stop a reported 800–1,000 people swimming in the river each summer in the 1820s and 30s, however.[15]

Nonetheless, the expectation developed among the middle classes that their own sort should be clean. *A Family Cyclopaedia* published in 1821 recommended frequent washing of the face, hands and feet, twice weekly changes of linen and occasional whole body washes; 'there is no objection to the use of soap', the author reassured his readers. Personal cleanliness was necessary for good health, he explained, but also 'becoming in our intercourse with society'.[16] Cobbett, in 1829, thought no man (at any rate, no

Englishman) could ever love a truly filthy mate.[17] To be clean was to be decent, and all good middle-class Victorians were desperate to be thought decent.

For most people, ensuring personal cleanliness – while nowhere near as labour-intensive or time-consuming as doing the laundry – was still a rather cumbersome business, achieved mainly by stand-up washes using water in a basin. These took place in a bedroom or dressing room while standing at a washstand and with water heated and carried up by a servant; others less well-off might wash in the kitchen. Since most bedrooms were unheated, and many were shared, people might remain partially clothed throughout for warmth and modesty, uncovering bits of the body in succession. Afterwards the used water was tipped into a slop pail and hauled away for disposal. Warm water was necessary if soap was involved, but soap (as well as the time and coals required to boil a kettle) cost money and the poor must frequently have skimped.

In the bath

And then there were baths. As early as 1789, the prison reformer John Howard reported approvingly on the excellent baths at Guy's Hospital, but criticised St George's, which had only one bath and never used it, and the London Hospital, which also had only one and kept it in a dirty cellar. The fact that they were in hospitals was no accident, because, until the mid-nineteenth century, baths were associated with health, not hygiene, and were taken under medical supervision, or at least on medical advice. The French revolutionary, Marat, famously met his end in a bath, which he was enjoying not because he was a luxury-loving sybarite beneath his radical exterior but because it was supposed to be good for his eczema.

The specialist manufacturers of baths that sprang up from the 1830s onwards marketed their wares on the basis of their therapeutic potential. They were small and portable – you could even buy travelling baths that folded up, and might double as a trunk in which to pack your clothes – and came in several shapes and sizes. There was the hip-bath, its variant the Sitz bath (from the German word for sitting), the moon bath, the Parisian sponging bath and smaller baths for washing feet and infants. There were shower baths, which relied on a servant or three to climb a ladder and fill the tank perched precariously atop the contraption. There were steam or vapour baths. And there were full-length, lounge or slipper baths in which the bather – or 'patient', as one manufacturer's catalogue in mid-century referred to them – could lie back and achieve near total immersion. The hip-bath was said to be 'very beneficial in various forms of cholera, colic, liver complaints, diarrhoea, and disordered conditions'; for the Sitz bath it was not necessary to undress completely, the catalogue suggested, and added:

> Dipping Sitz is a term applied to dipping the posterior part of the body a dozen or more times into cold water. This should be done slowly, and followed with friction. It is highly beneficial in cases of nervous debility or a relaxed condition of the generative parts.[18]

A very few people had dedicated bathrooms and some even had baths that were plumbed-in. The architect John Soane had one in 1820 in the house he had designed himself with all the latest accoutrements. The bath was filled from a boiler in the room above, and there was water on tap in several rooms in the house: visitors to the Sir John Soane Museum can still see the small wash basin and the pump used to fill it in Soane's own dressing room. But the system, fed with New River water and perhaps from a private well on the property, still depended on a footman, whose first task every morning was to pump water up from the basement to a cistern on the top floor. Originally Soane had supplied a bath for his servants as well, off the basement kitchen, but that was swept away when the house underwent one of its periodic modifications in 1825: perhaps they hadn't been using it.

Soane was unusual. In 1812, the Common Council of the City turned down a request to install a shower bath in the Lord Mayor's official residence at Mansion House, 'inasmuch as the want thereof has never been complained of', though they relented twenty years later; and, at the other end of town, even Buckingham Palace still had no bathroom in 1837, the year of Queen Victoria's accession.

One reason most baths were small was that someone had to fill and then empty them. It was usually a servant, rarely the man of the house. 'Men will do much for glory and vainglory,' wrote Florence Caddy in *Household Organisation* in 1877, '. . . but I never yet heard of a man who took the trouble to empty his bath after using it.'[19]

The labour entailed in having a bath was, of course, much increased if the water was to be hot, but often it was not. Warm baths for men were frowned upon as effeminate. In his 1857 *Manual of Domestic Economy*, J. H. Walsh recommended warm baths only for women and children. Hot baths could be downright dangerous: 'Hot baths are by no means a class of agents to be trifled with, and in medical cases where there is time to obtain it, regular advice should be had recourse to before using them.'[20] A household might have enough hot water for only one bath, and several members of the family might take turns using it, before the tub was then used for soaking laundry.

As for the cold bath, the country clergyman Francis Kilvert described one in his diary in 1870. It evidently made an impression:

> It was an intense frost. I sat down in my bath upon a sheet of thick ice, which broke in the middle into large pieces whilst sharp points and jagged edges stuck all round the sides of the tub like chevaux de fries [a medieval anti-cavalry device consisting of sharp spikes]. Not particularly comforting to the naked thighs and loins, I had to collect the floating pieces of ice and pile them on a chair before I could use the sponge, and then I had to thaw the sponge with my hands for it was a mass of ice.[21]

For those less inured to the discomforts of muscular Christianity, a warm bath might be taken before the bedroom fire, with a large flannel sheet spread beneath it to save the floor from getting wet. The writer Dorothy Hartley remembered both hip-baths and also moon baths, in which the bather stood upright. The hip-bath, she reported, used less water and kept it hotter, enabling one to soak luxuriously: 'For a prolonged wallow, one kept a can of extra-hot water alongside and draped a bath sheet around one, bath and all, leaning back in steamy content.'

The moon bath was set down on the floor next to the wash basin. Once the maid had brought your hot water, you first tipped a little into the bath, to take the chill off the cold tin. Then Hartley recalled standing in the middle of the bath, 'like a pink lighthouse', using half the water to wash her face and hands and soaping herself vigorously from top to toe till she was 'foam-flecked as Venus'. 'Then you filled up the wash basin with the remainder of the hot water, seized the sponge, and sluiced down.'[22]

By the 1870s, dedicated bathrooms were starting to appear in London houses. A whole new industry sprang up manufacturing baths, basins and WCs to equip them. Cast-iron baths were customarily covered with enamel paint, which got chipped after a time and needed a new coat. Mr Pooter, the Holloway clerk with pretensions to bourgeois elegance in the Grossmith brothers' satire, *The Diary of a Nobody*, repaints his bath red. The first time he uses it he gets the water so hot he can scarcely bear it, lies back for a good soak, only to discover the heat has dissolved the paint and his skin has turned bright red. 'My first thought was that I had ruptured an artery, and was bleeding to death, and that I should be discovered, later on, looking like a second Marat . . .'[23]

Hot baths posed other dangers, especially when gas was introduced as a fuel. Some of the earliest and most primitive heaters simply directed gas jets at the underside of the metal bath: misjudge the moment or the spot for stepping in and you risked serious burns to your feet, even if the water itself were only lukewarm. Later solutions to the problem were safer but took half an hour or more to heat enough water. One answer was the gas Geyser, developed in 1868, which was fixed above the bath and supplied instant hot water.

But home baths were a luxury, and unavailable to the poor. It was not until the 1840s that the first public baths and washhouses appeared, introduced in Liverpool. With the aid of campaigners such as the Bishop of London and acts of Parliament in 1846 and 1847, municipal baths spread slowly across the country in what became known as the Washhouse for the Million movement. Their popularity reveals how desperate the need: St Pancras baths in London opened in 1846 and attracted 280,000 bathers in its first two years, while over 90,000 used them to do their laundry. By the end of the century, the buildings themselves were often ornate and lavish, symbols of municipal pride. Dorothy Hartley, clearly a young woman who took personal cleanliness seriously, recalled using one of the surviving public baths as a student in London. It was run by two good-natured and gossipy women, with a third on the door. Sixpence in the early twentieth century got you twenty minutes in the bath, plus a small cake of yellow soap 'and two clean towels of huckaback texture [a distinctive towelling weave of linen or cotton, said to be especially absorbent] and board-like hardness'. The water was turned on by the attendant in the corridor, the temperature adjusted by a process of call-and-response.[24]

In time soap became cheaper and more widely used: the lifting of the tax in 1853 meant sales almost trebled from 82,000 tons in 1850 to around 200,000 tons in the 1880s. William Hesketh Lever spotted a business opportunity and first marketed his Sunlight soap in 1885: you could buy Lever's soap in separately wrapped bars, rather than queuing up for the grocer to carve it off a large block.

The nineteenth century saw a revolution in personal cleanliness, but it went at different speeds in different places and for different people. Keeping clean was still a challenge for the poor. Most working-class homes were too cramped to find room for even a portable hip-bath, and 'model' working-class housing was still being built without fitted baths well into the twentieth century. From 1919, it was mandatory to install a bath in the new-fangled council housing. But, as late as 1951, over a third of British homes still had no bath at all.

11

The Age of Engineers

In December 1861 John Hawkshaw was elected president of the Institution of Civil Engineers. Hawkshaw's career had taken him from his beginnings in Yorkshire around the world, building railways and harbours, bridges and canals. The year of his presidency, he began work on the Amsterdam Ship Canal. Later he was to build the Severn Tunnel. He was a fitting figurehead for industrial Britain's premier profession.

Hawkshaw's inaugural presidential address celebrated the transformative impact engineers were having on the world: the 'annihilation of space and time' brought about by railways, telegraphs and steam-boats, the way their 'adjuncts', such as bridges, docks and harbours, were remoulding and refashioning the material universe to the wants of men. The world was running ever faster and civilization was advancing ever more quickly, and it was all thanks to his profession. The idea is a cliché now, but it was new then. 'No man can look back on the last twenty or thirty years without feeling that it has been the age of engineers and mechanicians,' he observed.[1]

Victorian engineers were accorded high status. When Hawkshaw was speaking, the heroic age was not yet over, and pioneering figures such as Robert Stephenson and Isambard Brunel were still alive or only recently dead. Our image of these men is conditioned by photographs taken when they were old, but many achieved success remarkably young, in the era before photography: Stephenson was thirty when he became engineer of the London and Birmingham Railway, Brunel was only twenty-nine when he took charge at the Great Western. As one historian remarked, engineers 'were the folk-heroes of mid-Victorian England', with a 'ruthless eruptive animal energy'. Many were of humble origin, self-made men who were 'intensely individualistic even for an individualistic age'; reputedly it was an engineer who coined the term 'private enterprise'.[2] It's fair to say they did not take kindly to being told what to do.

Also in 1861, Samuel Smiles first published his *Lives of the Engineers*, which embodied a similar idea. 'Our engineers,' he wrote in an introduction to the 1874 edition, 'may be regarded in some measure as the makers of modern civilisation'. In the previous hundred years they had transformed the physical world, and, by their 'inventive genius', had rendered iron, fire and water 'the most untiring workers in all branches of industry, and the most effective agents in locomotion'.[3]

The profession whose achievements Hawkshaw and Smiles celebrated owed much of its existence to water: to the need to tame and accommodate a protean element that both succours and destroys, that can be dangerous and playful by turns, that is both shape-shifting and powerful and essential for life. The earliest engineers in Smiles's book almost all worked with water, such as those who came from the Netherlands to drain the fens, or indeed Sir Hugh Myddelton.

By the mid-nineteenth century, water supply was an acknowledged engineering specialism, and the London water engineers formed a distinct group. In an era when few companies had what we would recognise as a chief executive, they wielded enormous influence in the organisations they worked for, especially if they had a close relationship with the company chairman. Of course, not all engineers were equally skilled: chutzpah sometimes counted for as much as expertise. Nor were these men cheap. Many of the structures and much of the machinery built by Victorian engineers have lasted so long because they were over-specified. In an era when rule of thumb and tradition still counted alongside rigorous calculation, it was safer to incorporate a significant margin of error. The engineers' legacy is impressive, but it came at a cost.

And Victorian water engineers had the failings of the arrogant. Joseph Quick at the Grand Junction and South-wark & Vauxhall eventually lost his job, as we shall see, because of a financial scandal that may have amounted to fraud; Charles Greaves at the East London Waterworks vigorously denied, as we shall also see, that his company's water could possibly have been responsible for London's last cholera outbreak in 1866, though it later became abundantly clear that it had been. Sometimes one catches the whiff of corruption. Until the late 1870s it was customary for some London water engineers to award enormous (and lucrative) contracts without competitive tender, and the engineers' relations with their contractors were remarkably close by modern standards: they acted as executors of one another's wills; they sat together on the boards of overseas gas and water companies. And they were quite happy to take shares in the firms that supplied them with equipment such as valves. Some went further still. James Simpson simply awarded the contract for supplying pumping engines for the Lambeth Waterworks to his own manufacturing firm.

Simpson's Schmutzdecke

Simpson, like Hugh Myddelton, is one of London's unsung heroes. Chief engineer of both the Lambeth and Chelsea companies, he was also – uniquely among the tribe of top-flight Victorian water engineers – a manufacturer: he established his own works making pumping engines on the river at Pimlico. But what made him outstanding was not his engineering skill nor his capacity for making money but his far-sightedness and his recognition of the importance of water quality: thanks to his introduction of the slow-sand filter bed, modern Londoners owe him a very considerable debt.[4]

James was the seventh of Thomas Simpson's eleven children, and was another leading engineer who started young: he effectively succeeded his ailing father as engineer of both the Chelsea and Lambeth companies at the age of twenty-one; the appointments were formalised on his father's death in 1823, two years later. Two of his brothers, Joseph and William, also became engineers and, when Joseph died in the same year as their father, James was appointed his successor as 'Engine Maker under His Majesty's Office of Works', making this promising young man the government's chief adviser on the era's hi-tech wonder: steam – a bit like putting the youthful founder of the latest social media platform at the heart of government. He remained in the post throughout his life.

Successful nineteenth-century engineers were hard-headed men not noted for sentiment, but one of the things we know about Simpson and his brothers was that they apparently revered their father, and believed he deserved to be better-known and more highly respected than he was. When James became president of the Institution of Civil Engineers in 1853, he spoke of his father in his presidential address, recalling how the old man 'often, in his later years, recurred with pride to his communications with Smeaton, Jessop, Watt, Rennie, Telford and other of his contemporaries'. These were the engineering titans of the late eighteenth century and James clearly thought his father was their equal. And another brother, David, rather touchingly put Watt's and Rennie's names in letters as prominent as his father's when he erected a memorial tablet to Thomas in St Cuthbert's Church in Carlisle.[5]

But James's achievements comfortably outstripped his father's. He counted not only the government but also royalty among his clients – the manhole covers at Windsor Castle still bear his company's name – and designed and built waterworks throughout Britain as well as Southend's first pier. He was a diplomat as well as an engineer, more interested in resolving disputes than in conflict. His obituarist spoke of 'the suavity of his manner and the kindly geniality of his nature', which were valuable characteristics in the highly political world of Victorian engineering, where every scheme of any size required a private act of Parliament. He could be relied on to see the big picture: 'He was not brilliant as a witness, nor as a speaker, but his advocacy generally carried great weight with it, and his opinions were held in high esteem, not alone because of the soundness of his views, but of his known and admitted

honesty and uprightness of character' – which rather suggests that uprightness and honesty were sufficiently rare in
business to be worthy of remark.[6]

In 1825, two years after succeeding his father and two
years before the furore provoked by *The Dolphin*, James
Simpson built a small experimental filter for the Chelsea
Waterworks to purify water from the Thames. It impressed
the company's directors sufficiently for them to pack him
off on a research trip to other parts of the country. He saw
filters at work in 'Glasgow and a few dyeworks in the
manufacturing districts' as well as at paper mills and print
works, and after he returned, he designed the first full-size
filter beds installed in London: they began operating in
January 1829.[7]

Simpson's filters were built up in layers: fine sand on
top, then coarser sand, then a layer of seashells (which
always seemed to come from Harwich), then a layer of fine
gravel and finally one of coarse gravel, which in turn
sat on a network of earthenware pipes pierced with holes.
The raw water percolated slowly down through the layers,
and clean water was taken away in the pipes. The shells
ensured the sand didn't clog the pipes.

Simpson and his contemporaries believed the filters
acted mechanically, to strain out soil, dirt and impurities.
A leading water engineer told the Grand Junction company in 1877 that filtration 'separates or arrests suspended
matter only – it does not change the chemical character or
constitution of the water'.[8] In fact we now know the filters
mainly do their job biologically, something which only
became evident with the development of the new science
of bacteriology in the 1880s. A film of bacteria, fungi and
other micro-organisms forms on the top layer of the sand,

delightfully known as a '*Schmutzdecke*' (it means 'slime blanket' in German), which neutralises harmful bacteria and impurities.

Once in widespread use, filters proved their worth. Almost two centuries after Simpson built the first at Chelsea, Thames Water still uses his method to clean two-thirds of London's water, the only major city in the developed world which does so. Slow sand filters are simple and cheap to operate, they are robust and they don't use chemicals. They also have their disadvantages. They are not fast and they require space: some modern filter beds are larger than a football pitch and each water treatment works needs several. They also have to be periodically cleaned to prevent them clogging, which involves draining them and physically washing the sand before replacing it. After cleaning it takes a few days for the *Schmutzdecke* to reform and the filter to become effective – something the Victorians, who put cleaned filters back into service immediately, didn't realise.

Not all Simpson's contemporaries were fans of filters. In 1834 the engineer of the East London Waterworks, Thomas Wicksteed, believed it was a waste of time and money filtering the company's water when much of it was destined for manufacturers: private consumers ought to buy their own portable filters instead, he suggested, briskly passing responsibility for ensuring clean water on to his customers (and offering no suggestions as to what those who couldn't afford filters should do). Wicksteed's directors, like Simpson's, had despatched him on a fact-finding trip: he went to Birmingham, Lancashire and Glasgow to look at filter beds run by water companies and manufacturers and, on his return, told his board: 'A perfect mode of filtration would be so enormously expensive that I cannot conceive that the company would ever attempt it.' He later changed his mind. As late as 1851, his opposite number at the New River, W. C. Mylne, also thought filters unnecessary, though he too altered his opinion after the law required the company to install them.*

To Seething Wells

James Simpson also made a second great contribution to London's well-being. That was at the Lambeth Waterworks, which in 1852 became the first company to move its intake upstream from Teddington Lock, and thus beyond the upper limit of the river's tidal reach. Other water engineers and their directors were loath to admit that the Thames was becoming increasingly polluted and that purifying it even with filters had become next to impossible – particularly after heavy rains, when the river was in flood and thus 'turbid', or after one of the new-fangled steam-driven paddle

---

* Wicksteed's original views are recorded in LMA, ACC/2558/ EL/A/01/026, East London court minutes, 17 July and 21 August 1834. By 1851, he was publicly disagreeing with his directors on the subject, saying his personal view had changed and he now thought river water should be filtered (*Minutes 1851*, pp. 617–18). Mylne was in the opposite position in 1851: while he thought filtering was not necessary, his directors thought it was (*Minutes 1851*, p. 655); eight years later, he too changed his mind, writing that filtration 'has proved a *boon* to the Public which the majority of the Tenants would never have obtained, had it not been enforced on the Companies to execute' (LMA, ACC/2558/MW/C/15/239, letter 23 July 1859).

steamers going past a company's intake had churned up the river and its burden of excrement. Simpson and the Lambeth company were brave enough and far-sighted enough to admit the problem, and to do something about it.

In December 1845, Simpson wrote to his directors, calling their attention to the fact that their water intake was regularly being blocked, that the river had had to be dredged and that a barge had been hired that had taken away '210 cubic yards of material . . . of the most filthy description, so filthy indeed that I have every reason to apprehend the mass of the water will be affected in summer and autumn and baffle all attempts to purify it in the reservoir'.[9] The directors, urged on by Simpson, decided the company would have to move its intake. It probably helped the board in reaching this decision that it included Simpson's brothers, Charles, a doctor, and William, also an engineer, and James Gascoigne Lynde, the Chelsea Waterworks secretary who had also been a colleague of Simpson's father (and whose son was, for a time, in partnership with Simpson).

But when he came to write a share prospectus in November 1848, to raise new capital to cover the cost of the move, Simpson made no mention of his worries about water quality. Instead he made the case for extra investment on the basis of the growing demand for water, both from London's overall expansion and from a change in the way people used water, which the company's existing pumps and engines could not keep pace with. Openly discussing the poor quality of the company's product in a public document would obviously have been foolish. And the company no doubt calculated it was more likely to raise the money by highlighting a commercial rationale for the move than by appealing to Victorian investors' sense of responsibility to the public, which was rudimentary at best.

However the Lambeth directors were quite clear among themselves that they were going upriver at least partly on grounds of quality. The evidence for this is in a note written by a board committee that reviewed the company's options. 'The time must arrive,' the committee wrote, 'when the banks of the river to a great extent, and inland therefrom, will be occupied by buildings both of a manufacturing and domestic nature and consequently the river will become more impure than it now is from the certainty of an increase to the public sewerage.' A more distant intake would provide a cleaner supply. Privately, the company even thought it might be able to make some extra money from its scheme. Having spotted a source for a 'pure and ample supply of water to the Metropolis' that other campaigners and water companies had missed, it hoped to gain some commercial advantage by selling this purer water to its rivals.[10]

The new intake was at Long Ditton near Surbiton, at a point on the Portsmouth road south from Kingston with the rather charming name of Seething Wells. Simpson built new filter beds and engine houses there, first for the Lambeth company and a few years later for the Chelsea company. The waterworks buildings, less flamboyant than some others in London and now owned by Kingston University, are one of Simpson's monuments. Some lie empty, awaiting a suitable use, others have already been repurposed – one is a fitness centre. I was given a tour by Robin Hutchinson, Bob Roberts and Simon Tyrrell, who campaign for their preservation. They were knowledgeable, enthusiastic and excellent company, and Bob generously shared with me his research into Simpson's decision to move to Seething Wells.

But part of the site is beyond the campaigners' reach. The filter beds that Simpson built here have long been disused, and in recent years had become a haven for wildlife, including rare bats. Sometime between the summer of 2018 and the spring of 2019, someone sent in the bulldozers and stripped the old place bare of all vegetation. The four of us stared helplessly through the iron railings erected by Simpson, despairing at this act of ecological vandalism.

The new Lambeth works opened here in March 1852 – just as a head of steam was also building behind the legislation that would require all the Thames companies to move their intakes above Teddington. James Simpson and the Lambeth company had done it without being told to.

One beneficiary of the move was Simpson's manufacturing company. In the 1840s he had developed a pumping engine that became one of the workhorses of the water industry. His 'double-acting beam rotative compound engine' applied steam to both the upstroke and downstroke of the piston (hence 'double-acting'), translated the up and down movements of the traditional heavy beam into rotary motion with a crankshaft and an enormous flywheel (hence 'beam rotative') and moved the steam successively from the highest pressure cylinder to one or more lower pressure cylinders (hence 'compound'), making better use of its power potential.

Simpson's engines were installed at Seething Wells but, for a truly spectacular memorial to the man, pay a visit on one of its regular open days to the engine house at Kempton Park in Middlesex. It was constructed in

1929 by the Metropolitan Water Board to house two gigantic machines built by Simpson's successors at what, after merging with a leading American pump-maker, had become Worthington-Simpson Ltd. One machine is named for the board's then-chairman, Sir William Prescott, and the other for his wife, Lady Bessie, and they tower five storeys high at opposite ends of a cavernous machine hall, lit by floor-to-ceiling windows. These 'triple expansion' engines represent the apogee of steam power, though arguably they were already out of date when they were commissioned, because smaller and less labour-intensive steam turbine or diesel engines could do the job just as well. 'Sir William' has been restored and from time to time can be seen in operation, fussed over by men in white boiler suits on the surrounding gantries. In 2019, at a celebration to mark ninety years since the machines were installed, the entertainer Sir Richard Stilgoe manned the controls: his grandfather, Harold, had commissioned the machines as the Metropolitan Water Board's chief engineer. The television entrepreneur and arts bigwig Sir Peter Bazalgette, great-great-grandson of the famous Joseph, looked on. And so did Sir William and Lady Bessie's grandson, Sir Mark Prescott, a racehorse trainer who inherited his grandfather's baronetcy.

Simpson was among the best of a generation of brilliant men with nationwide consultancy practices as water engineers. But not everyone thought highly of Victorian engineers. The reformer Edwin Chadwick certainly didn't. 'A more ignorant or more jobbing set of men,' he wrote, 'less to be trusted (as the difference of their estimates and their expenditure will show) than the common run of men who dub themselves with the title of engineer and pretend to science I have rarely met with.'[11] Others agreed. As one of the Rothschilds is said to have observed, 'There are three ways of losing your money: women, gambling and engineers. The first two are pleasanter, but the last is much the most certain.'

12

The Invention of Sanitation

Why was London's water so dirty? There were several reasons – run-off from gasworks was one of them, despite William Matthews's protestations – but the most important reason was the growing popularity, from the late eighteenth century onwards, of the flushing water-closet.

For much of the city's history, Londoners had been emptying their privies and chamber pots into brick-lined cesspits under their property: the foundations of some houses were riddled with cavities full of ancient ordure, like a repugnant honeycomb, thanks to the practice of covering over the pits when they were full and digging new ones. Parts of the old City were said to have another ghastly 'cesspool city' beneath them.

In places without cesspits, privy waste was literally allowed to pile up. One surveyor in 1842 recalled inspecting two houses whose cellars 'were full of nightsoil to the depth of three feet', and another court in a slum in St Giles's where 'passing through the passage of the first house I found the yard covered in nightsoil from the overflowing of the privy to the depth of nearly six inches, and bricks were placed to enable the inmates to get across dryshod'.[1]

But most households had functioning cesspits that were periodically emptied by nightsoil men or gongfarmers. These tradesmen worked in teams of three – one man down in the pit, shovelling, the other two carrying out the waste in a tub slung from a pole: they usually had no choice but to carry the contents through the terraced house to their cart. It was dirty work, exceptionally smelly, and a slow process. When the nightmen emptied Pepys's cesspit on one occasion, he found them starting work when he got home at eleven at night – and his servant (who had had no sleep) cleaning up after them when he got up at six next morning.[2]

Henry Mayhew, in *London Labour and the London Poor*, reported on a night spent with these muck-shifters in the 1840s: the smell was 'literally sickening' for the first ten minutes, he wrote, but after that he got used to it. The nightmen themselves 'pronounced the stench "nothing at all"; and one even declared it was refreshing!' This attempt at Cockney wit may have been helped along by the bottle of gin provided by the householder, with two pots of beer and some bread and cheese[3] (did they wash their hands before eating?).

The nightmen took the fruits of their work either to their own yards or to riverside 'laystalls' to dry out. Then these heaps of dung were loaded on to carts or barges and taken out to the countryside to be sold to market gardeners as fertiliser: London was ringed with fields growing cabbages and cauliflowers, parsnips and peas. The Venetian ambassador in 1618 reported that this excellent manure was 'as rich and black as thick ink'. For centuries, then, Londoners metaphorically ate their own excrement – literally, if they happened to buy some of the vegetables brought back in the same carts and barges that had taken the nightsoil out of the city. Add to these towering heaps of human excrement the dung from the horses who provided the city's motive power, and from the cattle driven through the streets to market, and London must have stunk abominably. As one historian wrote: 'At mid-century Victorian England was in danger of becoming submerged in a huge dung-heap of its own making.'[4]

The water-closet was not a new invention. Elizabeth I had one installed at Richmond Palace, designed by a courtier called Sir John Harington. There are occasional references to them in the seventeenth and eighteenth centuries in the houses of the aristocracy: the Duke of Chandos had them in his London home in St James's Square in the 1720s, no doubt sluiced with water pumped up by the York Buildings' dragon.

In 1778 a cabinet-maker called Joseph Bramah took out a patent for an improved device with two valves that could be simultaneously opened by pulling a lever: one valve released water from an overhead cistern to flush the basin; the other valve emptied the basin's contents into a soil pipe through a D-shaped water trap. The trap was meant to prevent bad smells coming up from the drains but was itself a source of smell, because, unlike the U-bend in modern toilets, the water in it was not completely replaced with each flush. Bramah's WC did a decent job, and he claimed to have sold 6,000 by 1797, but it was an elaborate piece of kit, with many of the working parts inconveniently hidden under the floor, where they were awkward to repair or to clean. It was also expensive, so only the wealthy could afford it: you had to be flush to flush.

There were several rival designs. The most widespread was the pan closet, which was cheaper and replaced Bramah's outlet valve with a pan, which tipped the waste into a chamber beneath the bowl *en route* to the D-trap and the drains. Its principal design fault was that the underside of the pan was never rinsed during a flush, which meant it became encrusted with filth. The Victorian water companies were driven to distraction by the waste of water caused by customers tampering with their WCs so that water continually trickled through the basin in a futile attempt to get rid of the smell.

By the 1820s both Bramah's closet and the pan closet were in widespread use. The architect John Soane, always ahead of the curve, had WCs put into all three of the adjoining houses he built in Lincoln's Inn Fields, the first in 1794, the last in 1823. By 1847 almost half the houses in the parish of St Anne's in Soho had a WC, and two-thirds in the more prosperous parish of St James's in Westminster – though you could of course turn that last statistic round and marvel at the fact that a third, even in wealthy St James's, still made do without a flushing loo. In 1851 the engineer James Simpson reckoned the number of WCs in London had increased twenty-fold since 1821.[5]

No doubt these WCs improved the quality of life for individual homeowners, but for the city as a whole, they were a disaster. The problem was that all that dirty water and faeces had to go somewhere, and traditional cesspits could not cope with the extra load. If built to be water-tight, they overflowed and had to be periodically piped out – often simply into the street. If they had been left porous, the liquid gradually seeped into the surrounding ground, creating foul-smelling bogs. As late as 1840, cesspools in London were being dug deliberately deep so the liquid contents would drain away, which meant there would be less solid matter for the nightsoil men to shift, but also meant nearby watercourses and wells became polluted.

The city's sewers, meanwhile, had been designed merely to carry 'surface water': rainwater run-off and perhaps a few slops from neighbouring houses. In many parts of London it had been illegal to put anything else into them, and especially not the waste from privies. But, over time, whatever the regulations might say, most WCs and cesspits were surreptitiously connected to the sewers, and district by district the rules were changed not just to permit people to connect up but to make it compulsory. In 1848, cesspits were banned if a property was within 100 feet of a sewer, and by the end of the 1850s they had virtually disappeared from central London.

Meanwhile the city was growing relentlessly: its population more than doubled from one million to over two million between 1800 and 1850. The result was a tidal wave of effluent daily discharging into London's rivers. The builder and developer Thomas Cubitt summed up the problem succinctly in 1840: 'The Thames is now made a great cesspool instead of each person having one of his own,' he said. Dickens, in 1857, wrote in *Little Dorrit*, 'Through the heart of the town a deadly sewer ebbed and flowed, in the place of a fine fresh river.' It would, wrote *The Builder* in 1858, be 'an act of insanity' to dip a mug into the Thames and drink the contents.[6]

Under inspection

But this dreadful state of affairs was not simply the result of widespread adoption of a new technology. It owed something as well to one of the most remarkable individuals in Victorian Britain.

Edwin Chadwick was a giant of his age, a man who combined vision with rigour and – until he alienated almost everyone whose support he needed – was remarkably successful at getting things done. This clever, spiky, driven man was by far the era's most effective proponent of public health – in fact, he more or less invented the concept. He also invented much that we now take for granted in modern government, including the idea that governments have a duty to promote the well-being of their citizens and the right to interfere with the liberty of the property-owning individual in order to bring that about – two concepts that many of his contemporaries struggled with. Though John Wright, author of *The Dolphin*, and the MP Francis Burdett were energetic and articulate, their efforts changed little. Where they failed, Chadwick succeeded – after a fashion.[7]

Unhappily his far-sightedness and capacity for hard work were matched only by his ability to inspire resentment and dislike. A disciple of the utilitarian philosopher Jeremy Bentham, Chadwick had trained as a lawyer, worked as a journalist and then started work in 1832 with one of the new-fangled royal commissions, set up to reform the antiquated poor law; in 1834 he became secretary of the new permanent Poor Law Commission established as a result.

Chadwick's poor law reforms – and they were effectively his – made him notorious. The old system, which
went back to Elizabethan times, was a mess, inconsistent
and corruptly administered. The law made parishes
responsible for their own paupers and allowed them to
raise money from a property tax, the rates, to meet the
costs of keeping them in workhouses or supporting them at
home. This was an open invitation to corruption – jobbery – as local vestries awarded their cronies contracts
for supplying workhouses with food and clothing. And
ratepayers complained they were forking out to support
able-bodied paupers who ought to be working for a living.
With ruthless Benthamite logic, Chadwick proposed to
relieve the ratepayers' burden by, in effect, forcing the des-
titute to find work. The workhouses would be turned into
quasi-prisons, run on harsh and restrictive lines, which
would make the position of the dependent pauper 'less eligible', in his words, than that of the independent working
labourer. You could work; or you could go to the workhouse; or you could starve. Chadwick – a man who didn't
really do empathy – thought this would promote 'prudence
and forethought' among the working class. His approach
might (just) have been acceptable had work been plentiful,
but it condemned thousands to a life of misery in the workhouse in periods of economic slump when there was often
no work to be had.

Chadwick's policy was attacked from all sides.
The liberal-minded saw it as heartless and cruel. Conservatives resented the attack on 'local self-government'
represented by Chadwick's plan for ending corruption,
which involved replacing small local workhouses with
large, supposedly well-run establishments serving several

parishes, grouped together in 'unions', and giving a new central poor law board powers to override local decisions. Such 'centralisation' was seen as undermining essentially English traditions of sturdy independence; it was authoritarian, or, worse still, French. For the next fifty years, centralisation was deployed as a dog whistle term whenever vested interests – including the water companies – perceived a threat from government and wanted to rally conservatives to their support.

Chadwick was an enthusiastic centraliser. While preparing the poor law reforms, he was briefly side-tracked by government into the inquiry that produced the 1833 Factory Act, which for the first time limited the hours children could work in factories but also created a new type of centrally appointed official, the factory inspector.

At the turn of the eighteenth and nineteenth centuries, advanced thinkers had become increasingly interested in notions of inspection and control. They suited the emerging world of the textile mill, that striking manifestation of what we now call the Industrial Revolution, where owners were concerned to find ways of keeping their workers to a rigid timetable dictated by the operation of machines. They culminated in Jeremy Bentham's scheme for a prison, the Panopticon, in which all the cells are visible from a central observation point and all the inmates therefore under constant surveillance.

The title of inspector was not new. As we have seen, the engineer at the Chelsea Waterworks, Thomas Simpson, father of James, was originally styled 'inspector'. But now an idea familiar from civil engineering was applied to social engineering. In 1832 a temporary Board of Health set up to combat England's first cholera epidemic urged local authorities to appoint 'district inspectors' to tackle threats to public health. In time more and more areas of society, including London's water companies, became subject to the oversight and control of outside experts and government officials, appointed by the centre and managed from the centre. The first inspectors of schools were appointed in 1837. A railway inspectorate was established in 1840. A lunacy commission, with powers to inspect asylums, arrived in 1845. Ideas of what government could and should do changed. Governments became bolder, and more willing to shoulder the burden of protecting the public interest. Alongside the power to inspect, they asserted a right, on occasion, to compel. Railway acts specified the track gauges that should be used, and insisted companies run daily 'parliamentary trains' with cheap fares for poorer passengers. Mine-owners were barred from employing women and children underground. Vaccination was made compulsory. In due course London's water would be given similar treatment.

Such moves went down badly with a business class firmly wedded to *laissez-faire* economic ideas of individual freedom and a market regulated only by competition. But the regime of inspection that was a necessary adjunct of all this was Chadwick's most significant contribution to the machinery of modern government.

Centralising tendencies

It wasn't long before Chadwick turned his formidable talents to scrutinising the nation's health. In 1838 there was a serious outbreak of typhus, and the poor law board – really,

Chadwick – commissioned a wide-ranging investigation, which became the 1842 *Report into the Sanitary Condition of the Labouring Population of Great Britain*. 'Sanitary' was a new word for a new concept. Chadwick's report is the first recorded use in the *Oxford English Dictionary*, and the word's novelty meant that not everyone agreed on how to spell it: Chadwick himself had spelled it 'sanatory' in an initial 1838 report on typhus,[8] and others preferred 'sanatary' and 'sanitory'.

Chadwick was a great believer in both evidence and experts, and much of the report was derived from inquiries made by three leading medics and from a questionnaire sent to the medical officers of the new poor law unions. He also took evidence from experts such as John Roe, the surveyor of the Holborn and Finsbury sewer commission, who had invented a more efficient egg-shaped sewer made of small pipes, narrower at the bottom than at the top, which encouraged a rapid flow to sweep away obstructions. The report led to the setting up of a short-lived General Board of Health, with Chadwick as one of its members, and more government-appointed inspectors.

In time the sanitary movement launched by Chadwick developed into a formidable lobby, a coalition of polemicists and politicians, medical men and engineers, idealists and pragmatists that proved impossible to ignore. From 1857, when the Ladies' Sanitary Association was formed, the movement also provided a rare public outlet for the talents and energy of middle-class Victorian women, who published a stream of pamphlets with titles like *The Power of Soap and Water, Household Troubles and How to Meet Them* and *How to Manage a Baby*, which were full of sound advice on domestic hygiene and childcare. The association also sent an army of women volunteers — forerunners of modern health visitors — into the homes of the poor to offer practical help. Deploying women to do this work was deliberate: to the Victorian mind it would have been intolerable to have government officials enter private homes; earnest middle-class Lady Bountifuls were not a threat, though some of those they sought to help may have found them an unwelcome irritant.

But Chadwick's sanitarians also faced formidable opposition. Opponents of centralisation in the sanitary sphere found its implications unsettling. Partly this reflected the distrust of a classically educated elite for experts, especially scientific experts, particularly if they came with a brief from government to interfere. Partly it was because sanitary improvements cost money. Partly it was about straightforward party politics: Joshua Toulmin Smith, the man who coined the term 'local self-government', thought Chadwick's ideas were just cover for a Liberal national government 'engrossing under one central patronage the actual control over all local institutions, works, and arrangements' — in other words, politicians arranging jobs for their pals.[9]

But there were deeper concerns. City-wide sewerage projects implied a 'networked city' in which the interests of the individual and the mere neighbourhood might be ignored because the interventions required were too extensive, expensive and technically sophisticated for local self-government. Some thought such schemes unrealistically utopian, others thought them authoritarian. Intellectual underpinning for the sanitary sceptics came from Herbert Spencer, the man who came up with the phrase 'survival of the fittest' and first applied that Darwinian notion to human society. Spencer thought government intervention in matters of health and cleanliness represented a violation of privacy, and conjured a nightmare vision of a nanny state: before you knew it, a government that believed it had a duty to protect people's health would be poking its nose in everywhere, regulating what and how much people ate, what they wore, how much they slept . . . and employing an army of officials to enforce its diktat. The fortress-like sanctity of the Englishman's home would be breached.

The anti-centralisers were fighting a losing battle. In 1853 the government introduced compulsory vaccination against smallpox and enforced it from 1871 with the appointment of vaccination officers and inspectors. Vaccination was widely accepted, but the anti-vaxxers of the era vigorously protested the compulsory nature of the process, the 'dictatorial' behaviour of the government and the violation of local decision-makers' freedom. Resistance from local government to centralisation generally only started to crumble in the 1870s, when the Local Government Board made loans available for sanitary improvements – provided the local authority submitted to central government inspection and accepted central government's terms.

Chadwick set out to challenge the prevailing *laissez-faire* complacency, arguing, in effect, that there was such a thing as society and that its leading members had a duty to help those less fortunate. In a succession of reports, he and his collaborators spelled out in vivid and appalling detail the conditions in which many of the country's poorer citizens were forced to live: cramped, stinking, overcrowded hovels without water or drains. No wonder death rates were so high and life expectancy so short among the urban poor. Doing something to alleviate such misery was a humanitarian act; it was also enlightened self-interest. The middle classes themselves were at risk from contagion in the form of bad air or 'miasma' spreading out from the festering slums, and the risk was moral as well as physical; dirt and degeneracy went hand in hand. Chadwick's critique was based, as we shall see, on a faulty understanding of disease; but it caught the popular imagination.

It was part of Dickens's vision too. In *Dombey and Son* he described not only the 'noxious particles that rise from vitiated air . . . rolling slowly on to corrupt the better portions of towns' but also 'depravity, impiety, drunkenness, theft, murder and a long train of nameless sins . . . creeping on, to blight the innocent and spread contagion among the poor'.[10] To many the connection between dirt and moral degradation was axiomatic. The Dean of Westminster, preaching at a service of thanksgiving in the wake of a cholera outbreak in 1849, urged better sanitation and an improved water supply as remedies against a future visitation of the disease, and told his listeners that it was chiefly the 'unclean' and the 'intemperate' who suffered at the hands of the Angel of Destruction:

> . . . those that are guilty of the sins of uncleanness, and of filthiness, and of superfluity of naughtiness, guilty of reckless uncleanness of living, of uncleanness in their houses, uncleanness in their cesspools, gardens, and passages, those that are addicted to intemperance of any sort, excess in eating, excess in drinking, drunkenness and debauchery of every kind.[11]

One of Chadwick's fellow 'sanitarians', Dr Thomas Southwood Smith, who was both a medic and a Unitarian minister, thought living in 'a filthy, squalid, unwholesome

dwelling' led to selfishness and sensuality 'and the formation of habits of idleness, dishonesty, debauchery, and
violence; in a word, the training to every kind and degree
of brutality and ruffianism'.[12]

A lack of clean water contributed to all this. John
Simon, the first medical officer of health for the City of
London and a towering figure in the sanitary reform
movement, explicitly linked personal hygiene with moral
health – even though morality was not strictly his province: 'I have no hesitation in saying that I believe that in
having cleanlier bodies they [the poor] would have cleanlier minds, and so far be improved morally,' he told an
1851 inquiry, while admitting that such moral issues
were outside his competence as a physician. 'It is a point
on which I have of course no professional knowledge'.[13]

Christian reformers such as Southwood Smith and
Charles Kingsley – the Anglican churchman who wrote
The Water Babies – found a congenial billet in the sanitary
movement, and there is an evangelical tinge to some of the
sanitary literature. 'God . . . sends rain down abundantly
upon the earth to wash away decaying matters and dangerous filth', as one of the Ladies' Sanitary Association's
earliest tracts puts it, though the text is careful not to make
explicit the connection between sin and poor sanitation.[14]

Chadwick's own arguments tended to be practical and
economic – utilitarian – rather than moral. Respectable
members of society paid a price for the insanitary slums
because it made them potential victims of crime and disease, and because they were ratepayers who had to support
workers and their families laid low by fever and illness.
This being England, the debate about dirt and contagion
was also a debate about class.

Chadwick's views trickled down to others. Dr John Challice, chairman of the Bermondsey board of guardians, was clear that bad water produced bad effects. 'Bad water produces sickness, and anyone who has paid any attention to the subject is well aware that sickness is one of the greatest causes of pauperism,' he told the 1851 inquiry. 'A poor man cannot drink the water, it is so nauseous . . . not having pure water he resorts to intoxicating liquors.' And not only the poor were revolted, but respectable ratepayers like Challice himself. 'We are obliged to resort to pumps in the public streets; it is impossible to drink the water supplied to us through the pipes, it tastes so badly.' His evidence was supported by that of Edward Collinson, chairman of the board of guardians of the parish of St George the Martyr in Southwark and an active member of the Metropolitan Association for the Supply of Water. Collinson said of his supply: 'Sometimes the smell is offensive; the taste is always so.' (They were talking about Southwark & Vauxhall water.)[15]

Chadwick not only diagnosed society's failures, he offered solutions too. Better drains were obviously one – he hated smelly, insanitary cesspits; but another was a constant supply of water to flush the drains continuously, sweeping away the accumulated filth and ordure and reducing the risks of disease. The rich had water-closets; the poor needed them too. In time – deploying the metaphor of the city as a living body, like so many before him – he developed this idea into what he called his 'venous and arterial system': the city was to be kept alive and healthy with the aid of two comprehensive and complementary networks of pipes, one bringing clean water in, another taking dirty water out.

To bring this about to Chadwick's satisfaction, the water companies needed to offer a constant supply, with their mains constantly charged, and in London they could not or would not do this. But the bigger question was what to do with the effluent. Chadwick firmly believed it had commercial value as manure, just like the nightsoil from cesspits. But nightsoil was a solid, more or less, whereas the product of the water-closet was definitely a slurry. Chadwick and others tried for years to find ways to collect it, pipe it out into the countryside and generate the cash to pay for sanitary improvements by selling it to farmers. They failed: any remote prospect of making their product economically viable was destroyed in the late 1840s when the first artificial fertilisers were perfected and vast quantities of guano – solidified bird droppings stuffed with plant nutrients – were imported from South America.

So the only alternative, in London and elsewhere, was to flush all this human waste into the nearest river. As the author of *A Lecture on the Sewage Difficulty* wrote in 1867, 'The whole system of the hydraulic disposal of the excreta of town populations is nothing else than an ingenious method of polluting enormous quantities of water.'[16] The cleansing of London's slums so earnestly desired by Chadwick was to be achieved at the expense of the Thames.

Purging the sewers

The sewers that poured their contents so liberally into the river were the responsibility of ancient sewer commissions, established under Henry VIII. There were eight in all, part of an impossibly tangled and fragmented jumble of local authorities responsible for running London. The sewer commissions, like most of these bodies, were notorious for incompetence and corruption. The sewers themselves were brick-built, wide and flat-bottomed. They had to be large so men could get into them and clear them out, but the wider they were the more slowly the water flowed through them and the more readily they got choked up.

When Chadwick talked of veins and arteries, he came up against these sewer commissions. They reacted badly to his 1842 *Inquiry*, in which he criticised them explicitly, but it's a measure of Chadwick's standing at this period, and of how alarmed Londoners in general and the rich and powerful in particular were becoming at the stinking state of the metropolis, that the government backed Chadwick. At the end of 1847, all the old sewer commissions in London were swept away (with the exception of the one in the City) and a permanent Metropolitan Commission of Sewers was established instead.

Chadwick was a member, seeking to solve the problem he himself was helping to create. But cleaning up the Thames required an overall plan for the capital's sewage – at which point the difficulties began. Some were technical: the engineers the commission consulted could not agree on the best approach. Should London's sewers feed into a network of sumps across the capital, from which sewage manure could be pumped out to the countryside? Or should there be a huge tunnel under the Thames taking its contents out into the estuary (a kind of Thames Tideway super-sewer, 150 years ahead of its time)? Nor could they agree on the best size for the sewers: smaller than the existing ones, yes, but did that mean as small (and as cheap) as the ones John Roe in Holborn and Finsbury proposed and Chadwick favoured, or something rather larger?

Some of the difficulties were political and stemmed mainly from conflict between Chadwick and another member of the commission, John Leslie, a toffs' tailor and a former member of the Westminster sewer commission. Leslie had campaigned to expose corruption, so should have been on Chadwick's side, but was (according to Chadwick's biographer, Samuel Finer) 'a thoroughly unpleasant man, spiteful, offensive, and ungenerous' and Chadwick loathed him. Perpetual infighting between Chadwick and Leslie undermined the commission's work so badly that in 1849 it was dissolved, and reconstituted with a new set of commissioners, including neither Chadwick nor Leslie.[17]

Unhappily the new commission fared little better, and in all the Metropolitan Commission of Sewers was dissolved and reconstituted with new members no fewer than five times in eight years. At one stage the second commission asked for submissions from engineers who thought they had the solution to London's drainage problems and was then inundated, as it were, with 157 schemes, ranging from the plausible to the unintelligible; the third commission decided none of them were entirely satisfactory. It all went to show just how intractable the problems were. The commission was also short of money, with an income from the sewer rates of just £200,000 a year, when the problems it was trying to address would cost millions to put right.

The commissions did little for their own credibility when a brand new sewer in the brand new Victoria Street, intended as a showpiece, went dreadfully wrong and had to be rebuilt at horrendous cost after collapsing. In 1855, the sixth commission was finally abolished and replaced by yet another body, the Metropolitan Board of Works. The board inherited little of value from the commission – with two major exceptions: one was a workable (if expensive) plan for completely re-engineering London's sewers to keep filth out of the Thames; the other was Joseph Bazalgette, who had helped draw up the plan and, as the new board's engineer, would eventually carry it out.

Meanwhile, leading men in medicine and the emerging disciplines of natural science had started to ask questions about how exactly polluted water might harm those who drank it – physically as well as morally.

13

Science Applied

It was one thing to assert that the water of the Thames and Lea was dirty and unfit for use; it was quite a different thing to demonstrate why that was. This was a question for scientists. The debate over London's water was perhaps the first occasion on which science was deployed to help determine a matter of public policy. Alas, for much of the century it proved inadequate to the task. That was partly a consequence of pushback by the companies; but partly it reflected the fact that many of the scientists were asking the wrong questions.

The truth – though, for obvious reasons, scientists were reluctant to admit it – was that the laboratory techniques of the era were simply incapable of identifying with any certainty what it was in polluted water that made it dangerous. Even when the new science of bacteriology produced a breakthrough in the 1880s, it merely reframed the question in different terms, without providing a conclusive answer.

For much of the century the business of passing judgement on water quality was the province of chemists. Using methods originally developed for analysing spa mineral waters, boiling off the water itself and examining the residue, they could tell you how many grains per gallon of 'carbonate of lime' or 'oxide of iron' or 'common salt' or 'organic matter' any given water sample contained. But even if analyses by different chemists came up with the same findings – which they often didn't – there was no agreement about what they signified. It rather depended on who was paying the analyst's fees. As a writer in *Fraser's* magazine observed drily in 1834, 'It is curious and interesting to observe the manner in which palpable truths are frittered down, and become lost to the public, by the ingenuity and disingenuousness of scientific men when called upon to support particular interests.'[1]

The question the chemists did not ask, and could not have answered even if they had done, was how exactly their water samples might harm anyone who drank them. In this they were hampered by contemporary theories of what 'disease' was. To us it seems self-evident that particular diseases have particular causes: until well into the nineteenth century, that was far from obvious, even (or especially) to medical professionals. Nor were most scientists and medics prepared to accept that some diseases were carried in water. It was not until another new discipline – epidemiology – emerged that it was possible to demonstrate conclusively that dirty water was a killer; and even then the precise mechanisms remained a matter of conjecture for another twenty years.

There was plenty of scope for speculation and dispute, and the water companies took advantage of it. In our day, this exploitation of scientific uncertainty, as practiced by the likes of tobacco companies and oil companies, is known as 'manufacturing doubt'. London's nineteenth-century water companies pioneered this process: the scientific controversy around water quality was a dry run, you might say, for similar controversies in our own day.

The tendency towards wrangling and obfuscation was exacerbated by the chief mechanism through which science in the nineteenth century fed into policy-making. Royal commissions and select committees called witnesses who were questioned and cross-examined. This adversarial approach, derived from the conduct of trials in courts of law and deeply embedded in the British way of doing things, contaminated the process almost like a disease bacillus in the water supply. It was hard to achieve agreement when scientists on either side were so intent on defending their own positions and rubbishing their rivals'. 'The expert was the one who asserted and got away with it,' one historian of science observed. 'Experts didn't say maybe.'[2]

Common sense

To begin with, in the 1820s, scientists could often do no better than the layman when presented with contaminated water. A well-known surgeon, John Abernethy, was one of several doctors and scientists to whom John Wright in 1827 showed samples of Grand Junction water; his reaction when Wright asked him whether it was fit for use was recorded in *The Dolphin*:

> Never shall I forget the countenance of this eminent man at that moment! The very sight of the turbid fluid seemed to occasion a turmoil in his stomach. He began pacing the room backwards and forward, and the only words I could extract from him were 'How can you ask me such a question? There is such a thing as Common Sense!'[3]

One witness said something similar to the 1828 commission:

> A slender portion of common sense . . . authorizes me
> to affirm that a stream which receives daily the evacu-
> ations of a million human beings, of many thousand
> animals, with all the filth and refuse of various offen-
> sive manufactories . . . cannot require to be analysed
> except by a lunatic to determine whether it ought to be
> pumped up as a beverage for the inhabitants of the
> metropolis of the British empire.[4]

But this kind of rhetoric was a substitute for hard evidence.
An appeal to 'common sense' sidestepped the question of
what it was exactly that posed the danger – and this helps
to explain why the conclusions of the 1828 commission
were so anodyne: there was no scientific consensus.

On the one hand, the physician and enthusiastic vege-
tarian William Lambe told the commission that Thames
water was injurious to health because it was thick with
decomposing organic matter – code for sewage. On the
other hand, an analysis of the Grand Junction's sources of
supply commissioned by the company concluded that its
product was 'as perfectly harmless as any spring water of
the purest kind used in common life'.[5] To try to resolve the
differences, the inquiry commissioned an analysis from a
physician called John Bostock, who took more than thirty
samples from close to all the companies' intakes, though
he actually subjected only two of them (the 'best' and
'worst') to chemical analysis. The rest he evaluated on the
basis of their taste, their smell and their appearance, and,
if they looked sufficiently murky, thought himself 'fully
warranted in asserting' that they were 'improper to be
employed in diet', while, if the water looked clear, it was

fine to drink. This was common sense again, dressed up as science, and not much help.[6]*

By the middle of the century, questions were being raised about how useful all this analysis really was. In 1856 a study of the condition of the upstream Thames – adulterated with sewage from towns like Oxford, Reading and Windsor – concluded that 'chemical analysis does not at present convey an exact understanding of the danger to health which a particular water may occasion'.[7] That was written by engineers, but even some chemists were starting to admit their ignorance. Among them was Sir Benjamin Brodie Bt, Oxford professor of chemistry, who told an inquiry in the 1860s there was no scientific way of knowing at what point polluted water might become safe: 'I can only say that when you have once put sewage into the water I should be rather reluctant to drink it.' Common sense again.[8]

Brodie was an academic chemist and independently wealthy, so a man who didn't need to earn his living from analysis and could afford to be frank about his profession's practical shortcomings. Most mid-century analytical chemists did not have that luxury. Nevertheless, one of them did break ranks and, like Brodie, ask fundamental questions about what he and his colleagues were doing. Edward Frankland, who became the doyen of Victorian

* Six years later Bostock was commissioned to undertake another analysis of Thames water. This time it was the West Middlesex company paying him. He concluded that the river water was purer than it had been – which he put down to the demolition of old London Bridge, which had speeded the flow and carried impurities more rapidly down river. (Clay, *Remarks on the Water Supply of London*, p. 98).

water analysis, was professor of chemistry at the School of Mines (a forerunner of Imperial College) and, from 1865, the official analyst of the London water supply appointed by the chief statistician to the Registrar General of Births, Deaths and Marriages, William Farr. Every month Frankland analysed the different companies' water and published the results. Just over a year after his appointment, he made an interesting discovery. Cholera had arrived in the East End in July 1866 and Farr's statistical analysis of cholera deaths revealed that the area affected by the disease matched that supplied by the East London Waterworks.

Yet Frankland's chemical analysis of the East London's water at the peak of the outbreak showed it was actually purer than a month earlier and contained less organic matter than usual. He wrote to Farr to tell him this, and Farr published his observation in his return of 4 August:

> It must be borne in mind, however [Frankland added], that chemical investigation is utterly unable to detect the presence of choleraic poison amongst the organic impurities in water, and there can be no doubt that this poison may be present in quantity fatal to the consumer, though far too minute to be detected by the most delicate chemical research.[9]

It was a revealing and commendably honest thing to say: Frankland was admitting that his own science, chemistry, was for practical purposes irrelevant, and that Farr's statistically-based epidemiology was a far better tool for detecting the presence of cholera. And towards the end of his life, when the germ theory of disease had become widely if not universally accepted, Frankland was able to state flatly: 'You cannot detect the germs by chemical

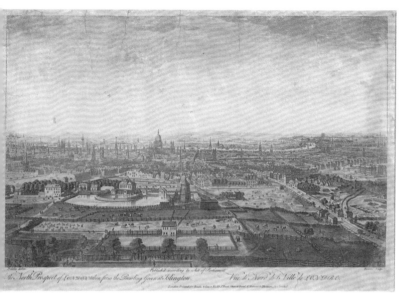

London from the North in the 1750s, by Thomas Bowles, showing the water house, windmill and reservoirs at New River Head.

The round pond and water house at New River Head in 1914, shortly before they disappeared to make way for the new headquarters of the Metropolitan Water Board.

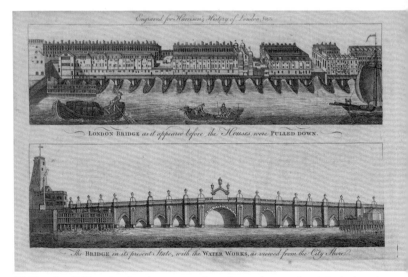

Old London Bridge, showing the waterworks at the northern end and, in the later image, the wheels at the southern end which pumped water to Southwark.

The York Buildings Waterworks around 1790, by Thomas Malton, with the smoking chimney of London's first steam engine.

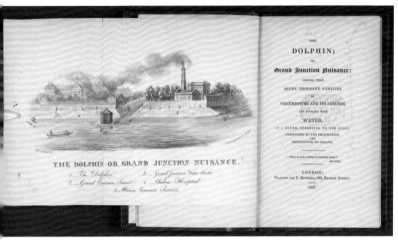

The frontispiece of John Wright's 1827 pamphlet, 'The Dolphin', showing the Grand Junction's intake and works at the mouth of the Ranelagh sewer.

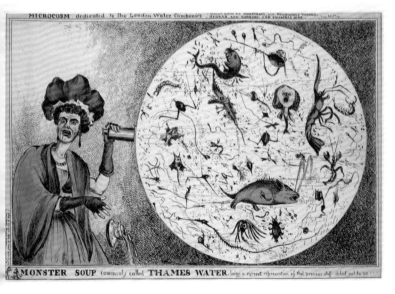

Monster Soup: Paul Pry satirises the microscopists' findings in 1828.

Salus Populi Suprema Lex: George Cruikshank's 1832 attack on the dreadful Southwark Waterworks and its equally dreadful owner, John Edwards Vaughan.

Thomas Shotter Boys's image of the Thames in 1842, showing the river busy with working vessels, many beached like badly-parked cars on the stinking foreshore.

A London water carrier with his distinctive tankard (left) and the Dutch artist Marcellus Laroon's much-reproduced but misleading version (middle). Horace Petherick's illustration of a London turncock on his rounds in the 1870s (right).

The Laying of the Water-Main in Tottenham Court Road by George Scharf, 1834. The introduction of cast-iron pipes at last made possible 'constant supply'.

OPENING OF THE NEW WORKS OF THE LAMBETH WATER COMPANY, SEETHING WELLS, DITTON.

The grand opening in 1852 of the Lambeth Waterworks' new intake and pumping station at Seething Wells as depicted in the Illustrated London News.

An abandoned 'miscast' of the largest Cornish engine cylinder ever made, for a pumping station in the Netherlands in 1849, pictured in the yard at Harveys of Hale, who manufactured it.

Cleaning the sand in the filter beds at the Hampton waterworks around 1880. In the background are the impressive pump houses of the Southwark & Vauxhall, Grand Junction and West Middlesex companies.

Three of the principal players in the Grand Junction and Southwark & Vauxhall financial scandal of the 1870s: (from left to right) Joseph Quick, Arthur Clay, and Allen Stoneham.

(above) Cathedral of sewage: the richly decorated interior of Joseph Bazalgette's Crossness sewage pumping station in Kent.

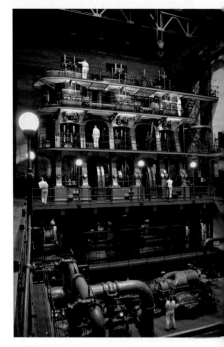

(right) Steam's last spectacular hurrah: one of the two enormous Worthington-Simpson triple expansion steam engines installed in 1929 at the Metropolitan Water Board's Kempton Park pumping station.

means . . . they are too minute in quantity and weight to affect the results of chemical analysis.'[10]

But it didn't stop him from continuing his analytical work on London's water supply right up until his death in 1899, or from giving highly contentious evidence to periodic official inquiries. He also served as the driving force of the second of two royal commissions on Rivers Pollution between 1868 and 1874. In 1867 he coined a term, 'previous sewage contamination', to describe water that contained inorganic nitrogen compounds, which he maintained came from decomposed sewage. It was a clever phrase and a useful stick with which to beat whichever company had been found supplying dodgy water that month, but it was largely meaningless. If the sewage had decomposed to the point where all that was left was inorganic nitrogen, you could argue the water had become pure and innocuous. Frankland must have known this but it didn't matter. Unable to put his finger on exactly where the harm lay in dirty water, he was acting on what we would now call the precautionary principle – assuming that water that had once been polluted might still be compromised by something which chemical analysis could not detect, and using provocative language to alert the public. He was, in fact, employing much the same tactics as the analysts working for the companies: manipulating evidence and marshalling facts so as to manufacture doubt.

Monster soup

There was another way of analysing water. The microscope had been around since the seventeenth century and it was an easy thing to put a sample of Thames water under the magnifying lens to see what it contained. In the library at the Wellcome Collection there is a print dating from around 1828 by William Heath, who went by the *nom de caricature* of 'Paul Pry'. It is entitled: 'MONSTER SOUP commonly called THAMES WATER being a correct represention [sic] of that precious stuff doled out to us.' It shows a woman looking through a microscope at an array of tiny creatures – fish, sharks, lobsters, millipedes, eels, worms, a dinosaur skeleton and nameless others – portrayed in a circular frame. The woman is horrified: her face turned towards us registers shock and disgust and her cup of tea is falling from her hand. Some of the creatures have been given human faces and look equally shocked: they certainly don't look like the kind of thing you'd want to drink in your tea. The Wellcome's notes on the print tell us that 'looking at a drop of water through a microscope was a popular entertainment provided by travelling showmen who carried the microscopes around in cases on their backs'.[11]

In 1850 a physician and botanist called Arthur Hassall put this showman's entertainment to work in the service of serious science and public health. In March that year, he published *A Microscopic Examination of the Water Supplied to the Inhabitants of London and Surrounding Districts*. The book – or at any rate its illustrations – caused a sensation: you can tell because they quickly prompted a parody in the humorous magazine *Punch*.[12] Hassall had borrowed William Heath's idea of displaying his findings in a circular frame, as if seen through the lens of the microscope. His samples of Thames water and company water were swarming with microscopic life – things he called *animalculae* or *infusoria* – and

the illustrations showed what they looked like: not caricature fish or monsters with angry faces but clusters of tiny
cells, hairy globules, tangled filaments, all wonderful and
fascinating, provided you didn't have to drink them.

Sewage pollution in the river showed up too, in the form
of potato cells, wheat husks, and fragments of muscular
fibre. These, Hassall wrote, came from 'faecal matter'. 'It is
thus beyond dispute,' he concluded, 'that according to the
present system of London's water supply a portion of the
inhabitants of the metropolis are made to consume, in
some form or other, a portion of their own excrement, and
moreover to pay for the privilege.' He backed up this assertion with a nauseating and overwritten description, worthy
of John Wright and *The Dolphin*, of what went into the river:

> The contents of . . . closets and urinaries; dirty and
> waste waters of various descriptions . . . the refuse of
> gas, chemical, and a host of other works and manufac-
> tories, some of which are of the most unclean and
> offensive description, as those of bone crushers, the
> makers of glue and catgut, soap boilers, tanners of lea-
> ther etc . . . the purpulent discharge, *cataplasmata*, and
> other *rejecta* of the sick of our hospitals.[13]

The circular vignettes in which his illustrations appeared
made it look as if each represented precisely what he had
seen through his microscope in one drop of water. In fact
he cheated, as he was forced to admit under cross-
examination at a select committee hearing: the tiny
animalcules *had* all been found in his samples, but no single sample contained all of them.[14] It didn't matter: the
point had been made. Londoners now knew what they
were drinking and it wasn't pleasant.

Hassall's discoveries were eye-catching, but they ran up against the same problem as chemical analysis. Were these creatures in the water bad for you, and if so why? Hassall himself ventured an explanation of why bad water was bad for health, but it was not wholly convincing. His *infusoria*, he said, were scavengers: their presence indicated the presence of the dead and decaying organic matter on which they fed, and to Hassall and his contemporaries, decay and putrefaction were a Bad Thing, if only because they gave off poisonous gases. But he struggled to explain the direct effects on people:

> What are the symptoms, it may be asked, which arise in the human frame from the use of water largely contaminated with organic matter? This question is not easy to answer in a satisfactory manner . . . We are not in general, or except in times of epidemics, to look for any violent or sudden injurious effects from the use of impure water; like the effects of vitiated air, those of bad water are doubtless in general slow and insidious, but not the less important, or the less to be dreaded.'[15]

Hassall was a prisoner of the assumption, near-universal at the time, that disease was linked to bad or 'vitiated' air.

Faced with Hassall's attack, the water companies had no difficulty finding scientific defenders. Some argued that if Hassall's *animalculae* were scavengers, they should be encouraged because they were helping to purify the water. Others simply refused to accept Hassall's premise. William Brande, the distinguished chemist who had served with Roget and Telford on the 1828 commission, was one. 'Should you consider water containing such insects as those to be noxious or otherwise?' he was asked in 1851. 'I should think it would not be noxious,' he replied, though without bothering to say why.[16]

Alfred Swaine Taylor, professor of chemistry at Guy's Hospital, was another. 'I cannot agree with Dr Hassall in the view of the injurious nature of the *animalculae* in the water,' he said. 'Speaking from 20 years' experience, I know no writer, chemist, physician or physiologist who has ever adduced a single fact to show the injury arising from the use of water containing these microscopic animals.'[17] But then Taylor and a colleague at Guy's were on the payroll of the West Middlesex company, whose water (unsurprisingly) they had recently found to be 'a good, wholesome and potable water, free from all noxious ingredients'.[18]

Bad air

What was needed for a breakthrough was a new way of thinking about disease. It took a surprisingly long time to emerge.

At the start of the century, the prevailing notion among medical authorities was that illness and disease were mani-festations of an imbalance in the body's constitution. This idea went back a very long way indeed, to the theory of the four 'humours' developed by the ancient Greek phys-ician Hippocrates and passed on to the medieval world in the works of the second-century physician Galen. Galen identified the humours as blood, yellow bile, black bile and phlegm. All are present in the body but the proportions vary from individual to individual and help determine character: more blood in your constitution makes you san-guine, more yellow bile makes you choleric, more black bile makes you melancholic, and phlegm makes you, well, phlegmatic. But if the balance of humours got seriously out of kilter, the result would be not just differences in temperament but enhanced susceptibility to illness.

Doctors in the eighteenth and early nineteenth centuries no longer talked of humours but they still believed that imbalances in the body's constitution were a 'predisposing cause' of disease, which lay latent until some external 'exciting cause' triggered actual illness. The poor were especially at risk – which helped to explain the higher death rates among London's more deprived communities – because their inadequate food and 'intemperate', 'ill-disciplined' and 'irregular' way of life undermined their constitutional balance.[19]

Among the exciting causes of disease might be bad water. But even worse – much worse, in fact – was bad air, or 'miasma'. The notion that the stink of decomposition associated with marshes and middens made people ill went back a very long way: it was part of medical orthodoxy. It was baked into terms like malaria, from the Italian for the bad air, 'mal'aria', which emanated from mosquito-ridden swamps. The idea was seized on by nineteenth-century sanitary campaigners because it helped to explain why smelly, ill-drained, poverty-stricken areas, such as London's East End, were so susceptible to disease, and because it served to alarm the middle classes and so mobilise them in the sanitarians' support: smells and miasmatic mists might travel.

The most forceful statement of the miasmatic idea came from Edwin Chadwick, who in 1846 told a parliamentary committee: 'All smell is, if it be intense, immediate acute disease; and eventually we may say that, by depressing the system and rendering it susceptible to the action of other causes, all smell is disease.'[20] Chadwick's fellow-sanitarian Thomas Southwood Smith suggested that 'poisonous matters', when inhaled, pierced the thin delicate membranes of the lung, 'and thus pass directly into the current of the circulation'. The consequence could be death within a few minutes or hours, or a progressive 'deterioration and corruption of the whole mass of the blood', which excited 'those violent commotions of the system which constitute fevers, choleras, dysentries and other mortal epidemics'.[21]

Mapping disease

The man generally credited with demolishing the miasma theory and demonstrating that at least one disease, cholera, was spread by water – and who also posited the existence of an identifiable cholera 'poison', thus laying the groundwork for the theory of germs – is Dr John Snow. Snow was one of those eminent Victorians whose achievements almost beggar belief. He was the son of a Yorkshire coal heaver, the eldest of nine children, apprenticed at the age of fourteen to a surgeon in Newcastle. At the age of twenty-three, he walked to London (via Liverpool), qualified as both an apothecary and a surgeon, set up in general practice and became a regular contributor to *The Lancet*. After studying at the University of London, he became a physician in his thirties, entitled to style himself 'doctor'. In 1846 he witnessed one of the earliest demonstrations of ether used as an anaesthetic, and within a month had published a table for calculating the size of doses and designed a device for administering the gas. When chloroform arrived as an alternative to ether, he experimented with the drug not only on small animals but on himself. By 1853 he was administering chloroform to Queen Victoria during childbirth – her majesty expressed herself 'much gratified with the effect', he wrote in his notes – and his reputation was made.[22]

Snow encountered cholera as a young apprentice in Newcastle in 1831–2, after it first made landfall in England at Sunderland. Known as Asiatic cholera from its origins in India, the disease had travelled remorselessly around the globe in the preceding decade. It's passage across Europe had been tracked, provoking what one historian called 'an ordeal of anticipation'.[23] Soon after Sunderland, it reached London – but no one knew why or how it spread. It was terrifying: sufferers sickened and died within days, vomiting and expelling vast quantities of clear water from their bowels, their body seeming to shrink and their lips turning blue as they suffered catastrophic dehydration while still remaining mentally alert: 'The mind within remains untouched and clear,' wrote *The Times*, 'shining strangely through the glazed eyes, with light unquenched and vivid – a spirit, looking out in terror from a corpse.' It was a ghastly way to die. We now know that there is a simple cure – rehydration, through saline solution given intravenously – and that the cause is a bacterium that travels in water polluted by the faeces of victims. But the doctors of the 1830s and 40s were powerless in the face of this horror.[24]

The disease appeared a second time in London in 1848–9, when a seaman from Hamburg died of it in Horsleydown, a district of Bermondsey. A week later the man who had moved into the sailor's room also contracted the disease. As it spread rapidly thereafter, Snow's restless mind was engaged. He studied the tables of cholera deaths compiled by William Farr for the Registrar-General – and he investigated in person. He went to Horsleydown and found a row of cottages, sharing a single well and a cracked open drain, where a dozen people had died, yet in a similar court next door, which got its water from a different source (untainted by the drains) only one person had died. Meanwhile, Farr's tables revealed that deaths from cholera were concentrated in an area south of the Thames, while in the East End – where living conditions were equally dreadful and the stench and miasma just as bad – hardly anyone had died. Snow concluded that foul air was much less likely to be the cause of the outbreak than polluted water and, in 1849, he published a paper, *On The Mode of Communication of Cholera*, which said as much. A Bristol doctor, William Budd, had come to a similar conclusion and published a similar paper the same year, claiming to have identified a distinct 'cholera fungus'. Budd was wrong about the fungus, but he and Snow were right that the organism responsible for cholera was transmitted principally in drinking water, and Budd later established that typhoid, too, was waterborne.

Both Snow and Budd were ignored. There were too many conflicting theories: their insights were just two among many, and, in any case, miasmatists held sway, intent on making the facts fit their pet version of the theory. Julius von Liebig, for instance, a distinguished German chemist and agriculturalist, developed what he called his 'zymotic' theory of disease, which blamed it on the fermentation and putrefaction of dead matter. The statistician William Farr believed the incidence of cholera reflected elevation: low-lying areas were more at risk than airier uplands, such as Hampstead, perhaps because they were more affected by the evil miasma coming off the river; the idea that the river water itself might be to blame simply wasn't canvassed. Others blamed the soil. Or electricity in the atmosphere. Or a lack of ozone. Or 'putrescent yeast' and the emanations of sewers and graveyards.

In 1854 Snow tried again. Cholera had returned and there was a particularly virulent outbreak in Soho, within easy walking distance of his home. What happened next has become the stuff of scientific legend. Snow began identifying the victims and establishing where they lived; then he plotted the results on a map of the area. A glance at the map showed the majority of deaths were clustered around one particular street. Snow investigated: in the street was a pump connected to a well from which many of the inhabitants got their water. Snow – convinced as he was that the disease was carried in polluted water – persuaded the authorities to remove the handle of the pump. And the outbreak ended.

Later investigation established that the source of the outbreak was a baby living in a house close to the pump. The water in which its nappies were washed had found its way into a cesspit and from there leaked through the fractured lining of the pit into the community's water supply. Not everyone in the neighbourhood suffered. The workers at a nearby brewery drank beer made with water from a different well. The local workhouse escaped largely unscathed because the inhabitants drank piped company water. But a woman far away in Hampstead died because she'd originally lived in the area and liked the taste of the water from the pump, a bottle of which her sons sent up to her daily: the taste, perhaps a seductive *petillance*, was in fact a consequence of the well's everyday pollution from neighbouring cesspits. No one has ever worked out how the baby became infected.

*

In the heart of Soho there is today a pub called the John Snow, with a plaque commemorating the doctor's achievement; outside is a pump with no handle. The pump is in the wrong place and the street name has changed from Broad to Broadwick Street, but this is the spot where Snow made his breakthrough – even if the geographical imprecision might have irked this most meticulous of researchers. When I first came to London and worked in an office round the corner, this was where I encountered Snow's story, marvelling over a pint after work at his insight and his readiness to challenge conventional wisdom, so obvious in retrospect, so challenging at the time. This was science as heroic endeavour, shining light into the darkest corners. Snow's legacy was not just his contribution to epidemiology and our understanding of diseases but also the establishment of a new type of hero, the scientist as lone figure standing out against an erroneous orthodoxy and overturning an established scientific paradigm – admirable, provided the scientist is proved to be right and the orthodoxy is indeed erroneous; less admirable when the scientific consensus is in fact (as it usually is) correct and the maverick merely gives ammunition to conspiracy theorists.

Of course, Snow's story was not quite so simple. There were others involved both in investigating the Soho outbreak – in particular a sceptical local clergyman,

Henry Whitehead – and in pursuing the wider cholera question, such as Budd. The local board took some persuading to remove the pump handle, because their initial investigation of the well had suggested it was sound. Removing the pump handle may not have ended the outbreak, because it may have been in rapid decline already. Snow's map came later, when he published his findings: during the outbreak itself, any map was probably in Snow's head alone. Though the published map can be seen as one of the founding documents of epidemiology, Snow was not alone in deploying statistics to study disease – William Farr, for one, was doing similar work.

But Snow deserves his credit, not only for his analysis of the Soho outbreak but for another even more extensive piece of research, which revealed not just a single polluted well but the pollution by cholera of the Thames itself. The 1854 outbreak once again affected south London (as well as Soho), and there Snow found a near-perfect opportunity to test his waterborne hypothesis. South of the Thames was the only significant area of London served by two water companies, the Lambeth and the Southwark & Vauxhall, the only part of the metropolis where houses next door to one another, alike in every other respect, got their water from different sets of mains. Snow again went knocking on doors. The result was another set of maps and charts, comparing cholera deaths by company.

Snow's findings – published in 1857, the year before his death – were stark. In households supplied with Southwark & Vauxhall water, the death rate was 315 per 10,000 houses. In those served with Lambeth water, it was just 37 per 10,000. The reason was not hard to find. The Lambeth company had been the first to move its intake above

Teddington lock, and was taking its water not from the polluted tidal Thames at Hungerford but from Seething Wells near Thames Ditton, where the water was free of London's sewage. The Southwark & Vauxhall was still taking water from the river at Battersea. The source of the cholera was in the Southwark & Vauxhall water, but not in the Lambeth water: this was not a case of a single infected pump, but of mass poisoning by one of London's water companies.

The evidence convinced Snow that cholera was a distinct 'poison' or germ passed from one individual to another in drinking water contaminated by a cholera victim's faeces, and not by some vague miasma. 'I consider,' he told a select committee in 1855, 'that the cause of cholera is always cholera; that each case always depends upon a previous one.'[25]

Lost in the mists

And that should have been that. Except it wasn't.

Compelling though Snow's analysis seems to us, his arguments were still not accepted. In the transcript of his evidence to that 1855 inquiry, you can almost hear the incredulity in the voices of his questioners: Did he really mean to say that smells didn't make people ill? That breathing air that was 'tainted by decomposing matter, either animal or vegetable', would not be 'highly prejudicial to health'? Was he not aware that people going into vaults full of dead bodies had sometimes died from the poisonous gases? Snow's response was that poisonous gases could only harm you if you were exposed to them in sufficiently high concentrations: the gases arising from drains or middens or 'noxious trades', such as boiling glue from old bones, were too diffuse to do real harm. But they didn't listen. The deadweight of miasmatic theory proved too hard to shift.

Snow's ability to think outside the box would have been remarkable in any age. It can be illustrated by a comparison with another doctor who was convinced cholera was linked to dirty water, but who lacked Snow's flexibility of mind and so was still a prisoner of conventional thinking. Dr John Challice was the chair of the Bermondsey board of guardians. 'Innumerable instances of cholera were directly produced owing to the foul water which was drunk by the inhabitants,' he told the 1851 select committee.[26] He'd said the same thing the year before to the Prime Minister, no less, when a deputation of water campaigners had been to see Lord John Russell in Downing Street: he deployed some elementary epidemiology by pointing out that deaths from cholera had been just ten per 10,000 people among users of Grand Junction water from Kew Bridge, but 156 per 10,000 among those who took Southwark & Vauxhall water from Battersea.[27] Yet when pressed under cross-examination to give specific examples of cholera deaths linked to bad water, he floundered: he could simply have pointed to the statistics, as Snow was to do, and suggested they told their own story; instead he came up with two (questionable) cases, and lamely fell back on the conventional notion that water was an 'exciting cause' of cholera.[28]

Given the close associations between stench and disease in Victorian Britain, there was nothing inherently absurd in assuming that the one might be causing the other, and that eliminating stench might eliminate disease. What is striking is how determined the experts were to dismiss any suggestion to the contrary. Steven Johnson, in his brilliant book on cholera in nineteenth-century London, *The Ghost Map*, marvels at the continuing power of the miasmatic model, even as it came under increasing attack from a growing body of evidence that disease was not somehow provoked by nasty smells. The model's persistence is especially strange, as Johnson says, given that many of the most convinced miasmatists were in other respects revolutionaries intent on challenging and overturning prevailing orthodoxies: Dickens, Engels and Henry Mayhew, for example, were, as he points out, 'not people naturally inclined to accept the status quo. In fact, they were all, in their separate ways, spoiling for a fight'.[29] Likewise Chadwick, and also Florence Nightingale. She did more than anyone to establish the profession of nursing, affirm the independent agency of women and revolutionise hospital practice; yet she, like Chadwick, went to her grave (as late as 1910) a convinced miasmatist.

In 1858 Snow died at the young age of forty-five, his views on cholera still not accepted by the medical establishment and public health campaigners. An official inquiry by the Board of Health into the 1854 outbreak had reviewed Snow's waterborne theory briefly before concluding: 'After careful inquiry, we see no reason to adopt this belief.' An editorial in *The Lancet* scoffed at his claims about Southwark & Vauxhall water: it was just a theory, he had offered no proof; his ideas came from the sewers, in which he had become trapped.[30]

Perhaps most surprising is that William Farr's statistical studies of the cholera outbreak of 1854 had pinpointed the same differential between the death rates of Lambeth and Southwark & Vauxhall customers, yet he and one of the era's foremost experts on public health, Sir John Simon, drew a subtly different conclusion from the figures. By 1855 Simon had moved on from the City of London to become chief medical officer of the General Board of Health (and later of the Privy Council, when the board was abolished). He was a rigorous scientist and a shrewd political operator, deft and emollient where Edwin Chadwick was confrontational. In 1856 he presented the results of Farr's analysis. His description of the 'almost incredible foulness' of the Southwark & Vauxhall's water was borrowed from Arthur Hassall's work. Simon was quite clear that this foul water contributed to a higher incidence of cholera in the homes that took it. But he was not prepared to go so far as to say that the dirty water *caused* the cholera: 'The present contribution,' he wrote of Farr's study, 'aims only at giving a more exact knowledge of one cause, not at gainsaying the existence of other causes', among which he numbered 'impure air or defective nourishment'. Correlation is not the same as causation, as the cautious Simon knew.[31]

But opinion did shift, albeit slowly. In some ways uninformed public opinion went ahead of expert medical opinion. Just as the Southwark Waterworks customers in Cruikshank's 1832 cartoon believed that polluted water would give them cholera, so an 1849 John Tenniel cartoon in *Punch* showed two children watching a turncock in action; one child is saying, 'I say, Tommy, I'm blowed if there isn't a man turning on the cholera.'[32] And an 1860 cartoon in the magazine *Fun* showed children and young people gathered around a parish pump, with Death working the handle.[33] This was Snow's idea in graphic form.

Within a few years Farr and Simon were coming round to the same position, even if the water companies preferred to stick with the miasma theory. In 1869 the companies' trade paper, the *Journal of Gas Lighting, Water Supply and Sanitary Improvement*, observed that 'the germs, the fungi, the cells, or whatever is supposed to propagate the disease [cholera] are only imaginary existences'.[34] But, by 1866, Farr was convinced that cholera was waterborne and paid tribute to Snow's work, observing satirically that the air had got the blame hitherto because it was supplied free to London's inhabitants rather than by commercial interests prepared to pay for expert testimony on their behalf: 'For air no scientific witnesses have been retained, no learned counsel has pleaded; so the atmosphere has been freely charged with the propagation and the illicit diffusion of plagues of all kinds.' Simon had been a staunch miasmatist at the time of his City of London appointment in 1848, but by 1870 he had likewise changed his mind, convinced by what he called Snow's 'bold conjecture'.[35]

Bugs to the rescue

By the 1880s a new science, bacteriology, had been developed in France by Louis Pasteur and in Germany by Robert Koch, which offered a revolutionary and at first sight more accurate way to assess the safety and purity of water. In 1876 Koch identified the organism responsible for anthrax and followed it up with the identification of the

tuberculosis bacterium, and, in 1883, the *Vibrio cholera*.*
The germ theory of disease, to which Snow's work had
made an important contribution and which had first
surfaced in the 1860s, was firmly established.

But it remained a theory, hard to prove definitively.
And when it came to water purity, bacteriologists faced the
same problem as that which had bedevilled chemical and
microscopic analysis. A bacteriologist could demonstrate
the presence of tiny organisms, but he or she could not tell
you whether they were dangerous.

By the mid-1880s British scientists were learning how
to culture bacteria by mixing contaminated water with
sterile gelatine and filtered meat broth and spreading the
mixture on to a glass plate; then they counted the colonies
that started to appear. But what were they counting?
Were these bugs the harmful ones? Did some bugs fail to
grow at all in these conditions? 'The method of gelatine
plate culture is excellent, if it is required to determine
which of several samples of water contains more organisms capable of growing in gelatine,' as a deadpan British
bacteriologist put it: this might be a sterile activity in
more senses than one.[36]

The water companies' defenders seized on this uncertainty as a chance to manufacture doubt. In 1886 one
chemist retained by the water companies as a consultant
was still doubting the existence of germs: 'People talk about
germs very freely . . . as though these things had been got

---

* The cholera *vibrio* had in fact been identified in 1854 by an Italian
scientist, Filippo Pacini, who spotted it through a microscope, but
his published paper went unremarked (Steven Johnson, *The Ghost
Map*, p. 99).

hold of,' he remarked, and demanded that a cholera germ be put on the table in front of him before he would acknowledge its existence. *The Engineer* considered 'microbes' harmless, given the numbers to which our bodies played host and the numbers we routinely breathed in and drank. 'If bacteria could slay, then would no man, woman or child be alive in a week', was the engineering verdict. As late as 1899 an official of the British Medical Association remarked of another germ: 'This insane hunt after the [tuberculosis] bacillus, as if it could be bottled up in a twopenny-halfpenny spittoon and got rid of, is the insanest crusade ever instituted on illogical lines.'[37]

So bacteriology also risked becoming a scientific dead end for Victorian water analysis – with one important exception. Edward Frankland's son Percy and his wife, Grace, were bacteriologists, and in 1885 Percy began a three-year series of tests on London company waters before and after they were filtered. He discovered that between 95 and 99 per cent of all the bacteria present in raw river water had disappeared once the water had passed through a slow sand filter.[38]*

Percy and Grace Frankland's discovery – they called it 'astonishing' – was an important one, but not quite the slam-dunk for bacteriology it might appear: there was still the question of whether the remaining 1 to 5 per cent

---

* Grace Frankland was a pioneering woman chemist and bacteriologist and got equal billing with her husband on their joint publications. It was not unusual for male scientists to rely on their wives or other female relatives for help with their work, but colleagues of Percy said he was 'the first man who had the chivalry to admit it'.

might be dangerous, and the possibility that some especially hardy types of bacteria might not be identifiable by the techniques then available and might slip through the barrier.

Later on, it emerged that the companies' alternative to filters – simply leaving water in a reservoir for a time so that the mud and impurities sank to the bottom – might actually have been quite effective had they left the water to stand for longer. Sir Alexander Houston, the chief scientist at the Metropolitan Water Board, established that typhoid and other germs in fact died naturally without a host, and that water could be rendered safe even without filtering just by letting it stand for thirty days in subsiding reservoirs. His proof was simple: he infected a sample of raw Thames water with 218 million typhoid germs, then tested the water every few days until he could find no trace of typhoid. He then drank half a pint of the water every day for five days. He suffered no ill-effects.[39]

14

Regulating the Flow

In 1849, in the wake of the cholera visitation that year, Henry Mayhew went to Jacob's Island, a notorious waterside slum in Bermondsey. This was the place so ghastly that Dickens had Bill Sikes meet his death there in *Oliver Twist*. Mayhew, a journalist of genius, wrote up his visit for the *Morning Chronicle*. He shared with Dickens a campaigner's anger at the degradations of slum life and a writer's fascination with its lurid horrors, and the piece is a memorable contribution to the literature of disgust accumulated over three centuries by writers on London's water.

Jacob's Island was a place of stinking creeks and ditches. Mayhew called it 'the very capital of cholera, the Venice of drains'. He described water 'covered with a scum almost like a cobweb and prismatic with grease':

> In the bright light it appeared the colour of strong green tea, and positively looked as solid as black marble in the shadow – indeed it was more like watery mud than muddy water; and yet we were assured this was the only water the wretched inhabitants had to drink. As we gazed in horror at it, we saw drains and sewers emptying their filthy contents into it . . . We saw a little child, from one of the galleries opposite,

lower a tin can with a rope to fill a large bucket that
stood beside her . . . As the little thing dangled her tin
cup as gently as possible into the stream, a bucket of
nightsoil was poured down from the next gallery.[1]

Before using the water, Mayhew reported, the inhabitants
left it to stand for a day or two, until the worst of the muck
had settled to the bottom of their tub. One told him they
had spoken to their landlord about getting piped water
laid on: 'And he says he'll do it, and do it, but we know him
better than to believe him.'

Mayhew was writing to shock, and for the inhabitants of
Jacob's Island their lack of clean water was indeed appalling. But by 1850 Jacob's Island was exceptional. Most people
in London had access to company water, and newly built
houses were routinely connected to the mains. Sir William
Clay reckoned that, in the affluent Grand Junction district,
there were just ninety-five houses without any known supply
of water. Even in the poorer Southwark & Vauxhall district
south of the river, which included Jacob's Island, only 1,300
had no known supply. The Board of Health estimated the
number of households without access either to company
water or to their own wells or rainwater tanks at 17,000, or
6 per cent of London's total.[2]

But 'having a supply' didn't necessarily mean having a
tap in your home. Slum landlords might pay for a service
to each house but the poorest properties were rented by
the room, so the residents at best had shared access to a
butt or cistern filled from a single tap. Many others had to
make do with a standpipe at the end of a court or alley,
queuing for water at the mercy of a sometimes arbitrary
company turncock.

As to the communal butts, John Simon testified in 1851 to the frequent complaints about the quality of water stored in them: 'It is spoken of with disgust.'[3] And no wonder, when you read some of the descriptions. One speaks of a butt kept in a dark and windowless basement where the drains had burst and people had to wade ankle-deep through 'abominable slush' to reach it. Others speak of people washing their chamber pots in the water their neighbours were supposed to use for drinking, and of the 'solution of dropped leaves, bits of plaster, old boots and various kinds of rubbish' that filled the tanks. Of one butt it was said:

> Besides the ordinary sources of pollution from the dust and smut in the atmosphere, and from slops thrown out of the top windows, this cistern is resorted to by boys in the street, the house door being always open during the day, to wash their hands and play all sorts of pranks such as dipping sprats when they are in season, drowning mice, etc etc.[4]

The water stank, and the butts were rarely if ever cleaned out; people tried if possible to catch water from the tap before it reached the cistern, because then it might be clean enough to cook with.

The water companies had an ambivalent attitude to these cisterns. They agreed they were often dreadful and should at the very least be cleaned regularly. On the other hand it was often tempting to use them as a way of shifting the blame for polluted water on to their customers, especially the poor, deemed too ill-educated or too feckless to store their water properly.

On Sundays, for the most part, there was no water for anyone: the turncocks stayed at home. That was fine for middle-class customers with a good-sized cistern that was regularly cleaned and always had something in it, but harsh on the poor, who could get no water on the one day of the week when they weren't working and so had a chance to do their laundry.

Constant supply

One answer to the problems posed by places like Jacob's Island and by people having to collect water from standpipes was to compel slum landlords to pay for a supply to their properties. The water companies – who stood to gain by getting as many households as possible signed up wherever they had spent money on laying mains – encouraged property-owners to lay on water for their tenants by 'farming' the rates, in effect giving the landlord a bulk discount with the chance to make some extra money if they got their tenants to pay for water. But in Manchester the city had given itself the power to levy a compulsory water rate on owners of cheaper properties. 'They may take or leave the water, but if they do not take it they pay for it,' the town clerk told the 1851 select committee. 'That is the only way of taking it into cottages.'[5] There were calls for a similar approach in London.

Another possible answer to the problem was 'constant supply', keeping the mains charged all the time and water always available at the turn of a tap. That might do away not only with turncocks to manage delivery but also the need for storage cisterns. Edwin Chadwick pushed strongly for constant supply, and public opinion backed him. Copious quantities of water available all the time would help keep houses clean and flush dirt and disease away.

In the days of wooden pipes, constant supply had not been an option: they would have leaked unstoppably under the higher pressure. Once iron pipes arrived, that particular objection vanished, but the London water engineers had others, some more, some less convincing. Thomas Wicksteed of the East London suggested that, if there were a constant supply to standpipes, the middle classes (or at any rate their servants) would join the poor in the queue for free water instead of paying to have it piped into their houses, and the companies would lose out. He also argued that, if constant supply were general, there wouldn't be enough water to go round: to supply 20,000 houses would require a main 71 inches in diameter, against only 20 inches for intermittent supply. A rival expert challenged his maths and argued that this was only true if all the houses turned their taps on at the same time.[6]

James Simpson of the Chelsea and Lambeth offered a more substantial objection: existing water fittings, such as the pipes and taps in customers' homes, weren't up to the job. They would leak under the higher pressure: all would need to be replaced. Nor could customers be trusted to turn their taps off, or to have a functioning ballcock that would prevent their cistern from overflowing if the water was always on. Under intermittent supply, people got used to leaving the tap feeding their cistern open, so as not to 'miss the water' when it did come on, and when the cistern was full, the overflow simply ran to waste: Simpson wasn't confident they would voluntarily change their behaviour. There would have to be draconian powers of inspection to ensure people were doing the right thing. Asked to create a system of constant supply for Liverpool, he argued that it would be exorbitantly expensive and useless, because 'thousands of pipes and cocks in private places are not susceptible of hourly and immediate inspection and control': as a result of his views, Liverpool ended up for a time with two separate water systems, one providing constant supply under public control for fire-fighting and street watering, the other only intermittent for domestic use.[7]

Simpson's views were backed by colleagues like W. C. Mylne of the New River and Joseph Quick of the Grand Junction and Southwark & Vauxhall. In 1865, Quick argued that constant supply had been a failure wherever it had been tried, whether in Britain or America, 'either from wilful or accidental waste'. A constant supply from the main would, he claimed, cost each house between £5 and £10 because they would have to install a proper cistern, and an 'approved ballcock' for every WC; and consumers would end up paying between 5 and 25 per cent more to cover the cost of the wasted water and of the company inspectors, or 'water police', who would have the right to enter customers' properties and if necessary summons them for non-compliance with the rules.[8]

Waste was a serious issue for the companies, forever playing catch-up as London grew and demand increased. The archives are full of leaflets and handbills exhorting consumers not to waste water and threatening them with dire penalties if they did. But Quick's intervention in 1865 provoked a string of letters from other water engineers to the *Journal of Gas Lighting* taking issue with him. Plenty of towns, it seemed, offered a constant supply and, no, it didn't mean large quantities of water went to waste. Quick's intermittently supplied Southwark & Vauxhall recorded consumption of 30 gallons per head per day; the majority of the water companies outside London offering constant supply and cited in the correspondence recorded less than that.[9]

The *Journal* thought the companies were deliberately dragging their feet, because a switch to constant supply would be expensive and difficult. And as Chadwick had pointed out, it would also cost the companies revenue, because under the intermittent system they charged customers extra for delivering a 'high service' of water to upper floors, and with local turncocks no longer managing delivery these differential charges would no longer be possible.[10]

Confusingly, while Quick and Mylne and Simpson were worried about water going to waste thanks to leaky fittings and careless customers, one of Chadwick's principal arguments in favour of constant supply was that it would *reduce* waste. This was because people would no longer need cisterns so there would be nothing to overflow. Chadwick's optimism turned out to be misplaced, partly because a WC still required a cistern even if the house as a whole could do without. But in the 1840s none of this was clear cut. So it was quite possible for Joseph Quick's chairman, Sir William Clay, to take a different view from his engineer and support the idea of constant supply. Clay was a Liberal MP and saw it as a way to get rid of polluted water butts. But Clay the water company chairman also insisted on a *quid pro quo:* people would have to tolerate the water police.[11]

Interference and a lie

One consequence of the widespread take-up of company water was that its cost and quality were of near-universal interest; certainly every property-owning voter had a stake in it. On the subject of water, aristocrats, petit bourgeois shopkeepers and even radical Chartists could make common cause. Such a broad coalition was hard to ignore and slowly, after decades of procrastination, Parliament and government conceded the need to 'interfere'.

The first sign of this came in 1847 with the Waterworks Clauses Act. It sounds underwhelming, a piece of technical legislation of the driest kind, and it was; but it sent an important signal. The act was part of the wider reform of parliamentary procedure that also saw select committees modernised. Private bill legislation took up enormous amounts of parliamentary time; each new project needed its own private act and its own committee; and the quirks of different private acts meant that different provisions often applied in what were essentially the same circumstances. So campaigners pressed Parliament to pass a series of model acts with standard clauses that could be cut and pasted (perhaps literally in those days) into draft private legislation, and to which private bills were expected to adhere unless there were good reasons not to. Between 1845 and 1847 eleven of these 'consolidated clauses' acts were passed, covering, among other things, railways, company formation, cemeteries – and waterworks.

The new act sought to tackle accusations that the companies were overcharging by capping their profits. It limited water company dividends each year to a maximum of 10 per cent of the company's nominal capital: if there was more profit available for distribution it was to be ploughed back into price cuts. In London the companies before the 1880s rarely 'divided' more than 8 or 8½ per cent, so, in the metropolis, the legislation was little more than a gesture. But it set a precedent: here was the first legislation to target the water industry as a whole and to prescribe limits to shareholders' freedom.

When the idea of limiting profits in this way had first been canvassed, it had prompted one company to engage in a monumental piece of dishonesty – a barefaced lie that it maintained right through till 1904 and which it ensured by buying the silence of the one man who had stumbled on the truth.

To restrict a company's dividends to a percentage of its capital, you had to know how much its capital amounted to. Most of the water companies were relatively recent and had the figures at their fingertips: they had acts of Parliament authorising their capital, and records of how many shares had actually been issued and paid up. But the New River went all the way back to 1613, and many of the company's records had been destroyed in the fire at its offices in 1769. Modern historians have established that the river cost roughly £18,500 to build, financed by shareholders who, as we saw in Chapter 2, bought shares worth £100 apiece and then contributed £189 per share to the construction cost. If a dividend limit of 10 per cent of nominal capital were imposed, then holders of the New River's original shares would be permitted to split a maximum of just £1,850 between them each year. Yet one of the seventy-two adventurers' and king's shares had sold for £15,200 in 1827, giving the company at that point what we would call a 'market capitalisation' (not a term in use in the first half of the nineteenth century) of well over £1 million. The actual dividends paid out after 1800 on the original New River shares, expressed as a percentage of their nominal £100 value, ranged from a nadir of 23 per cent in 1814, at the height of the competition, to 200 per cent in 1819, 516 per cent in 1827 and 706 per cent in 1840.[12] If you believed that capitalists were blood-sucking parasites who enjoyed utterly extortionate returns at the expense of hapless consumers, then here was your evidence.

It was embarrassing, and the company dealt with the problem by lying. In 1812, when its charges were under attack from rivals, it put out a leaflet saying the belief that the shares had originally cost only £100 (which they had) was 'absurd', and that 'the formation of their works at the time of Sir Hugh Myddelton cost, according to the best authorities, £500,000'. It didn't say who 'the best authorities' were meant to be. When there was talk of a merger with the West Middlesex in 1815, the company put its capital even higher at £750,000.[13] These estimates could perhaps be defended when (or if) the directors were genuinely ignorant. But by the 1840s they certainly knew the truth. One of the company's collectors with an antiquarian bent, Alexander Wilkinson, had compiled a 'History of the New River' from documents in the archive of the Land Revenue, in an unlined foolscap volume bound in vellum. Among the documents were the copies of Hugh Myddelton's original account books kept by royal officials; Wilkinson had gone through them and totted up the total cost of construction. He made the cost of the river and of laying the first pipes just over £32,000 – much more than £18,500, true, but a very great deal less than £500,000. When the horrified directors found out they spent almost five months procrastinating, before in January 1845 making him an offer he couldn't refuse: he was given £50, a considerable sum for the time, on condition that he handed over his history, which breaks off in 1685. They then buried his deeply compromising manuscript in the company's archive.[14]

And so, for the next sixty years, with this awkward evidence out of the way, the company went on baldly stating something that wasn't true. By 1851, the capital, taking into account modern investments in pumps and machinery and new reservoirs, was said to be more than £1.4 million. The story was always the same: the original records had been lost in the fire, so W. C. Mylne in 1815 had estimated the cost of the river itself at then-current prices, and that was the basis on which the capital valuation rested; the current management knew no more than that. Towards the end of the century it became even more important to keep the lie going, because it was clear that at some point the government would buy the companies out, and the price was likely to be based partly on their share capital. In the formal arbitration hearings that preceded the takeover in 1904, the New River initially asked for £13.2 million for its shareholders and ended up with a fraction over £6 million. The award was made by the arbitrators in total ignorance of the actual cost of construction.

Ferment

The year after the Waterworks Clauses Act, Edwin Chadwick's relentless campaigning produced the first Public Health Act. Severely watered down by the anti-centralisers and their allies in Parliament, it was a rather feeble response to the foetid, disease-ridden state of the country's towns and cities but it gave local municipalities new powers to clean up their own backyards, should they choose to use them. Among them was the right to run their own water supply, and over the next thirty years more than 150 local authorities duly went into the water business, either buying up an existing water company or starting their own. London was exempt from the new law, and in any case had no city-wide municipality, but one effect of the act was to show that leaving an urban population at the mercy of private water suppliers was no longer the only feasible option.

By 1849 there was renewed ferment around London's water, reminiscent of that provoked by *The Dolphin* twenty years earlier. A Parochial Water Supply Association was formed to campaign to put water under parish control, and in March 1850 the Prime Minister, Lord John Russell, listened patiently if noncommittally to speeches made by a deputation from the association. 'Competition, animated by mere selfishness and gain, has totally failed to secure the necessary advantages of enterprise to the public,' the association argued. 'The consumer has been sacrificed, that the producer might be enriched.' An MP introduced a bill to put London's water under parish control. Schemes were put forward to bring water from distant sources rather than the Thames. *The Times* ran a series of articles on London's water supply that were positively vituperative about the companies and about the 'corrupt and oppressive system' from which they benefited. Sir William Clay responded with a pamphlet, *Remarks on the Water Supply of London*, which defended the water companies' record but also – rather surprisingly – argued for their takeover by what he called 'some authorities, municipal or other, acting on behalf of the public'. Among his reasons he cited water's importance 'not only to public health, but even to public morals', and the need to protect against the dangers of a monopoly – but also his discomfort at the idea of the 'inquisitorial powers' needed to police the proposed constant supply being exercised by a private body. Opinion was clearly shifting: twenty years earlier it would have been unthinkable for a water company, or indeed any kind of company, to suggest a takeover in this way.[15]

And in 1850 Chadwick's Board of Health – newly established by government and thus hard to ignore – published a report on the metropolitan water supply that called for the Thames to be abandoned as a source, for the introduction of constant supply, and for London's water companies to be amalgamated. If there had been a municipality in London, a governing body for the whole of the metropolis, the report would have recommended transferring responsibility to this central body. But there was no such municipality and its absence provided a ready excuse, if they needed one, for politicians not to pursue the idea – and may also have provided cover for Clay. Though he personally claimed to favour a takeover, he must have known it would go down poorly with some of his shareholders, and may have welcomed a good reason not to pursue it.

Bludgeoned relentlessly by Chadwick and his chums, in 1851 the government finally agreed to legislate. But it had to have two goes. Its first attempt, drafted by the Home Secretary Sir George Grey with the help of Clay, pleased nobody. It proposed amalgamating the companies under state supervision; the rates consumers paid would be defined by law, and the new company would be answerable to the Home Secretary. There was fierce opposition from all sides.

What Dickens dubbed 'vestrydom' saw the Home Secretary's involvement as an example of detestable centralisation. *The Times* saw the hated water monopolists confirmed in their privileged and lucrative position. Chadwick was against it because water and drainage had not been amalgamated under a single authority and because the bill did not mandate constant supply. Proponents of alternatives to the Thames as a source of water complained that their schemes were being ignored. The water companies (despite Clay's involvement) complained that the terms proposed amounted to confiscation; the bill might have done better if the government had taken the trouble to consult the companies first, but it hadn't.

Evidence was taken on the bill at a lengthy series of select committee hearings. The minutes of this 1851 inquiry provide a handy summary (albeit over several hundred pages) of the state of the industry and of the arguments on all sides at this midpoint of the century, and I have cited them several times already in this book. It was clear almost from the outset that the bill was a dead letter. Clay's proposals for an amalgamated company were shredded in cross-examination: he and his colleagues, the Southwark & Vauxhall secretary and Joseph Quick the engineer, had done little more than back-of-an-envelope calculations to substantiate their claims that big cost savings could be made.

But the companies' main opponents, representing the parishes, fared little better. The public meetings in churches or the upstairs rooms of pubs where the campaigners gathered were easy targets for water company counsel trying to depict them as ill-organised amateurs more interested in

convivial debate over a glass or two than in anything serious, and quite incapable of running something as important
as water.

A water bill

After this battering, the government withdrew its first bill
at the end of 1851 and a new one was introduced, this time
by the First Commissioner of Works, Lord Seymour, an
unlikely sponsor for such ground-breaking legislation. He
was no social reformer and held to an extreme interpret-
ation of the *laissez-faire* notion that government should keep
out of other people's business. He once told Chadwick that
'his rule of action in office was never to act until obliged
and then to do as little as possible'. He deplored the Public
Health Act, which he thought permitted 'an interference
with every trade and every occupation of the most arbitrary and stringent character'.

At one point during the select committee's inquiry Sir
William Clay remarked that 'the real question for the
consideration of the committee' was the role government
should play. Seymour had a clear answer to the question:
it should have no role. It was not the job of government, in
Seymour's view, to interfere with the freedoms enjoyed by
private property owners by an insistence that the companies amalgamate, let alone to control them through some
sort of commission: 'All that it behoved Parliament to do
was to require that water should be supplied of good quality, in sufficient quantity, and at a cheap rate. The companies
had better be left to act separately, or in conjunction, as
they should find best,' he said. 'It was unnecessary there

should be any further interference, and if unnecessary it would be unwise to interfere further.'[16]

Seymour also shared a prejudice widespread at the time in favour of private enterprise over public ownership: he had 'more hopes from companies than he had municipal corporations', he told MPs. Company directors or 'proprietors' with a personal interest in a venture were seen as energetic, committed and highly motivated; they were the people to get things done. Public officials lacked their drive (how Seymour could think this when he knew Chadwick personally is a mystery – though, like many others, he detested the man), while public bodies, especially the parish vestries, were seen as inefficient, cheese-paring and corrupt. Sir William Clay agreed with that last bit. When he advocated a takeover by a public authority in his *Remarks on the Water Supply of London*, he added a rider: 'I need hardly add that by the authority referred to in the text I mean something very different from the "Water Association", to be constituted of parochial deputations, which of all conceivable modes of dealing with the question would assuredly be the worst.'[17] The vestries were beyond the pale.

Given Seymour's views, it's remarkable that what became, in 1852, 'An Act to make better provision respecting the Supply of Water to the Metropolis' went as far as it did. The companies were left in place and the parishes sent packing. But it brought in three big changes. The first was that those companies taking their water from the Thames had to shift their intakes upstream from Teddington lock, above the tidal reaches of the river where sewage surged backwards and forwards for days, getting sucked into the companies' intakes before being blithely recycled to consumers. The Lambeth company had already done this;

the others were given until 1855 (or 1856 in Chelsea's case) to follow suit. The second requirement was that, wherever they got their water from, they must filter it 'effectually' (though it was never quite clear what 'effectual' meant in practice). And the third condition was that, once filtered, this relatively pure water should be stored in covered service reservoirs to keep out soot and other rubbish and to guard against recontamination. All this would be expensive: the companies would need parliamentary authorisation to raise additional capital, and, in 1852, the companies duly sought and obtained a series of private acts.

But there were several things the act didn't do, or did only half-heartedly. It made no new rules on what the companies could charge. There were price controls in some of their individual private acts, but there was no consistency. The act said nothing about the drains – much to the frustration of Chadwick. It paid lip service to another of Chadwick's shibboleths by nominally requiring the companies to deliver constant supply, but they had lobbied hard to water down the provision. In the end the act instructed them to offer the service only if four-fifths of householders on a particular main requested it in writing. The four-fifths never materialised anywhere in London.

Chadwick was inclined to see the act's shortcomings as the result of lobbying and improper pressure by the companies, whom he viewed as a menace: outright enemies, part of a gigantic conspiracy to oppose and undermine him. There was some truth in this. For a start, large numbers of water company shareholders and directors were also MPs. Chadwick estimated the number in Parliament at eighty (or on another occasion 100). He also thought the companies 'retained' two-thirds of the press. And indeed a

Private Enterprise Society set up to counter his ideas numbered among its leading members two well-known water engineers with whom Chadwick had frequently clashed – one of them was James Simpson – and was bankrolled by the Lambeth, the New River and the Grand Junction companies: its prospectus is in the latter company's files, while payments to Simpson and others were approved by the Grand Junction directors.[18]

The 1852 Metropolis Water Act prompted a blizzard of activity on the part of the companies, and a bonanza for their engineers and their contractors. The Chelsea company moved to Thames Ditton, next door to the Lambeth company's new facility. The New River Company installed filters. The Grand Junction moved its intake once more, this time to Hampton, a mile or so upstream from Hampton Court; the Southwark & Vauxhall moved in next door, and both built reservoirs and filter beds and enormous pump houses. A later Southwark & Vauxhall addition dating from 1898, with the company crest on the central gable, is especially handsome, perhaps to try to appease Hamptons' affluent residents, who objected to their views of the river being ruined. A third company, the West Middlesex, also moved its intake to Hampton but kept its existing reservoirs and filter beds at Barnes, linking the two sites with a gigantic pipe that went under the river at Richmond. All this would have been financially unsustainable were it not for the continuing rapid growth of London, which meant more and more potential customers and more and more revenue with every passing year.

Alternative sources

For a time, the 1852 act put an end to active water politics. But there was unfinished business. One unresolved question was whether to replace the Thames as London's main water source, and, if so, how. The search for alternatives lasted for decades. In 1831, Thomas Telford had been asked to survey the possibilities and he submitted a report in 1833. He was old, he was ill, it was one of his very last jobs – the celebrated engineer died in September 1834 – and it was a poor piece of work, which was almost immediately denounced. Much of the actual surveying had been done by Telford's assistant, according to the scurrilous William Matthews in his book, *Hydraulia*, supervised by the ailing Telford from his post-chaise. Later, Matthews alleged, Telford and the assistant fell out over how they should divide the fee. This sounds like malicious gossip: Telford certainly surveyed at least one waterworks in person, travelling down the Lea in the company of 'Mr Cubitt' (probably the influential engineer and contractor William Cubitt) from Stamford Hill to the East London's works at Old Ford, where he expressed himself 'perfectly satisfied with everything they had seen'.[19] But the alternative sources Telford suggested wouldn't produce nearly enough water: one, the River Verulam, dried up in summer. And it was all going to cost the colossal sum of £1.17 million, which Telford said the government should lend the water companies. Nothing happened.

Telford was not the only one to address the question. Engineers, entrepreneurs and eccentrics produced a steady stream of proposals, some more sensible and affordable than others. One of the most eccentric was concocted by the artist John Martin, who, in 1828, first came up with a scheme, which he constantly adapted and revised, for bringing water from the Colne near Uxbridge in a spectacular aqueduct, featuring waterfalls, fountains, an 'ornamental water' in Buckingham Palace Gardens, and a vast open-air bathing pool at Paddington, with space for a thousand people at a time. Martin had made his reputation with a series of monumental canvases of biblical cataclysms, full of swirling storm clouds, collapsing classical temples and tiny figures running in terror from the judgement of heaven. His scheme reads like a politer version of one of his paintings. It was, wrote William Matthews, 'chiefly aimed at the public good by superadding beauty to utility'. Later the Colne and the aqueduct were dropped in favour of the Thames as a source, but Martin's schemes all came to nothing.

John Martin's credibility suffered from the antics of his brothers: Jonathan, who in 1829 set fire to York Minster; and William, who had once patented a perpetual motion machine and lived in Newcastle, where he published a stream of books attacking Newton's theory of gravitation. John seems to have suffered from the family mania, because around the time he first published his water scheme, he started to neglect his artistic career and published an *Outline of Several New Inventions for Maritime and Inland Purposes*, including an elastic iron ship and an elastic cable chain. But he was a genuine visionary: in time he extended his water scheme to include sewage disposal – an exercise in venous and arterial integration that must have delighted Chadwick – proposing intercepting sewers north and south of the river to stop the effluent entering the

Thames and diverting it eastwards. It was not so very different from the scheme implemented thirty years later by Joseph Bazalgette.[20]

The Colne had been suggested and rejected as a possible water source several times in the eighteenth century, long before John Martin hit upon it, and a good many other schemes were likewise simply variants on earlier proposals. Springs at Bushey near Watford were put forward more than once; so were artesian wells sunk into the chalk around and below London. In 1850, the General Board of Health thought it had found a perfect source around Hindhead and Farnham in Surrey, where the rock was a type of sandstone and so furnished water markedly softer than the city's existing supply; soft water was better both for doing the laundry and for making tea and the board thought the Farnham water would save £5 million a year in soap and half the capital's annual tea consumption. The Thames between Henley and Marlow was canvassed; so were tributaries of the upper Thames, such as the Churn, Windrush and Ock, and the upper valley of the Lea.

But the truth was that, in south-east England, with its low rainfall and its low chalk hills that sucked up rainwater like a sponge, the Thames was really the only possible source from which to get the quantity of water required by the world's largest city. If it really wanted an alternative, the metropolis would have to turn to sources very much further away. So when, in 1866, yet another royal commission was set up, chaired by the Duke of Richmond, it was told to ascertain 'what supply of unpolluted and wholesome water can be obtained by collecting and storing water in the high grounds of England and Wales . . . at a sufficient elevation for the supply of large towns', including London.

That prompted a further flood of proposals for new 'gathering grounds', including the Peak District and the upper Wye in Wales. But it was two especially ambitious plans that really caught the commissioners' imagination. One envisaged bringing water no less than 270 miles from Thirlmere in the Lake District; the other, proposed by the leading water engineer of the era, J. F. Bateman, identified the headwaters of the Severn in North Wales as a possible source. Both schemes were considered in detail.

Bateman, who gave himself some extra cachet late in life by adding his mother's fancy surname La Trobe to his own, deserved to be taken seriously. He was in his mid-fifties, and had built many dams and waterworks, including a series of reservoirs in Longdendale, north of Glossop, to supply Manchester. His crowning achievement, completed in 1859, was to bring water from Loch Katrine in the Trossachs 36 miles south to Glasgow in a series of tunnels, aqueducts, bridges and pipes constructed through rugged, uninhabited terrain. 'I leave you a work as indestructible as the hills through which it has been carried,' Bateman said at the opening, and the system still supplies 230 million litres (or 50 million gallons) of water a day to the city.[21]

Grand schemes like these were in vogue in the industrial north, where hills abounded. Dams were built, villages drowned, entire landscapes re-engineered to keep sometimes far distant cities watered. Liverpool had built a series of reservoirs at Rivington near Chorley and a 17-mile pipeline, and later (in the 1880s) the city built a dam and 68-mile pipeline to bring water from an artificial lake in the valley of the River Vyrnwy in North Wales. Sheffield had a network of reservoirs in the hills to the west of the city – at one of which, Dale Dyke, the dam collapsed disastrously in

1864, killing almost 250 people. These monumental water-works were commissioned and paid for by the self-confident municipalities of fast expanding industrial cities, which recognised that their manufacturers and their population alike needed clean water and plenty of it. They were excitingly modern, statements of urban pride. And London had nothing like them.

Bateman's scheme for London – which also identified the Vyrnwy as a possible source – dwarfed all of these in its scale and in the distance the water would have to travel. Bateman spent £3,000 of his own money over several years surveying the sources and the route and gave nineteen hours of evidence to the Richmond commission. What he proposed would have delivered 230 million gallons a day: the Longdendale system delivered 38 million gallons, Rivington 16 million and even Lake Vyrnwy when complete provided only 46 million to Liverpool. But the cost was equally gigantic: £11.4 million.

Despite the attractions of both schemes, the commission had reservations. One, obviously, was the cost: who would pay? Another was the capital's vulnerability if it relied for most of its water on aqueducts snaking hundreds of miles across the country, prone to leaks, Fenian outrages or the attentions of a hostile invading army. And the companies were implacably opposed: they saw these proposals for alternative sources as a plot to sideline them completely, for who would need their elaborate and costly systems of pumps and filters and reservoirs if pure water from the mountains of Wales or Cumberland were being delivered by gravity alone?

The companies fought a vigorous and successful rear-guard action in defence of their existing sources.

When Richmond's commission reported in 1869, it not only joined the long procession of inquiries that recommended that control of London's water should be handed to a public body, but also concluded that 'the existing sources of supply available from the Thames Basin were ample for all the wants of any possible increase in the population'. The companies, in 1869, were already supplying 180 million gallons daily and the commission thought that, between them, the Thames, the Lea, the chalk and a network of storage reservoirs could supply up to 300 million gallons. The commission was also convinced that, with proper filtration, the water of both the Thames and the Lea could be made 'perfectly wholesome, and of suitable quality for the supply of the Metropolis'.[22]

More than once in the intervening century and a half, the idea of supplying London with Welsh water has been resurrected. But the Richmond commission's judgement has been vindicated by time. London still gets two-thirds of its water from the Thames.

15

Volcanoes of Filth

Stand today on Waterloo Bridge, in the heart of London, and two things may strike you. One is the splendour of the view. The other is the dreariness of the river itself. The eye is drawn not to the water, which is largely devoid of interest save for the tourist boats, but to the manmade structures along its edge, by turns monumental and elegant, sometimes overbearing, occasionally absurd. In this magnificent curving sweep, London presents its best and most alluring face, a vista worthy of a great global city and a playground for architects since the eighteenth century.

This view is a modern construct. Nothing like it was available before the 1860s. Partly, of course, that's because many of the buildings you can see are modern, but also it's because the early nineteenth-century Thames was a working river, not a show pony. With rare exceptions, most of the buildings lining the central section of the river were wharves and warehouses. There were no embankments from which to drink in the sights and sounds of the river, not to mention its smell. Until the 1750s, there was only one bridge, and that was lined with shops and houses that hid the water from sight. But this unseen river was alive with activity. Eighteenth-century views of the river are crammed with incident. A 1750s drawing by Canaletto of

London Bridge shows more than fifty working boats on the river, and others beached among casks and lumber.[1]*

By the mid-nineteenth century the watermen's wherries and skiffs that ferried foot passengers up and down and across the river had largely vanished, to be replaced by fancy new paddle steamers, their tall chimneys echoing the industrial smokestacks that lined the river banks. Thomas Shotter Boys's 1842 views of the Thames show it crowded to the point of congestion with barges and shipping. In one image, which shows the river at low tide, the exposed foreshore is lined with beached lighters like badly parked cars: they have settled on wide and reeking mudbanks whose load of sewage contributed greatly to the river's notorious smell.[2]

The river was a place of striking contrasts, full of dead cats and expensive yachts alongside working boats and coal barges. There were waterside pubs and crazy, slimy stairs and mudlarks, 'and everywhere muddy water and restless currents – all moving – all commingling – and over all a canopy of ever-rolling smoke'. Artists might revel in the scene, but most commentators thought the ramshackle wharves and industrial premises that lined the river were an embarrassment. *The Times* complained of 'meanness and shabbiness and discomfort' and thought the banks were 'disfigured by every unsightly erection that trade and manufacture could devise for their convenience.'[3] What's more,

---

* Canaletto's drawing shows the tall water tower of the London Bridge Waterworks and the wooden posts of the dolphins protecting its waterwheels under the northernmost arches. Shotter Boys's image shows a similar view, but old London Bridge with its houses has been swept away, and so has the waterworks.

the river was a corrupting presence in the heart of the city, carrying a burden of dirt and degradation. Not only did it reek, but it was the haunt of social outcasts and petty criminals, vagrants and scavengers and dredgermen, like Gaffer Hexham and Rogue Riderhood in Dickens's *Our Mutual Friend*, who cast their nets in search of flotsam to sell, and of dead bodies with pockets to rifle. The river was the haunt of prostitutes and suicides – the two were closely linked in the Victorian mind – and a place where the homeless slept. It was unworthy of an imperial capital.

Thomas Shotter Boys's pictures are in a very English tradition: the picturesque topographical view. But nine-teenth-century London and its river also lent themselves to a different treatment. Where some might see factories and warehouses as ugly, others saw them as manifestations of the sublime, provoking astonishment and terror in the viewer. Transformed into art, they could be made to conjure a vision of power and grandeur, of repetitive vistas and dramatic contrasts of light and dark. The most memorable, though not always the most accurate, images of the cauldron of commerce and maritime bustle which constituted mid-Victorian London and the Thames are by the French artist Gustave Doré, published in *London: A Pilgrimage* in 1872, and they are black-and-white gems of sublime art, invoking terror and astonishment at every turn. The river loomed large in Doré's perambulations through the city. His paddle steamers are hulking monsters looming out of the fog, crowded with anonymous passengers; his cargo vessels a confusion of spars and rigging, jammed together hugger-mugger; his bridges a chilly haven for rough sleepers. A hay boat lies at anchor in the moonlight, its crew asleep atop their cargo: night scenes brought out Doré's dramatic feel for the city's mystery and grimy splendour. But the figures that people his drawings are often featureless creatures out of Dante's Inferno, in ragged clothes, their eyes and mouths reduced to dark hollows like creatures in a horror film. He returned several times to depict the narrow streets on either side of the river, vertiginous canyons crossed by high bridges straight out of Piranesi or Escher, lined with vertical openings where men stand precariously on platforms, ready to seize the barrels and sacks and bales hauled up by cranes: you hold your breath lest one of them falls.[4]

This was the world's busiest port, and, in economic terms, the river was never more alive than in the 1850s and 60s. In ecological terms, it was all but dead, the fish killed off by pollution. We owe both today's views and the river's recovery to Joseph Bazalgette, who designed not only London's sewers but also the Chelsea and Albert and Victoria Embankments, which hem the river in, narrowing it so that it flows faster, and ensuring that, even at low tide, the narrow foreshore is thankfully free from sewage. The embankments are his memorial, in the literal sense that there is a modest bust of the great man tucked away on a plinth in Victoria Gardens behind the Embankment, with the motto *Flumini Vincula Posuit* ('He placed chains on the river'), and in the wider sense that his other even more colossal achievement is buried out of sight.

Bazalgette and the Board

Like several of his distinguished contemporaries, Bazalgette was of French extraction: the renowned Isambard Brunel's engineer father, Marc, was French; John Simon, son of a wine shipper and the chief medical officer first to the City of London and later the government, was also French (the name was pronounced *Simone;* Bazalgette was and is pronounced *Bazzle-jet*). Bazalgette's grandfather came to England in the 1770s, and his father was an officer in the Royal Navy. There is nothing new about European immigrants enriching Britain, and it seems apt that the man who remade London just as his contemporary, Haus-mann, was remaking Paris should come from French stock. (But then, Hausmann's parents were German . . .)

At seventeen, young Joseph was taken on as a pupil by a leading civil engineer, and then set up on his own account at the height of the 1840s' railway mania. There was no shortage of work – in fact, too much – and it didn't go well: he suffered a nervous collapse and had to take a year off, which is why he ended up working for the Metropolitan sewer commissioners on a salary. But, despite his earlier breakdown, he proved extremely robust. One modern writer characterises him as 'a man of heroic patience and exemplary persistence in the face of frustrations and opposi-tions which many would have found daunting'.[5] When the sewer construction campaign was at its height, he worked frequently until midnight or one in the morning, and as his fame spread thanks to his work in London, he developed a lucrative consultancy practice alongside it. Where Brunel was flashy and entrepreneurial and prone to overreach, Bazalgette was measured and meticulous, occasionally iras-cible, and exceedingly effective. For thirty years – until he retired when the Metropolitan Board of Works was handed over to the London County Council in 1889 – he presided successfully over one of the biggest civil engineering pro-grammes in the world, including not only the sewerage and the embankments but new Thames bridges and a whole series of new streets, such as Northumberland Avenue, Shaftesbury Avenue and Rosebery Avenue.

Building the embankments and cleaning up London's river proved a long and contentious business. The Metropolitan Board of Works, which took over from the discredited sewer commissioners, came into being on 1 January 1856. There was ample evidence of the need for action. In July 1855 the distinguished scientist Michael Faraday wrote to *The Times*, decrying the 'fermenting sewer' into which the Thames had degenerated. He described a journey in a steamboat from London Bridge upriver to Hungerford:

> The whole of the river was an opaque, pale brown fluid. In order to test the degree of opacity, I tore up some white card into pieces, moistened them so as to make them sink easily below the surface and then dropped some of these pieces into the water at every pier the boat came to; before they had sunk an inch below the surface they were indistinguishable, though the sun shone brightly at the time.[6]

Punch followed up with a cartoon, 'Faraday Giving his Card to Father Thames', showing the scientist holding his nose and leaning over the side of a boat to present a *carte de visite* to a figure dripping with black ordure. Something, Faraday said, must be done.

Yet, more than two and a half years after its establishment, the new board still hadn't even begun to tackle the problem, even though its act of Parliament had instructed it to take steps to prevent 'all and any part of the sewage of the metropolis from flowing into the River Thames in or near the metropolis', and one of its first moves had been to appoint Joseph Bazalgette as its chief engineer and ask him to report on plans for the sewerage works 'at the earliest possible opportunity'.

This delay, reminiscent of the prevarication that had doomed the earlier sewer commissions, wasn't entirely the board's fault. The plans that Bazalgette had inherited and developed envisaged a system of massive sewers running east to west, three north and two south of the Thames, intercepting the existing sewers that ran down into the river and directing their contents eastwards. One problem was that they would be expensive to build, and the board didn't have the resources. Another problem was that the effluent would still go into the Thames, albeit a long way downriver from the built-up area. North London's sewage would go into the river at the entrance to Barking Creek; South London's would go in at a place called Crossness on Plumstead marshes.

The trouble was that both these sites were 'within the metropolis', if the metropolis was taken to be the area covered by the board. The government minister who had set up the board, Sir Benjamin Hall, and who had given himself the power to veto its decisions, wasn't happy. Hall was the government's First Commissioner of Works, responsible among other things for overseeing the completion of the rebuilt Houses of Parliament after their destruction by fire in 1834, which is why Westminster's clock tower and the bell it contains are jointly nicknamed Big Ben in his memory. He was also a genuine believer in sanitary reform (though, like many other people, he didn't get on with Edwin Chadwick) and a former president of the Board of Health.

He was not being obstructive just for the sake of it. The wording of the legislation had been deliberate, because it had become evident over many years that sewage flowed backwards and forwards in the river with the tide; the outfalls might be a good distance downstream, but that didn't mean the discharged effluent would not come back upriver on each tide, and that would be no remedy at all. As *The Lancet* wrote in apocalyptic terms in July 1855: 'The abominations, the corruptions we pour into the Thames, are not, as some falsely say, carried away into the sea. The sea rejects the loathsome tribute, and heaves it back again with every flow. Here, in the heart of the doomed city, it accumulates and destroys.'[7]

In December 1856 Hall referred Bazalgette's plan – and the question of where to site the outfalls – to three independent referees, including James Simpson. In July 1857 they recommended putting the outfalls much, much further east – 20 miles beyond the metropolitan boundary at the aptly-named Mucking on the north side, and near Higham (less aptly named, I feel) on the opposite shore. But this would also cost much, much more: roughly twice as much as Bazalgette's plan. However much London's ratepayers might want the sewage removed from the river, it became clear they were not prepared to pay to get it any further than Barking and Crossness. Hall decided the government wasn't prepared to pay either, and deadlock ensued. It's not clear what might have broken it had the hottest summer ever then recorded not intervened.

The Great Stink

The summer of 1857 had seen record temperatures, but 1858 was even hotter. On 16 June the temperature, in a city with no modern comforts, such as air conditioning or refrigeration, reached 94.5 degrees Fahrenheit, or 34.7 Celsius, during a fortnight of extreme heat. No one could be unaware of it and – if they were anywhere near the filthy river – no one could fail to notice the stench, exacerbated by the heat. Paddle steamers stopped plying their trade because they had no takers – a pleasure cruise was no pleasure at all when the smell was, as *Punch* put it, 'perfectly loathsome'. The Thames was 'black and beastly', 'opaque and black as ink', 'a deadly cesspool'. But there was more to it than mere disgust: there was also the terror provoked by the threat of creeping miasma spreading deadly poison along with the smell.

'Whoso once inhales the stink can never forget it and can count himself lucky if he live to remember it', one newspaper wrote. A lawyer living in the Temple, on the river's 'festering shore', wrote to *The Times* to complain that he was being 'killed by inches'. Londoners, *Punch* said, were 'living over a far worse poison than an apothecary can sell, and are inhaling it day by day until they are killed'. This was hysterical stuff and sanitary campaigners tried to play down the exaggeration and the 'strange stories flying of men struck down with the stench, and of all kinds of fatal diseases upspringing on the river's banks', but the notion that the stink of the river spelt death had taken fast hold – and of course it served the sanitarians' interests.[8]

In any case, there was no gainsaying the smell. Rich and poor, famous and anonymous were all equally affected. Dickens testified that, on the short trip across London Bridge to catch the train to his country home at Gad's Hill, the smells were 'of a most head-and-stomach distracting nature'. The historian Thomas Carlyle in Chelsea, about to leave for Scotland, bemoaned the 'Thames River with a stink worse than Acheron'.

Queen Victoria went to see the *Great Eastern* or *Leviathan*, the largest ship ever built and the engineer Brunel's last great folly, which was moored at Deptford after her launch and serving as a tourist attraction to try to raise the funds to complete her fitting out. 'We were half poisoned by the dreadful smell of the Thames – which is such that I felt quite sick when I came home,' she wrote to her daughter. Three weeks later *Punch* suggested the ship would make 'a first-rate floating sewer', and that London's sewage should be loaded into her many holds and discharged into the middle of the ocean.[9]

At Westminster the law courts abandoned their sittings in Westminster Hall, driven out by the 'pestiferous exhalations'. And *The Times* memorably described the moment a House of Commons committee considering new banking legislation was overwhelmed by the stench and the members, including two future Prime Ministers – the Chancellor of the Exchequer Benjamin Disraeli and William Gladstone – 'hastened in dismay from the pestilential odour', handkerchiefs pressed to their noses.[10] That was on Wednesday, 30 June; two weeks later, on 15 July, Disraeli introduced legislation, which, by 2 August, after just eighteen days, had passed into law. Contemporaries noted that it was only thanks to an accident of history and geography – the fact that the Houses of Parliament sat right at the riverside, where the smell was most offensive – that anything was done at all to deal with a problem that had been evident for years. 'The stench of June was only the last ounce of our burden,' *The Times* observed. 'That hot fortnight did for the sanitary administration of the metropolis what the Bengal mutinies did for the administration of India.'[11]

The state of the river, said Disraeli, when he introduced his bill, was a 'calamity' and a 'catastrophe'. 'That noble river, so long the pride and joy of Englishmen, which has hitherto been associated with the noblest feats of our commerce and the most beautiful passages of our poetry, has really become a Stygian pool, reeking with ineffable and intolerable horrors.'[12] The public health, he added, was at stake, with the implication that it was government's job to do something about it. This was a striking position for a Victorian Tory to adopt, and a striking victory for the sanitary reformers, who thirty years before had failed to persuade a Conservative minister, Peel, to intervene directly in the public interest, and had tried and failed again less than a decade earlier with a Whig, Seymour. Disraeli's bill amended the 1855 act, which had established the Metropolitan Board of Works. The key change was a subtle one, but crucial: the board was still expected to keep sewage out of the Thames within the metropolis but only 'as far as may be practicable'. It had become evident that outfalls at Barking and Crossness were practicable; anywhere further east was not.

The question of who should pay for cleaning up the Thames had been one of the unresolved issues that had hamstrung progress and it came up several times in the parliamentary debates on the bill. Most MPs were clear that London's excrement and London's river were London's problem, and London ought to pay to sort them out. 'The inhabitants of a very fine town,' said the member for Stirlingshire, 'put an enormous quantity of dirt into their very fine river, and then they wanted the inhabitants of smaller and poorer towns to come and take it out for them.' But others took a different view. London was the national – indeed the imperial – capital and so a special case. If an invading army were to attack London, suggested the member for Bradford (a major-general), 'it would not be urged that the provinces ought not to assist'.[13]

The outcome was a compromise. Londoners *would* pay: a threepenny rate would be levied for forty years and the proceeds used to service a £3 million loan that the act empowered the board to contract. But the loan would be available at low rates of interest and would be guaranteed by the government. Later the board was allowed to borrow more money against the security of its rate income, which rose constantly thanks to London's relentless expansion. And in due course it was assigned the revenue from old-established duties levied by the City on coal and on wine to fund the building of the embankments. Disraeli also gave the board the freedom either to sink or swim in London's putrid river without government intervention: the ministerial veto that had hobbled progress over the previous two and a half years was abandoned.

Sublime sewerage

The intercepting sewers that the board and Bazalgette forthwith began building have been justly celebrated. Without them, not only the Thames but the whole of London would have become intolerable. Though designed for a city of three million, they still do duty for one with a population three times that. Sometimes buried deep below ground, sometimes running across the lowlands of east London in what look like railway embankments, they were sufficiently well-built to have survived largely unaltered into the twenty-first century.

The scheme was hugely ambitious in conception and construction, and had more of it been above ground – and had it not been devoted to something most people would prefer to ignore – Bazalgette's sewers might have become as famous and admired in our own day as lofty Victorian railway stations like Paddington or St Pancras. They needed a Doré to do them justice – or perhaps that other master of the sublime, John Martin, who had in any case first imagined them in the 1830s.* As it is, we must make do with photographs of arched brick tunnels, curving out of sight and artfully lit, or with the pictures of construction in progress in the 1860s. Formally dressed engineers stand atop the works alongside labourers in shirt sleeves and open waistcoats, holding technical drawings and shovels, as the twin tunnels of the northern outfall drive towards the viewer, or the arcades of the storage reservoir at Crossness, as yet unroofed, march into the distance. The cameras of the day required them to stand still for several seconds: it gives them an heroic cast, like

---

* Martin's plan envisaged a covered sewer running alongside the river, with above it rows of classical colonnades straight out of one of his paintings. You can see images on the World of John Martin website at http://www.wojm.org.uk/plans/plans.htm: one includes a fanciful Egyptian galley rowing down the Thames.

ancient statuary in top hats. In their evocation of strength and purpose, these pictures recall one of the defining images of Victorian engineering, the photograph of a diminutive and ageing Brunel in mud-splashed trousers, stovepipe hat and cigar, standing in front of the massive chains of the Great Eastern.

The scale of the project was huge. It required 318 million bricks – so many that the country ran short and the price went up by more than 40 per cent, while bricklayers' wages went from 5s to 6s a day. Most of the sewers were dug using the cut and cover technique employed for the first underground railways – one of which, the Metropolitan, ran alongside the sewer behind the granite frontage of the Victoria Embankment – but some involved tunnelling, long before the deep tubes of the London Underground: there was a mile-long tunnel beneath Woolwich (five men died during its construction) and another four miles long carrying the northern mid-level sewer deep below Oxford Street, from Notting Hill to Saffron Hill.

In places you find evidence of this subterranean wonder at the surface. On the Chelsea Embankment, by the railway bridge into Victoria, where the Chelsea Waterworks intake once stood, is a handsome structure with tall windows on both its floors, a curved mansard roof punctured by curious oval louvres and a spectacular Italianate chimney: this is the western sewage pumping station, built to raise the material brought from the low-lying ground around Fulham and Chelsea up into the sewer running past Westminster and along the Embankment. At Abbey Mills in West Ham, where this northern low-level sewer joined its mid- and high-level equivalents, the system needed another pumping station, a flamboyant Gothic affair to lift the low-level contents so the whole lot could flow together along the northern outfall sewer to Barking. South of the Thames at Crossness yet another enormous pump house lifted the sludge 21 feet into a reservoir to await high tide, when the sluice gates were opened and 25 million gallons flowed into the river, to be taken (in theory) out to sea with the ebb tide. The sewage now bypasses the pump house here, but its four huge beam engines, the largest ever built, are still *in situ*. One, Prince Consort, has been restored to working order and is steamed on open days. Just as impressive as the engines is the wrought-iron decoration of the machine hall interior, a riot of colour and curling tendrils. It is tempting to see the iron figs scattered among the foliage as an arch Victorian joke. You get there along Bazalgette Way.

Crossness opened in 1865, Abbey Mills in 1868, the western pumping station in 1875, by which time the system was substantially complete. For some the new workings and tunnels were a site of potential horror: 'volcanoes of filth; gorged veins of putridity', in the words of the journalist John Hollingshead, 'ready to explode at any moment in a whirlwind of foul gas, and poison all those whom they fail to smother'.[14] But in general the whole thing was a triumph, and seen to be one. The problems emerged only as the years went by.

The most pressing was that the whole scheme had merely shifted the sewage a few miles downstream: the river was still horribly polluted – just a different section of it. When the effluent was discharged at Barking and Crossness twice a day, the water started 'hissing like soda-water with baneful gases, so black that the water is stained for miles, and discharging a corrupt charnel-house odour',

The Times reported in December 1878.[15] There were allegations, eventually deemed to be unfounded, that the outfalls were creating mudbanks that interfered with navigation. And in September 1878, an overloaded pleasure steamer, the *Princess Alice*, sank in Galleons Reach just upriver from the outfalls after a collision with a coal ship: 130 survived, 500 or more died, and there were claims the unfortunate victims had drowned in sewage that had floated upriver with the tide. Eventually Bazalgette and the board of works were forced to act. He devised a method of chemically precipitating out the solids in the sewage before the remaining relatively innocuous liquid was discharged. The question was what to do with the residue: burn it, sell it as fertiliser, or dump it somewhere? The cheapest option was to dump it, and so, from 1887 until the practice was banned by the European Union in 1998, the sludge was taken out to Barrow Deep off the Essex coast and tipped into the sea. Six specialist vessels were built to do the job: the first was named the *Bazalgette*.

Lost rivers

Sorting out London's sewers wasn't just a question of building new ones. There were the old ones to be tackled as well. In 1861, as work on Bazalgette's project was well under way, John Hollingshead took a trip down one of them, known as the King's Scholars' Pond sewer, and wrote about it in a pamphlet, *Underground London*.

Hollingshead was an ebullient character who wrote for magazines edited by both Dickens and Thackeray and later went into theatre management, where he introduced

Londoners to the French can-can and first brought Gilbert and Sullivan together. His 'day below' in the company of half a dozen sewer flushers was a bit of a lark, as well as educational. He was especially tickled that the sewer's route took them beneath Buckingham Palace: 'Of course my loyalty was at once excited, and taking off my fantailed cap, I led the way with the National Anthem, insisting that my guides should join in the chorus.'

Hollingshead entered the sewer near its start in St John's Wood (watched by a sceptical rank of hansom cab drivers) and descended its entire length, travelling the last few hundred yards in a punt. As they walked he exchanged banter with his companions – who, he said, evidently expected him to pass out – and listened to their stories of what they and their colleagues had found in the sewers: German silver, scrubbing brushes, bad half-crowns, whole sets of false teeth, a live hedgehog, dead children. He described a well-ventilated tunnel, knee-deep in water, with a smell that was 'inoffensive' and no rats. But its condition deteriorated as it neared the river: many of the lower bricks had been washed out and the 'jagged and uneven' flooring made it hard to walk. And some of the lesser sewers that connected with it were in a deplorable condition: a disused branch sewer was 'almost blocked up to the roof with mountains of black, dry, earthy deposit' and the bricks 'were as rotten as gingerbread; you could have scooped them out with a teaspoon'.[16]

The King's Scholars' Pond Sewer had begun life as the River Tyburn, and many of the other larger sewers that Bazalgette's new works intercepted had also once been natural watercourses, tributaries of the Thames and Lea, which had been culverted over as they became increasingly noxious. One, the Hackney Brook, was repurposed as the northern high level sewer. The rest were rebuilt and likewise incorporated into the new system. Today these 'lost rivers', with their evocative ancient names – Westbourne and Tyburn, Effra, Peck and Neckinger – are beloved of London's psychogeographers, hidden evidence of the ancient city persisting under the surface (literally) of the modern one. Though long buried, you can trace their course at street level from declivities in the ground, in street names like Turnmill Street, Spring Path or Effra Parade, and in oddities of the streetscape. The Great Northern Hotel at Kings Cross was reputedly built on a curve to follow the bank of the Fleet, and the Fleet valley is deep enough to justify not only Holborn Viaduct (another water-related name, a corruption of 'Oldbourne') but also a more modest cast-iron bridge a few hundred metres north, carrying Rosebery Avenue.

The route of the Tyburn is evident on the map in a line of back streets and alleys snaking south through posh Mayfair from Marylebone Lane, disrupting the street grid. Famously, passengers on the platform at Sloane Square station can see the Westbourne above their heads in an enormous cast-iron tube. And in some places you can still hear the rivers, fed by springs that no amount of Victorian engineering could wish away: the musical sound of flowing water trickling up through gratings from deep below. At one of the best-known spots to hear the Fleet, just off Farringdon Road, the local council has helpfully extended the pavement into the roadway to incorporate the grating, so urban explorers no longer risk death by delivery driver if they stop to listen.

At the points where these lost rivers once joined the Thames (the Fleet comes out beneath Blackfriars Bridge, the Tyburn in Pimlico, the Effra at Vauxhall) there are now massive iron flaps, which for most of the time stay firmly closed: under normal circumstances the lost rivers' flow is diverted wholesale into the northern and southern low-level sewers. But where the new and the old intersected, Bazalgette built weirs, over which the floodwaters could spill at times of exceptionally heavy rainfall, to run on down the old course, push open the iron flaps and empty into the Thames. It was a failsafe, designed to prevent sewage backing up and flooding homes in a deluge.

As Bazalgette pointed out, the sewage thus discharged would be heavily diluted by rainwater, and he estimated that the overflows would be needed no more than a dozen times a year. But since his day, London has continued to expand inexorably and the number of houses connected to the system has grown dramatically. Extreme weather events have also increased thanks to climate change. And a growing fashion for garden patios and hard-standing for cars has meant less rainwater absorbed by the earth and more flowing into the sewers. In consequence these storm drains now come into operation on many more occasions, sending thousands of gallons of sometimes toxic effluent into the river to poison the fish.

The Thames Tideway super-sewer, a spectacular piece of hard engineering, is meant to be the answer: a £5 billion, 16 mile-long tunnel deep below the river. It's big enough for a London bus, and into it thirty-four of the biggest 'combined sewer overflows' will empty on days of heavy rain, diverting the effluent both from the river and from Bazalgette's intercepting sewers. The consortium building it is called Bazalgette Tunnel Limited: the great engineer has his memorials.

As for his embankments, the most visible part of his legacy, they gave London a succession of promenades to rival those of European cities, but they never quite enjoyed the success that was hoped for them, and not everyone was pleased. Some of the attributes of the old river obstinately migrated to the new Embankment when it was finally completed. The homeless still slept there. It was still the haunt of the outcast poor and the petty criminal. The letter-writing classes complained of 'ruffianism', of colonisation by 'the wild boys and tomboys of the streets', of public urination. It was deemed unsafe for respectable pedestrians, especially after dark, despite its splendid gas lamps (and, for a time, London's first experimental electric street lighting). This may have reflected the fact that even wheeled traffic often shunned it: 'A few foreigners or country people, or hansoms with uncommonly knowing drivers, have the Embankment almost entirely to themselves', wrote *Building News* in 1874.

Inexplicably, drivers still preferred to take the old streets between the City and Westminster, despite the frequent gridlock depicted by Doré – with a satirical exaggeration that owes more to the grotesque than the sublime – in his extravagant evocation of a horse-drawn traffic jam, *Ludgate Hill – A Block in the Street*. 'The failure of the Embankment to relieve the congestion of the Strand and Fleet Street suggest[s],' wrote one historian, engagingly if a little unprofessionally, 'that London has a mind of its own, pursuing inscrutable ends according to a logic that eludes the cleverest entrepreneurs and planners'.[17]

16

Choleraic Poison

In one sense, Joseph Bazalgette's gigantic work came too late: by the time he embarked on its construction, no London water company was using the tidal Thames as a source. But there remained a desperate need to cleanse the waters of the river, and the new sewerage played its part in making London a healthier city. Evidence for this is to be found in London's last cholera outbreak in 1866. But, examining that outbreak in detail, as I have done, also tells us important things about the water industry at the time; it tells us about the newly acquired self-confidence and rigour shown by the servants of the state charged with keeping these private companies in line; and it tells us about the continuing spinelessness of their political masters.

On 27 June 1866, a labourer called Hodges and his wife, living near the mouth of the River Lea, both died of cholera. The disease quickly spread. Over the next two months it claimed more than 4,300 victims; they were scattered across London but just under 3,800 of the dead – nearly 90 per cent – were in the district served by the East London Waterworks. The statistician William Farr quickly noticed this and drew attention to it in a commentary in the Registrar General's weekly bulletin at the end of July.[1]

To Farr, and to experts like him, familiar with the latest scientific thinking, the outbreak was important evidence in support of John Snow's claim that cholera was waterborne – an hypothesis that Farr certainly accepted by 1866. But many others rejected it, including most of the medical officers of health in the East End. The medical officer in Limehouse later produced a lengthy report on the cholera outbreak in which he said he was originally attracted to the 'water theory' but now thought it was wrong: 'water drinkers', including teetotallers, had not been much affected, he claimed, while it was hard to explain why some succumbed to the disease and others did not if they were all drinking the same water. 'The action of a poison . . . is uniform over a community. But this Old Ford water acts capriciously; it skips about finding its victims; here its devastations are heavy, but there passes by multitudes untouched.'[2]

Local officials reacted to the crisis not by treating the water with caution but by demanding more of it 'for sanitary purposes', to help people keep themselves and their houses clean. The East London company (along with the New River) found itself pressed to turn the taps on for the poor on a Sunday. It agreed to do so temporarily.

Farr, of course, was right: the water was to blame and the Lea was a deeply compromised source. Upstream, as the vestry of Mile End Old Town discovered when they sent their surveyor to investigate, the river and its tributary, the Stort, were awash with sewage. His report listed some of the recent housing developments, such as that for the 1,500 men employed at the government's small arms factory at Enfield and their families, whose household waste went straight into the Lea. He noted the privies built over open ditches connecting with the river, and the town drains disgorging their contents into it. It was worst at Bishop's Stortford, where he saw long rows of privies overhanging the banks of the Stort and huge masses of excrement sliding into the water. He called the sight 'sickening', as well he might. The East London company was aware of the problem, and had even thought of going to law to compel the local authority in Bishop's Stortford to do something; but it had held back, fearful that, if the legal action failed, it might have to pay for a clean-up itself.[3]

The New River also got its water from the Lea, higher up than the East London and just below the town of Hertford. In the 1840s it had put in an intercepting drain to take Hertford's sewage downriver beyond the company's intake. But it wasn't much bothered about what happened downstream from there. Wouldn't the East London company still catch the sewage at Lea Bridge, the New River's engineer W. C. Mylne had been asked in 1851? 'No doubt, if it is in the river,' he replied laconically. Which was the East London's problem, he implied, not his.[4]

Downstream from Lea Bridge, where the East London had its filter beds, the state of the river was even worse than upriver. And here, though Bazalgette's sewers were finished, the pumping station at Abbey Mills was not. 'It is unfortunately,' Bazalgette wrote to Farr in August, 'the locality where our main drainage works are not complete.' The area's drains were still emptying into the Lea. 'We are deodorising the sewers and gullies freely with chloride of lime,' he wrote, 'and tomorrow I shall recommend the board to erect a temporary pumping station at Abbey Mills to lift the sewage of this district into the northern outfall sewer.' But that would take three weeks. Farr published

Bazalgette's letter, alongside Frankland's revealing admission (noted in Chapter 13) that the 'choleraic poison' was too small to be detected by chemical analysis. He also added a further gloss on the East London's arrangements, a day after he had visited the works himself.

During the visit he saw the company's filter beds; but also remarked that two of its customers had reported finding eels in their water pipes – which suggested the filters were either inefficient or being bypassed somehow. In his published report he pointed out that the East London's water came down from the filter beds at Lea Bridge in a closed pipe into covered reservoirs at Old Ford, as it should; but that next to the covered reservoirs there were two that were uncovered and which were still connected to Lea Bridge by an open canal. Alarmingly, one of these reservoirs had recently been emptied and had refilled by itself, perhaps from water that had soaked through its walls from the polluted river. The company said it didn't use these reservoirs; why then, Farr asked, did it still have them? And why did it still have the old feeder canal that connected with them?[5]

Taking the hint

What is especially remarkable is how unperturbed the East London's directors appear to have been when faced with the potentially devastating allegation that their product was killing their customers. If they discussed it, their board minutes show no evidence. And for some six weeks, while the epidemic raged, they took no proactive steps to deal with it; they merely responded with every appearance of bemused complacency to the initiatives of others.

There was, they were told, a 'misstatement' in the Registrar General's first report on the cholera outbreak; the board's attention was directed to this and to a letter of 'correction' from their engineer printed in *The Times*. John Simon wrote to them about a shortage of water during the epidemic in Stepney; a reply was approved. Dr Frankland suggested water could be rendered cholera-free by filtering it through animal charcoal; it would be expensive, but the engineer would conduct an experiment.[6]

If anyone senior in the company was responding constructively to the crisis, it was not the directors but their engineer, Charles Greaves. He was another member of the Mylne dynasty of water engineers: Robert Mylne had been his grandfather, W. C. Mylne was his uncle. He had had a varied career, including time in India and a stint making a survey of the New River, before, in 1861, at the age of forty-five, he succeeded Thomas Wicksteed at the East London. He was a details man, who worked immensely hard, constantly building more reservoirs and pumping stations as the company's district and the need for water mushroomed, and worrying that there simply wasn't enough water in the Lea to meet demand: after toying in 1864 with taking water from the Bedfordshire Ouse more than 50 miles away, he eventually built a new intake for the company on the Thames at Hanworth in 1871, and an 18-mile-long pipeline to bring the water east to a covered reservoir in Finsbury Park.[7]*

---

* The Finsbury Park reservoir was completed in 1869 and drained in 2012, after concerns about its structural safety: the interior is an imposing exercise in monumental Victorian brickwork, of which there are numerous photographs online, some actually taken with

Greaves' letter to *The Times* was his first public move. Farr's original description of the company's arrangement of intakes and filter beds and feeder canals had been wrong, and Greaves corrected it. The Registrar General, he said, had been using an out-of-date map. He also asserted 'that not a drop of unfiltered water has for several years past been supplied by the company for any purposes'. Before writing the letter he had visited the Registrar General's office at Somerset House and invited Farr to see the works for himself, which he duly did. The key question that concerned Farr – and Greaves – was whether untreated water had somehow got into the East London's mains. After Farr's visit, Greaves told his directors that Farr had seemed satisfied there had been 'no improper admission by intention or otherwise, although he affects to think it possible and would wish all chances removed'.[8]

Greaves took the hint. The company had been planning to cover its two open reservoirs at Old Ford so that they could store filtered water for distribution to the mains. On 13 September, Greaves told the directors he was abandoning that plan. A week later he told them that 'to put the earliest stop to the suspicion of an habitual use being made of unfiltered water, uncovered reservoirs, and channels that have been disused', he had blocked up the old canal and the head of the old reservoirs with dams of clay, 'and

---

(cont.) the knowledge of the owners (see, for instance, *My London News*, 12 November 2020, https://www.mylondon.news/news/ north-london-news/inside-secret-london-underground-reservoir-16245724 or *28dayslater*, https://www.28dayslater.co.uk/threads/ finsbury-park-underground-reservoir-north-london-may-2013. 80759/).

had laid a large heap of clay so as to effectually stop up the only sluice way by which water can be admitted from the uncovered reservoir'. And he went further still, recommending that the Old Ford works – which lay below the level of the Lea at high tide – be abandoned entirely in favour of Lea Bridge, where the company should install more pumping engines and more filters. 'I am not saying there is anything going on wrong or known to be wrong,' he wrote, 'but as has been said by others so much of the works and operations are submerged and hidden that proof positive of the perfect state of all things is not at any time immediately to be had.' It would cost money now, but it would help to avert a public relations disaster in the future: if the 'common malady' (presumably he meant cholera by this) were to return, it 'may lead to opinions more adverse and hostile and which it may not be possible to meet at all in a reasonable way'.

This all reads like a tacit admission that Farr's criticisms were justified and that the company's water had been to blame for the cholera. The engineer's half-yearly report to the shareholders in September proved unusually difficult to write: a heavily amended draft survives, addressing, among other things, the 'very strong aspersions' levelled at the quality of the company's water.[9] The Old Ford site was finally shut down in 1892, and now lies under the Olympic park. The Lea Bridge site, too, was abandoned in the 1970s; its extensive filter beds are now a park and nature reserve at the north end of Hackney Marshes.

Breaching the defences

The difficulty for Greaves was that, like many people under pressure, he was being economical with the truth. It was indeed the case, as he said, that no unfiltered water had been supplied 'for several years past'; but the vagueness as to dates was intentional. Unfiltered water had been banned under the 1852 act, yet the East London's board minutes record at least one occasion as late as the winter of 1860–61 when the company's filter beds froze and Greaves admitted using water from the company's old reservoirs, thus mixing filtered and unfiltered water and breaking the law. The filters were out of action for over a month. There were problems in summer too, when the Lea's flow was liable to shrink. And in spring the filter beds could become clogged with fast-growing weed, which, Greaves reported in 1865, 'almost beat us in filter bed cleaning': did the company sometimes resort to unfiltered water on these occasions as well?[10]

More seriously, because it directly addressed the possible cause of the 1866 cholera outbreak, in December Greaves was forced into a public and very damaging admission that unfiltered water had indeed been allowed into the mains from one of the old reservoirs the previous spring. It would, he told an inquiry by the Rivers Pollution Commission, be difficult to fix the precise date, but it was probably in June. The senior commissioner, Robert Rawlinson, pressed him to say why he hadn't looked into the matter 'when the charge of supplying impure water was brought against the company'. Greaves failed to give a straight answer, but replied that his foreman had opened the reservoir in question 'on a kind of quasi-sanction from him [Greaves] . . . because he thought it would be wanted'. Greaves told the inquiry he had felt justified in keeping the reservoirs full, 'considering that the question of quantity was at times of such importance'.[11]

In his defence Greaves pointed out that Henry Letheby, John Simon's successor as the City of London's medical officer, who was paid by the company to carry out monthly analyses of its water, had given the stuff in the old reservoir a clean bill of health. And Letheby had indeed – in defiance of the statistical evidence – told anyone who asked that East London customers had shown a 'singular' exemption from the cholera, and that since his chemical analysis had shown the water to be good, it simply could not have been the source of the disease.[12] This wasn't 'manufacturing doubt' so much as straightforward fabrication – a wilful untruth.

But the following year another inquiry carried out for the Board of Trade by the formidable Captain Tyler – a one-time railway inspector, who, as Sir Henry Tyler, later became a Conservative MP – established that one of the company's employees, a twenty-four-year old carpenter, had let in water from the old reservoir no fewer than three times, in March, June and July. 'The use of such unfiltered water so stored in an uncovered reservoir is indefensible,' Tyler wrote, 'and was a distinct infringement of the Metropolitan Water Supply Act of 1852.'[13] Did Greaves know his employees were routinely breaking the law by mixing filtered and unfiltered water? If he did, why did he not tell his directors? Was he perhaps in denial, as we say nowadays? Or had he been deliberately hiding the truth all along? Greaves comes across as neither a charlatan nor a crook, but it seems he *was* prepared to let his staff break the rules while he himself turned a blind eye, in order that the mains should be kept full.

*

The East London wasn't alone. The Southwark & Vauxhall also came under attack on a later occasion for cutting corners and compromising the quality of its water. An official inquiry in 1869 was carried out by one of two public health inspectors newly arrived on the staff of the Privy Council. He found that the level of demand had overwhelmed the S&V's capacity to supply clean water: it wasn't letting its water settle for long enough and it didn't have enough filter capacity. There was also a suspicion that, rather like the East London, it had allowed water into its works from its old inlet at Battersea to top up the supply.

John Simon thought the distribution of unfiltered water had been deliberate in the S&V's case, and that the law was inadequate to counter such perils to the public safety. The water companies' 'colossal power of life and death is something for which till recently there has been no precedent in the history of the world', he wrote. 'And such a power, in whatever hands it is vested, ought most sedulously to be guarded against abuse.' One newspaper went further. It accused the S&V of 'criminal indifference to the public safety' and 'homicidal antecedents on a really stupendous scale'.[14]

The investigations by Farr, Rawlinson and others showed that a Chadwickian system of inspection and inquiry was capable of holding private companies to account. But that wasn't quite the same as robust enforcement, even when it was clear that the law had been broken. The government had the power to fine companies for a breach of the 1852 act; it never bothered. One reason may have been the continuing reluctance to accept that dirty water could kill. In 1866 the East London was trying for a new act of Parliament to authorise further extensions to its works, and that required a select committee. 'We think it right to observe,' the committee said in its final report, 'that the evidence leads to the opinion that the spread of cholera might equally be ascribed to defective sanitary arrangements and to other causes.' The miasmatists had not yet conceded.[15]

The whole business brought out the water campaigners once again and the campaign for public ownership received a boost. The *Standard* thought the state of the capital's water unworthy of a Christian city:

> The facts of the day are against the existing water companies, which have bolstered up their interests and magnified their dividends so long. We ought to be ashamed of our municipal government, and ashamed of our own common sense, were it to be believed that, after so many examples of calamity and so many proofs of failure we should long continue to leave the operation of our metropolitan water supply open to doubt or cavil, or subject to the selfishness of monopolies.[16]

But it is by no means clear, to me at least, that public ownership of the water supply would have prevented the 1866 cholera outbreak. There would still have been the threat to health posed by the company's legacy infrastructure, by the sewage from upstream communities and by the unfinished state of Bazalgette's main drainage. And the immediate failures at Old Ford were a consequence of human error, wishful thinking and wilful blindness – qualities not limited to the private sector.

Water watchdogs

Three years after London's last cholera outbreak, the Richmond Commission reported, and though it concluded that the water of the Thames and Lea could be made safe to drink, it did call for public ownership. Legislation duly followed in the form of the Metropolis Water (Amendment) Act of 1871. Except that, once again, the government dodged the ownership question: the companies were left in place. That has left some historians to conclude that the 1871 act, like that of 1852, was a failure. But it was not entirely toothless. Two new government posts – Chadwick-style inspectors working for the Board of Trade – were created to keep the companies in check: a water examiner to oversee quality and a government auditor to scrutinise their accounts.

The examiner post went to Major Francis Bolton, a military expert on 'visual signalling' (i.e. semaphore and flashing lights etc) and the founder, in 1871, of the Society of Telegraph Engineers and Electricians. Bolton's career suggests a man of quite unusual drive and talent, though his record as water examiner was a mixed one. The son of a doctor who had died while he was still a child, flashy Francis started as a lawyer's clerk before enlisting first in the Austrian Army and then in the Royal Artillery, where he rose through the ranks to become sergeant-instructor in gunnery. He was commissioned at the age of twenty-seven into the Gold Coast Artillery, saw action in one of Britain's many imperial wars and then transferred to the infantry, who sent this restless and inventive man off on attachment to the Royal Engineers. He devised a system of visual signalling for the army, and wrote the codebooks to go with it, but he was also responsible for a long list of other inventions as well, including improvements to military rifles, to lighthouses and to batteries. He must have been hard to keep up with. His obituarist remarked on his energy, intelligence and self-reliance, before adding: 'He was slow to admit the possibility of failure, and probably for that reason was generally successful in matters where caution in a business sense was not a necessary qualification.'[17] He held the water examiner's post until his retirement in 1881 and remained a serving army officer: he was promoted to Lieutenant Colonel while in the job. He published monthly reports on the water supply, inspected the companies' works from time to time and responded to public complaints.

The auditor post went to a career civil servant called Allen Stoneham, the son of a Greenwich master tailor, who had joined the Board of Trade as a clerk, probably in his teens, and had risen to assistant secretary by the time of his retirement in the 1890s. His descendants have a splendid photograph of him taken in 1903, when he would have been seventy-six: he sits in a conservatory or winter garden, dressed in the spectacular white beard and flowing locks of an Old Testament prophet and the equally spectacular three-piece check tweed of a respectable Victorian patriarch. He is looking down at his grandson Donald, lying across grandfather's knee in his christening robe, and next to them stands Donald's father and the eldest of Allen's ten children.*

When I first came across Stoneham, I naively assumed, from my twenty-first-century perspective, that his post had been established to protect the public – to ensure that shareholders did not feather their own nest at the expense of the customers. Only later did it occur to me that just as important was protecting the shareholders themselves, which may be why Stoneham came from the board's railway department: the railways had been notorious for ripping off their investors, and his experience there would stand him in good stead in the water business.

Stoneham, as we shall see later in Chapter 18, did an effective job. Frank Bolton, however, has been criticised by some historians for being politically naive and too close to the companies: perhaps he was a victim of that bureaucratic variant of the Stockholm syndrome known as regulatory capture? His obituary suggests he sometimes acted more like a consultant than a watchdog, and *London's Water Supply*, a handbook published under his name in 1884, offers a thoroughly sanitised account of the history:

* Marty Burn kindly supplied a copy of the photograph. Stoneham's son, Allen junior, followed in his father's footsteps to the extent of being a chartered accountant, but he had an entrepreneurial streak and, at the time of the photograph, had recently bought the land near Etaples on the north coast of France, which he was to turn into the resort of Le Touquet: he ended up a rich man (https://web.archive.org/web/20171107002936/http://www.letouquet-lemascaret.co.uk/LeTouquetHistory.htm). Another of Stoneham's sons, Sydney, on the other hand, qualified as a solicitor but was convicted at the Old Bailey in 1888 of embezzling a client's money. (https://www.oldbaileyonline.org/browse.jsp?div=t18881022-975).

much of it seems to have been written by the water companies themselves.* His enthusiasm for the water industry was such that it may eventually have killed him: in 1884 he devised a display financed by the companies of coloured illuminated fountains for an international health exhibition in South Kensington, and personally controlled the constantly changing display from a tiny control room every night. The fountains proved so popular the display was repeated in the following two years, but the repeated exposure to the cold night air supposedly brought on chills and a fatal attack of laryngitis.

Whatever Bolton's shortcomings, he began energetically enough. His early reports consistently highlighted several companies' lack of filter capacity and subsiding reservoirs, especially the Southwark & Vauxhall. In June 1872, a group of residents in Bermondsey complained that their S&V water supply had failed for three days. Bolton concluded that the company's filter beds had been overwhelmed by 'rapid vegetable growth' and that, with more reservoirs, the problems would not have arisen. But he also went to see for himself, visiting all the houses that had signed the complaint between 5pm and 8pm one evening

* But he explicitly censored a contribution to the book from three water analysts working for the companies, calling it 'controversial'; in it they criticised the conclusions of the official water analyst, Edward Frankland, whose monthly reports Bolton published, and whose contribution to the book went in unchanged (Col. Sir Francis Bolton, *London's Water Supply*, p. 64). The company analysts, eagerly manufacturing doubt, tried hard to get Bolton to publish their monthly reports as well, to give them the appearance of official backing, and he was not always successful in resisting (Christopher Hamlin, *A Science of Impurity*, pp. 193–201).

with Joseph Quick, the company's engineer, and got the local turncock to turn on the water. He concluded that a large part of the problem was a result of consumers' 'defective fittings'. There was some truth in this, but in saying it Bolton was endorsing the companies' questionable practice of deflecting blame for poor water quality on to their customers; in his July 1883 report, he observed that all the companies' investment was 'rendered nearly abortive and of little value by the continued apathy and carelessness of a great number of the consumers'.[18]

This was letting the companies off the hook: Bolton might have done better to adopt the role of the consumer's champion. As the century wore on, the idea of 'the consumer' came into sharper focus. To begin with it meant 'he (or sometimes she) who paid the water company'. Those who called for consumer representation or for consumer control over water in the 1840s and 50s meant the rate-paying public, usually as represented by the local vestries. Many users of water were not rate-payers and had no direct relationship with the water company, but instead paid indirectly through their landlord.[19]

But the idea was taking root that, in a democracy, it wasn't necessary to be a property-owner to have a voice. Definitions of the consumer widened, helped along by London water politics. A network of Water Consumers' Defence Leagues sprang up in the 1880s that represented not just rate-payers but poorer tenants too. By the end of the century a trade union felt justified in pressing the local government board on behalf of its members in East London to improve their water supply, despite the fact that few if any of its members were likely to pay water-rates directly.

Often, disgruntled consumers went to court. The most successful was a man called Archibald Dobbs, a progressive barrister, who, in 1882, sued the Grand Junction over the basis on which his water rates were assessed. Since 1852 most of the water companies' charges had been fixed in their private acts of Parliament: they were allowed to charge only a certain percentage of a property's 'annual value' – the amount the property would bring in each year if rented out – but how that value was to be arrived at was not spelled out. Was it the same as the rateable value assessed by the parish? (Different parishes' assessments varied considerably in any case.) Or could the company make its own assessment (often based on the number of rooms or chimneys a house had)? The arrangement was a good one for the companies, since property prices in London boomed as the city expanded and water rates rose much faster than other prices. But it meant consumers in different parts of the city paid very different amounts: the owner of a house rated at £50 in 1890 paid £2 4s in the New River and Chelsea districts, for example, but £3 17s in the Lambeth district.

The Dobbs case turned on the technical question of whether his water company's charges should be based on the gross or net annual value of his property – in his case £140 and £118 respectively. The Grand Junction had been charging on the basis of the gross value; Dobbs argued it should charge on the basis of net value, a lower figure meant to take account of the deductions a landlord made from rental income to allow for the costs of repairs and maintenance. It made a small difference of just over £4 to Dobbs, but a big difference to the company if it were forced to switch to net annual value for all its customers. Dobbs lost at first instance but appealed all the way to the House of Lords, where he won the case. The outcome was a substantial dent in the revenue of most of the water companies.*

War on waste

The act of 1871, like that of 1852, in theory mandated constant supply. It led to a surge in investment, as the companies built more of the covered service reservoirs and associated pumping stations they needed to keep all their mains supplied at constant high pressure. Yet constant supply was still slow in coming.

The act laid down detailed and costly regulations to prevent waste, which customers had to abide by – including specifying the sorts of pipes and taps which were allowed – but the companies had wanted even tougher rules. The *Journal of Gas Lighting* thought these rules would be so expensive to comply with that most householders wouldn't bother (which was no doubt the point): 'The unfortunate householder will probably think that he may buy the joy of a constant service too dear, and decide to leave his water arrangements as they are.'[20]

Constant supply was only very gradually introduced, starting with newly built estates. The East London went

---

* But not all. The Chelsea company's income increased because the House of Lords judgment also tied water company rates to rateable value as defined by the local vestry, which was generally higher than the Chelsea's own valuations (*Aquarius*, 1905, p. 14).

first – giving constant supply to just under 2,900 houses in 1854, a figure which had risen to 25,300 (out of 92,000) by 1866. But the water was rationed: a flow limiter restricted it to around 20 gallons per head per day. Other companies gradually came aboard. By 1891 some of them had made great strides: 98 per cent of East London customers had constant supply and 77 per cent of Southwark & Vauxhall, but only 24 per cent of customers in the Chelsea district: this was less surprising than it sounds, because the Chelsea's largely affluent customers had large cisterns, which gave them, in effect, a constant supply already.[21]

Once the service was introduced, the customers proved as incorrigible as the engineers had always feared. Inquiry after inquiry heard of pricey new lead pipes and taps installed by landlords that were stolen to sell for scrap, and of ballcocks tampered with so as to produce a continual trickle running through WCs in the hopes of clearing the drains and making them smell less bad (it rarely worked).

In 1852 the inspector of the East London Waterworks had said that when the company installed ballcocks they were often taken off immediately: 'We know cases where within two hours after the men have left they have been taken away, and the water suffered to run to waste; they just have the ballcocks while the men are there, and then the moment they are gone the balls are sent back.' This wasn't necessarily being done in order to steal the ballcocks for the money – their cost was trivial and it happened even in 'good houses': 'They say it is done for cleanliness, for sanitary purposes.'[22] W. C. Mylne of the New River told of one builder who installed a ballcock on the cistern in each house he completed before inviting the company's inspector to take a look. A few days later the inspector was invited back to look at the next house. 'And so he moved the ballcock from house to house the whole way up the street, and in 16 or 17 houses there was but one ballcock for the whole street.'[23]

As the engineers feared, the introduction of constant supply produced a short-term increase in consumption. In 1893 the average per head was put at 32.68 gallons (or 148.5 litres), though perhaps a fifth of that was for trade use and a large but uncertain proportion disappeared thanks to leaks. The real consumption per head was probably around 16 gallons or 73 litres, compared with modern Londoners' consumption of 146 litres; given that Victorians lacked the water-intensive paraphernalia of modern life, including washing machines, dishwashers and a bath and shower in every house, that sounds about right.[24] But then the quantity consumed started going down, partly because people soon fixed their old and leaky pipes, but largely thanks to the new water police.

Most of the companies employed teams of inspectors who visited customers' homes to check fittings and in some cases modify them free of charge. The Lambeth company had twenty-two inspectors and a supervisor in 1884.[25] For a company like the East London, which had difficulty matching supply and demand and was always on the brink of a shortage, inspectors were vital, though not always very effective. In 1893, the East London's engineer reported that his customers were 'reckless' in the way they wasted water. 'A staff of over 30 inspectors constantly employed . . . is incompetent to prevent this waste, because it is not mainly due to defective fittings but to the fact that taps are deliberately left running for hours and sometimes days together,' he complained. Members of the 'poorer classes' simply stuck their laundry under a tap, turned it on and left it, rather than using 'a little labour and soap'.[26] This lack of sympathy for the hard-pressed housewife or laundress with aching back and chapped and bleeding hands doubtless reflected the fact that, as a male member of the middle class, he would never have had to do a day's laundry in his life.

Problems of a different kind arose when the companies dealt with customers who wanted water not for use in the home, for cooking and cleaning, but for commercial purposes.

17

Cow-keepers and Firefighters

In 1850 the Nottingham water company issued a price list
for supplying water for 'trades, manufactures and other
special and public purposes'. The London companies must
have had similar price lists, but perhaps none were as comprehensive as Nottingham's, which is why this one was
appended to the evidence produced at the select committee
hearings that preceded the 1852 Act. It runs the gamut of
Victorian institutions and businesses, from asylums through
bakers, bonnet makers, day schools, fish-curers and tripe
boilers to wine and spirit shops (retail) and wine and spirit
shops (wholesale with vaults). Each was charged a different
price. Large users, such as breweries, bleachers and public
washhouses, were charged according to consumption
measured by meter. Marble cutters were charged per saw,
nail-makers per hearth, printing offices per compositor
and places of worship per 100 places. Hydraulic cranes
and lifts were charged 'by special arrangement'.[1]

Water was used in countless ways, and each represented
a chance for the companies to earn a few extra shillings.
The mainstay of their business was supplying households,
but there was money to be made from selling water at premium rates to commercial and industrial users as well.
The Nottingham company derived a third of its income

from sales to non-domestic users, though the proportion was lower in London because the companies couldn't always furnish the constant supply that really large users – breweries, for example – required: these often dug their own wells.

There were sometimes tensions. Not every business paid its dues. In 1804, Sadler's Wells Theatre, next door to New River Head, was transformed in great secrecy and at great expense into an 'aquatic theatre', with a giant water tank that was revealed when the stage was lifted and on which pretend sea battles were fought. The tank was filled with New River Company water, but, in 1824, the theatre was cut off for non-payment of its water rates, and the new owners, including the famous clown Jo Grimaldi, had to beg to be reconnected.*

Then, too, the companies could be ambivalent about some uses to which their water was put, such as supplying ornamental fountains in private gardens: there was a fine line between earning extra revenue and wasting a scarce resource on fripperies. And in an era when many trades-men lived above the shop, it wasn't always easy to distinguish between domestic and trade users. The companies were always on the lookout for customers pulling a fast one by running water-thirsty businesses on the sly.

Thus, in 1821, the East London Waterworks increased the rates of a tripe merchant called Allinson in Shoreditch from £2 2s to £7 7s when they discovered he was not only a pork butcher but a slaughterman, who needed water by

* A performance at the theatre, with what looks like Neptune in his chariot being drawn by sea-horses, is pictured in Thomas Row-landson and Auguste C. Pugin's *The Microcosm of London*.

the bucketful to sluice away blood, and a wholesale tripe boiler: 'He is consuming as much as would supply ten ordinary houses,' the company's engineer said, after Allinson had complained about the price increase.[2]

Occasionally the companies resorted to industrial espionage. When, after the 1817 general arrangement, Hatchett's hotel in Piccadilly complained about its water charges, and a shortage of water now that the Grand Junction was no longer offering constant supply, the company employed one of the hotel's waiters as a spy, to ascertain how often its WCs were flushed.[3]

A tale of Tubbs

Some customers could be exceptionally difficult. In 1840 a cow-keeper called Thomas Tubbs complained when the New River Company increased his rates, after the company discovered he was watering his cows in the yard behind his premises without telling his supplier. Dealing with him must have been a nightmare. He was a persistent thorn in the company's side, the kind of truculent Cockney businessman who knows his rights, holds officialdom and its representatives in contempt, and isn't going to let anyone get the better of him. He was also plainly dishonest.

We know about him because he gave evidence to a House of Lords select committee on London's water supply in 1840, proceedings that were effectively hijacked by Tubbs. The committee was chaired by the Marquess of Westminster, busy at the time developing the Grosvenor family estate in Belgravia, which was to make his successors the country's richest commoners. Tubbs was rather lower on the social scale, with premises at the junction of Tottenham Court Road and the New Road, roughly where the Euston Road underpass now sits.

The marquess and his committee listened with fascination and not a little confusion as first Tubbs gave evidence, then the New River company's engineer, then the company's secretary, then Tubbs again, then the New River's secretary again, then the company's inspector and finally its collector. As the story unfolded, it became clear that Tubbs, who initially presented himself as the put-upon little man, valiantly protesting the outrageous impositions of a big bad water company and even beating them at their own game, was in reality a menace.

The short version of this convoluted story is that Tubbs had been paying the company £2 12s a year for a domestic supply to his house facing the New Road, but had also been using the water for his cows without paying anything extra. Behind the house he had a large yard with two cowsheds, in one of which he had thirty-seven cows when the New River inspected it and in the other seven cows, and space for seventy in total. He also kept horses. He had surreptitiously run a pipe from the front of his premises to the yard, and attached a hose, from which he filled the cisterns in his sheds. When the company discovered this, it told him he would have to pay its standard charge to cow-keepers of 3s 6d per cow, which brought his water-rent to between £30 and £40. Tubbs refused to pay, and appealed to the New River's board, who told him the charge stood. When he still wouldn't stump up, he was cut off. At which point he rented the empty premises next door, and ran a pipe from them to the cowsheds instead. He was asked to stop, became belligerent . . . and next door was cut off too.

The story was complicated by the fact that Tubbs's premises backed on to a small reservoir maintained by the New River Company at the top of Tottenham Court Road. After he was cut off, Tubbs started digging a well, but complained to their lordships that the New River Company had promptly dug its own well just the other side of the boundary wall, installed a pumping engine and taken all the water. 'I sank a well, but then they sank one against me, and took the water away, and rose me to £50 per annum,' he said – before immediately undermining his own story by claiming that the company's attempt to pump his well dry had in fact failed, that the company's well had been abandoned and that he now had an abundance of water and supplied some of his neighbours as well.

The company's version was rather different. The war of the wells was in Tubbs's imagination. W. C. Mylne, the New River's engineer, said he had decided to sink a trial well because there were proposals to supply the whole of London from artesian wells and he wanted to see how feasible that might be. (It turned out not to be cost-effective, he told the committee.) He declared 'most solemnly' that 'there was not the least interruption given to him [Tubbs] during the work by the New River Company's workmen. We never worked the engine, or made him any extra charge, on account of his attempting to supply himself.'

But, Mylne observed, 'There was a great deal of unpleasant feeling upon the business', and he cited a row over what he called a 'waterspout' against the back wall of Tubbs's property, on the other side of which was the bedroom in which the New River's site foreman slept. Tubbs's spout made the wall behind the foreman's bed damp: 'In fact the wall became so exceedingly wet we were compelled to complain of it to him,' said Mylne, 'but he could not be persuaded to take it away. We were obliged to bring an action against him; it went against him and he had costs to pay; he was exceedingly obstinate.'

Tubbs was called back by the noble lords and confronted with the company's evidence. A wiser man might have backtracked. Tubbs kept digging, changing his story to fit whatever new facts were put to him. At one point he said the company had wanted to charge him not 3s 6d per cow but 5s. They had told him this when he had attended the board meeting to lodge his appeal. 'The chairman himself told me it would be 5s a head,' he said. Unfortunately for Tubbs's credibility, the company's paper trail showed this was nonsense.[4]

In trade

London was full of cow-keepers, not all of them as awkward as Tubbs. By the 1830s, the city was thought to be home to some 12,000 cows, and some large cow-keepers had as many as a thousand. The unfortunate animals rarely if ever saw grass but were kept in sheds: until the advent of railways and the early morning milk train, it was the only way to supply city-dwellers with fresh milk.

The cows needed a lot of water – and not only to drink. Unscrupulous dairymen (the majority, it seems) used water to dilute their milk: chalk was then added to make it look whiter. One cow-keeper south of the river nicknamed his pump 'the black cow', because it yielded more than the rest of his herd put together. Another cow-house simply dipped the milk pails into the nearby stream into which drained the dung and urine from the herd. Milk was generally so adulterated that it was never drunk by itself except by infants, and was used mainly in cooking.

Modern London has been deindustrialised: manufacturing represents barely 2 per cent of the city's economy. But in 1861 around one-sixth of Britain's manufacturing workers were in London, in workshops and factories scattered throughout the city. Many of the processes involved water. Water companies' finances could be directly affected by the ups and downs in particular industries. The East London's area included a good many sugar refiners, whose business was seasonal. Supplies of raw material ran short during the winter and the company was frequently asked to grant discounts or rebates. In February 1834 a refiner called Martineau was one of several sugar-boilers negotiating for a reduction because he required only one-third of his normal supply of water until June, 'when the new sugars are expected to arrive'. Forty years later, in 1876, the East London's finances were reported to be affected 'disastrously' by a depression in the sugar trade.[5]

In general businesses were charged whatever the water companies thought they could get away with. In 1821 the Grand Junction charged laundresses the domestic rate, but more if they employed several other women; and the New River supplied Henry Meux's brewery for a price equivalent to what Meux previously spent on coal for a steam engine to pump from his own well. Later in the century, the Southwark & Vauxhall was charging the brewers Barclay Perkins 7½ pence per 1,000 gallons by meter (or a minimum of £150 a year) – a modest amount compared to the London Brighton & South Coast Railway, which was paying £2,000 a year for a supply to its stations and depots.

It probably helped that Robert Barclay was the S&V chairman's brother-in-law. The S&V also supplied water to an ice rink, while the Grand Junction was asked about connecting a small hydraulic engine for blowing the organ at Trinity Church in Paddington, but replied that it couldn't guarantee a particular pressure (or indeed any pressure at all) and that Sunday was the day for repairs, so that interruptions to the supply might occur 'at the most inconvenient periods'.[6]

Meters were crude and not always reliable. In 1879, the S&V directors heard a complaint from one business that for the past two years its meter had been stuck and the dial so covered with dust as to be unreadable; the S&V's inspector had nonetheless struck a match and pretended to take a reading.[7]

In 1874 Howell James & Co – a firm of jewellers with a large store in Regent Street – were paying the Grand Junction £31 10s a year against £17 17s previously and asked for a reduction, saying their premises were mostly sale rooms and all their men lodged in Golden Square nearby. The company sent inspectors round, who found two low service and six high service cisterns, thirteen WCs, one bath, two lavatories, a steam boiler in the kitchen and meals prepared for eighty people daily, plus urinals with four standings – all of which seems a lot for a mere shop. Given such a sizeable investment in sanitary ware and such a profusion of plumbing, Howell James were told they were paying the right amount – and would have to pay extra via meter for their new-fangled urinals.[8]*

* Urinals were a novelty in the 1870s, and the companies shared tips on how much to charge for them. In 1876 the Grand Junction

Road watering was an important source of revenue. Pre-modern city streets were made of cobbles or stone setts or 'macadamized' crushed stone: the weight and iron-bound wheels of horse-drawn traffic gradually ground down the surface and created dust in summer (and mud in winter), and regular watering in hot, dry weather helped to lay the dust. The water companies contracted with the parishes in their areas to supply water, and erected special standpipes for filling the water carts. One is pictured on a postcard dating from around 1900 showing the residential street in which I live. A horse-drawn borough water cart is filling up from the standpipe, which has a bollard-like base and then a vertical pipe that curves over above the cart: presumably it could be swung back over the pavement when not in use so as not to brain any passing drivers. I can report that today an outsize Thames Water cover in the pavement marks the spot.

The water-cart in the picture has four wheels, but often the carts were two-wheeled affairs, which had a tendency to bounce up and down as the horse moved forward and meant the road got watered in alternate wet and dry strips. There was a horizontal perforated pipe set low down at the back to distribute the water, sometimes supplemented by revolving wheels that splashed it out to either side. Earlier road-watering carts were hand-drawn: Thomas Shotter Boys's 1842 'Entry to The Strand from

(cont.) learnt via the Southwark & Vauxhall that the New River Company charged £3 15s for urinals in the City with a continuous stream flowing through them, and 6d per 1,000 gallons for urinals with meters (LMA, ACC/2558/GJ/1/14/1, Grand Junction court minutes, 1 November 1876).

Charing Cross' has two men in the foreground dragging a water cart round the base of Charles II's statue at the top of Whitehall; and, in 1828, George Scharf sketched three hand-drawn carts drawn up for refilling at the pump in Bloomsbury Square, their operators slumped at rest in the heat.[9]

Ah, Captain Shaw

There was one important use of their product for which the companies did not charge. Tudor London had been a wooden city, perpetually braced for the devastating effects of conflagration, and right from the start the companies were obliged to supply water for firefighting, if necessary by allowing firefighters to cut their pipes open.

After the Great Fire of 1666, the town was rebuilt in brick, but the risk of fire remained. By the mid-eighteenth century, insurance companies were operating their own fire engines, manned by Thames watermen. There were parish fire engines as well, and, after 1708, the law required parishes to insert 'fire plugs' in water mains and put up notices on a nearby house to mark where they were – the first step on the road towards the bright yellow metal plates marked with an H that show the location of modern fire hydrants. In the event of fire, the plug was pulled and water was directed on to the blaze by means of hoses attached to an engine. Often the water was first allowed to pool in the street, where it mingled with the refuse in the gutters. When the Grand Junction first launched, one of the benefits it advertised from its constant supply was clean water that would not, in the event of fire, 'tarnish the furniture' (though one would have thought there were worse outcomes to worry about if the house caught fire).[10]

The engines were pumps on wheels, worked by long handles down either side, and dragged to each location by hand and later by horses. It took twenty-six men to operate an engine. Pumping was hard work and most men could only manage a few minutes before they needed a break. They were all volunteers, plucked from the crowd that gathered to watch a fire, and were paid in money or tokens to buy beer: there are stories (perhaps apocryphal) of arsonists deliberately starting fires in order to volunteer as pumpers and qualify for a free drink.

The water companies willingly co-operated with the parishes and the insurance companies. It showed they were good citizens, and it was also a chance to boast about their copious supplies and the pressure in their mains and to burnish their image in the newspapers. When, in 1759, the West Ham Waterworks was applauded in the press for providing water to fight a fire in Queen Street in Ratcliff, the clerk of the rival Shadwell Waterworks was quick to write in, pointing out that actually the fire had been in Narrow Street and it was *his* company's water that had helped put it out. When the London Bridge Waterworks was criticised for being slow to respond to a fire, the secretary rejected the charge and took the opportunity to add, 'it is very well known that no mains belonging to any works in London, of equal diameters, can vent so great a quantity of water as those of these works'.[11]

Before the era of constant supply, the charge that they were 'slow to respond' was often levelled at the companies, because, when a fire broke out, the local turncock had to be found to redirect the water into the relevant pipes, and because, at night, the mains weren't always kept charged and so someone had to run to get the pumps fired up. The first turncock at the scene of a fire got a cash reward, which helped speed response times. First, though, he had to find the fire plug: in 1807 the New River distributed a notice to members of the various vestries whose residents it served, complaining that workmen undertaking road repairs 'frequently carry their pavement completely over the fire boxes, and obliterate every trace of them in the street'.[12]*

As with the water supply, firefighting was a hybrid: a public service mainly provided by private companies. And as with water, but a good deal sooner, it eventually ended up under public control. The first step came in 1833, when ten insurance companies combined their firefighting operations in the London Fire Engine Establishment (by 1848, only two insurance companies did not belong), and recruited James Braidwood as its superintendent. Braidwood had been born in Edinburgh and trained as a builder and surveyor; in 1824 Edinburgh's insurance companies had joined forces to better fight fires in the crumbling Old Town, and Braidwood had been put in charge at the age of just twenty-four. London borrowed both Edinburgh's idea and Edinburgh's man.[13]

* The notice has been amended in pen and a note has been scrawled at the bottom: 'Badly printed. Lines too close together. Ungentlemanly paper – a new printer to be employ'd next time. The business of the company done in so bad a name.' The New River Company had its reputation to maintain and shoddily printed circulars might damage the brand.

In London, Braidwood started with a team of eighty full-timers based at thirteen stations, mostly former sailors – preferred, he said, because they were taught to obey orders and were used to day and night watches and because, as one newspaper put it, they had 'acquired the knack of keeping a steady footing'.

Of course, Braidwood's arrival didn't eliminate the scourge of fire in London: soon after his appointment, the old Houses of Parliament burned down, though Braidwood and his men did help to save Westminster Hall. But he and his teams soon acquired a reputation for bravery and efficiency; it was just that, as the city grew, there weren't enough of them. Braidwood himself was a charismatic figure and a man who liked to lead from the front, which is how he lost his life in 1861, directing operations at the disastrous Tooley Street fire. A building full of inflammable goods at Scovell's Warehouse, next to Cotton's Wharf on the south bank east of London Bridge, had caught fire one Saturday afternoon in June, and the blaze quickly spread along the bank of the river through other wharves and warehouses full of oil and tallow, sulphur, saltpetre and spices. The Thames itself was aflame, as burning oil and tallow flowed out across the water, and anchored ships were set alight.

Soon there were fourteen of Braidwood's fire engines at the scene, and others from parishes and private fire brigades maintained by factory-owners, not to mention 30,000 spectators packing the bridges and wharves, perched atop omnibuses, hanging from the lampposts at London Bridge station or dodging the burning flotsam in small boats on the water. Braidwood's floating fire engine arrived, but was unable to draw enough water to be effective because the tide was low and the river too shallow. The fire eventually destroyed properties covering eleven acres and burned for a fortnight, the worst in London since the Great Fire of 1666. Braidwood himself was killed on the first evening, when a wall collapsed on top of him; one account has him distributing nips of brandy to his tired men, another says he'd paused to wrap his neckerchief round a fireman's gashed hand.

The £2 million cost of the Tooley Street fire brought the insurance companies to their knees and one upshot was a select committee inquiry into London's fire service and a recommendation that firefighting in London should become a public responsibility. The insurance companies were reluctant to go on paying for it, and there was now an organisation, the Metropolitan Board of Works, capable of taking it over. So, in 1865, a Metropolitan Fire Brigade was established, subsuming both the parishes and the insurance companies and later the escape ladders operated by the Society for Protection of Life from Fire; the new brigade was paid for partly out of the rates and partly from a levy on the insurers.

By 1870 it had 378 firemen, fifty stations and 110 engines, twenty-five of them steam-driven – more than the old fire engine establishment, but still not enough. Its first chief was Captain Eyre Massey Shaw, an Irish soldier who, at thirty, had become Belfast's chief constable, only to be poached a year later, just as Braidwood had been, to become Braidwood's successor. Shaw, too, became famous – enough to merit a mention in Gilbert and Sullivan's *Iolanthe*, written in 1882, where the love-struck Fairy Queen asks 'Ah, Captain Shaw,/Type of true love kept under,/Could thy brigade/With cold cascade/Quench my great fire I wonder?' Shaw himself is said to have been in the stalls for the first night to hear himself immortalised in song. Gilbert probably had his tongue in his cheek when he wrote the lines: Shaw was a noted ladies' man who was cited in 1886 as a co-respondent in a divorce case.

Shaw's relationship with the water companies was sometimes testy. Constant supply was a long time coming, there were wide variations in mains pressure between the different companies and too often there simply wasn't enough water. Shaw and the board of works frequently pressed the companies for measures to make life easier for the brigade, such as depositing duplicates of turncock's water keys at local police stations, or distributing a schedule detailing when each set of mains was supposed to be full.[14] Shaw wanted to replace old-fashioned wooden fire plugs, which simply opened a hole in the main, with hydrants that came with a device to which a hose could be attached: the board agreed to pay for fitting them but it took years of wrangling to agree on their design.

He was an able man and an adept politician, and the companies were often on the back foot in their dealings with him. He had a platform and he knew how to use it – and whenever a public inquiry was held either into fire-fighting or water supply, you could be sure of Shaw, who would be there giving evidence and adding his powerful voice to the clamour from those arguing for constant supply, for the amalgamation of the companies and for public control of London's water.

18

Watering Capital

One hot day in July 1874, members of the Richmond vestry came to a meeting with samples of creatures they claimed to have found in their household cisterns, filled with water supplied by the Southwark & Vauxhall company. The event had all the hallmarks of a stunt aimed at the newspapers, who duly reported that the creatures included fish, eels and – in perhaps the first appearance in print of an enduring urban myth – what the vestry chairman Admiral Stopford declared was a baby crocodile, though others thought it was a lizard.[1]*

The aim of the exercise was to demonstrate that the S&V's water was dirty and inadequately filtered: the vestry was seeking to build a case against the company ahead of a forthcoming public inquiry. The upshot was the episode with which I began this book: the S&V's decision to cut off the entire town in January 1877. Neither the vestry nor the water company came out of it well, and the industry trade paper, the *Journal of Gas Lighting, Water Supply and Sanitary Reform*, called the whole business 'a fiasco'.[2] The affair – which had its farcical moments but must have been grim

---

* Stopford had served in the eastern Mediterranean, so may actually have seen a crocodile in Egypt.

for Richmond's residents – was a product of pig-headedness on both sides exacerbated by incompetence and bad luck.

As it happened, it coincided with another crisis that threatened the very survival of the Southwark & Vauxhall and of its sister company, the Grand Junction, and from that crisis the directors emerge with as little credit as they do from the Richmond affair. But this second crisis also demonstrated the value of the new Chadwickian system of inspection to which the water companies had been subjected, in the shape of the government auditor.

The full story of both crises is told here for the first time. Drawn from the archives and from the newspapers of the day, it shows how a group of men, typical of the capitalists who ran Victorian companies, thought and acted. Who were these men who showed such disdain for their customers and such care for their dividends, who questioned the science and fought government attempts to limit their freedoms (and those dividends)? How did they run their businesses?

The Richmond affair

In 1861 the Southwark & Vauxhall had taken over the small independent water company serving Richmond, and integrated it into the S&V network. The locals had not been happy. There had been complaints about the quality of their own water, so they had begun negotiations for a takeover not with the S&V but with the Grand Junction Waterworks. What they hadn't realised was that the Grand Junction and S&V shared a chairman, engineer, solicitor and several directors, and without asking the Richmond

folk, Sir William Clay and his colleagues had quietly sub-
stituted one purchaser for another. This mattered because
the S&V had the right to charge higher rates.[3]

As part of the takeover, the S&V went to Parliament for
a bill authorising it to extend its area of supply to Richmond.
The bill was opposed by the locals and was withdrawn, as
was a second bill in 1865. Opposition on both occasions was
led by a thrusting young solicitor called Charles Burt, who
lived in the town and worked for a City firm called Bircham, Drake and Co., who were solicitors to the New River
Company; Burt thus knew a thing or two about the water
business.[4]

Despite the initial froideur, the town and the company
seem to have rubbed along tolerably well until January
1870, when the historic Star and Garter Hotel at the top of
Richmond Hill was destroyed by a fire. Fire engines were
sent – but found no water in the mains. A man had to be
despatched on horseback to the S&V's pumping station at
Battersea, five miles away, to get the necessary pressure
applied. The water didn't appear until more than two
hours after the fire started.[5]

Then, two years later the S&V put up its prices, not
just in Richmond but across its whole area, by up to 25
per cent. Resentment in Richmond rose to a level at
which the vestry – of which Charles Burt was a member –
unanimously decided to ditch the company and start its
own waterworks instead. It offered to buy the S&V's network of pipes in the town, but the company refused to
sell. So the vestry applied to the Local Government
Board for a £28,000 loan to set up its own supply, and
began its campaign by claiming that there *still* wasn't
enough water in the mains at the top of Richmond Hill

to fight a fire after midnight: Sergeant Howard and the men of the parish fire brigade turned out at 1.15 in the morning, telegraphing Battersea to fire up the pumps as they did so, to demonstrate as much.[6]

Though municipal takeovers of water companies were becoming commonplace outside London, on this occasion the company determined to resist the vestry's plan because of the loss of revenue it would entail, and protested at what it called the 'confiscation' of its property.

The company lobbied the Local Government Board against a Richmond breakaway, and the board sent an inspector down to hold an inquiry – the inquiry was necessary in any case before the loan could be approved. A number of distinguished engineers gave evidence in support of the vestry's scheme. One whose water also came from the S&V claimed it was indeed dirty: 'When the water was 18 inches deep in the bath it was impossible to see the bottom,' he claimed.[7]

When the inspector approved the vestry scheme despite the company's protests in December 1875, the S&V directors announced they would take what they called 'active measures' to protect the company's interests. Privately they had calculated that the move would cost them the considerable sum of £5,200 a year in revenue.[8] They sought an injunction against the vestry but failed to get one: their position was shaky because they had no Parliamentary authority to supply Richmond. They tried once more to get an act to remedy that, but failed yet again.

Meanwhile, the vestry bought the site of a former brewery next to the river and began digging an artesian well. By December 1876, it was promising its new supply would be ready by 30 March 1877, and some 2,200 householders – virtually the whole town – had apparently signed up to take it. The S&V feared that, once Richmond's own water was available, the locals would refuse to pay their S&V water rates, which were collected in arrears. It was not, it decided, prepared to supply water for three months to Richmond with no real prospect of getting any money: consumers were already threatening non-payment.[9] The *Journal of Gas Lighting*, which tended to side with the water companies in any dispute, sympathised with the S&V's directors. The S&V was perfectly justified in treating 'a particularly cantankerous authority with the severity they have justly merited', the editor wrote at the height of the dispute, though he felt sorry for local residents, 'who may, in a fortnight's time, be obliged to pay threepence per pail for water taken from the Thames at Richmond Bridge'.[10] All this helps to explain, but not to justify, what the company did next.

On 14 December, its engineer told his directors that the vestry's new artesian well was in trouble: the diggers had struck water 190 feet down in such quantities that the well was flooded and part of the brick lining had collapsed. On the same day the company told its shareholders at their half-yearly general meeting that it doubted the vestry would find enough water to supply the town. So the S&V knew the likely consequences for local residents of the decision it was taking.

But it chose to go ahead regardless and announced it would cut off Richmond's water from 13 January 1877. The engineer wrote the Richmond vestry a letter, using the lack of parliamentary sanction as an excuse for cutting off the supply, and improbably claiming: 'It is far from the wish of my directors or myself that anything should be done that may be distasteful either to the vestry or to the inhabitants.'[11]

No doubt he was advised on the wording of his letter by the Southwark & Vauxhall's new solicitor. The company had just fired its old lawyers and instead appointed Bircham's, who advised the New River, and Bircham's gave the business to their junior partner, none other than Richmond vestryman Charles Burt. Astonishingly, and despite a glaring conflict of interest, Burt continued both to attend vestry meetings and to advise the S&V on Richmond affairs up until February 1877. Fellow members of the vestry weren't impressed. On 30 November 1875, there was what one newspaper described as 'a sharp discussion' about Burt's position. Though he had promised to take no part in debates about the water supply, some thought his presence would enable him to pick up useful intelligence: 'I don't think Mr Burt ought to sit here to collect stones to throw at us afterwards,' one member said. Burt claimed in his defence that he had always been opposed to the vestry's plan to start its own waterworks – a claim rather undermined when someone pointed out that, in 1871, he had been a member of a committee that came down in favour of it. Remarkably, the episode did nothing to damage Burt's reputation in the long term; he ended up a Richmond alderman, with a knighthood.[12]

The S&V's move threw the vestry into a panic. It was frantically laying new mains, but with its new well not ready, its bluff had been called. On the Monday morning it produced a hastily printed handbill, regretting that 'continued heavy rain' had delayed connecting up households to its new pipes, but making no mention of the problems with its well.[13] The vestry's water committee met thirteen times in three weeks. It considered going to law but was advised that the S&V's lack of an act also meant there were no grounds on which the vestry could insist on a supply. But it did find that a well sunk years earlier by the old Richmond waterworks was still serviceable and could supply 20 gallons per head per day. Unfortunately a house had been built on top of it . . . so the vestry bought the house, and began installing steam engines and pumps.[14]

Despite the vestry's efforts, Richmond's residents were soon up in arms, because there was nowhere near enough water to go round. Only 600 out of 2,000 homes were connected, as the work of laying the new mains had been delayed by the heavy rains and there were standpipes in the streets. A fleet of watercarts was distributing the stuff free, and the town had pressed a motley collection of sources into service, including an old aqueduct supposed to have supplied Richmond Palace in the time of Queen Elizabeth.[15]*

The *Journal of Gas Lighting*'s editor decided to see for himself what was going on, and paid Richmond a visit. One woman told him she had to beg water from neighbours with private wells. He noted the work of connecting houses to the mains was going very slowly, and blamed the British workman and his 'usual characteristics'. The labourers, he claimed, with rather ponderous humour, sat in their trenches apparently expecting the coils of lead service pipes to connect themselves. 'They used their pickaxes in a way which suggested they were afraid of inflicting pain on the roadway.'

---

* The *Journal* criticised the S&V for failing to offer the vestry a deal, evidently unaware that the company had offered to sell its pipes to the vestry and been refused.

The editor was in the town to report on a public meeting of ratepayers in the Freemasons Hall of the Greyhound Hotel. He was not the only reporter there, attracted by the prospect of fireworks. They weren't disappointed. The meeting was crowded and evidently rowdy – or, in the language of Victorian journalism, the accommodation was 'taxed to its utmost capacity' and 'the whole proceedings from first to last were of a very tumultuous character'. It became clear the town was in fact deeply divided on the water issue, and that whatever political support the vestry had originally enjoyed for setting up its own supply was rapidly eroding.

The meeting passed not only a resolution condemning the S&V, but also another demanding the 'ample supply of pure water' from the vestry that had been promised, 'the sources of supply at present relied upon having proved absolutely insufficient, and having occasioned much inconvenience and distress'. The local doctor, who insisted on the inclusion of the word 'distress', and warned there was a risk of epidemic disease, was attacked by a vestry partisan who said he was 'ashamed' of him.[16]

The vestry negotiated with the Thames Conservancy to take more water from the river: because it was not a metropolitan water company, the ban on taking water from the tidal Thames and the obligation to filter it did not apply. But in February the *Journal* reported that Richmond's water supply was still 'of the scantiest, and the quality of the water must be regarded as of doubtful nature . . . Some of the water distributed is described as in colour like that of the "Yellow Sea".'[17]

In April, with warmer weather coming, the Southwark & Vauxhall's engineer met two town representatives, neither of them members of the vestry, who presumably came to ask the company to turn its supply back on; the following month the vicar and parishioners of Holy Trinity added their voices to the chorus of discontent. The company offered the town a bulk supply, to alleviate the shortages; the vestry turned down the offer.[18]

Richmond's water troubles dragged on through the summer and into the following winter, provoking much commentary in the newspapers. It was a perfect opportunity for critics of both the water companies and the vestries to mount the grandstand. The Conservative *Pall Mall Gazette* – whose readership included just the kind of affluent mid-Victorian gentlemen who took shares in water companies and served on suburban vestries – thought both sides were at fault. The Southwark & Vauxhall had behaved high-handedly, and demonstrated the case, if not for public ownership of water, then for tighter regulation. As for the Richmond vestrymen: 'If they had stood on their dignity a little less and thought of the convenience of their constituents a little more, all that has happened might have been avoided . . .' They had been too angry to do the sensible thing and negotiate with the company. 'A vestryman who is willing to go thirsty and unwashed rather than negotiate with a water company which he thinks has behaved ill may be almost a hero. But a vestryman who is willing to let his constituents go thirsty and unwashed . . . has a more questionable title to our admiration.'[19]

Not until 8 January 1878 was the Richmond vestry at last in a position to give a daily supply of water to the whole parish. It had taken almost exactly a year.[20]

The S&V hadn't given up completely. The following month, showing quite spectacular insensitivity to the feeling in the town, the company appointed a temporary collector to try to bring in £600 of unpaid rates for water supplied before Christmas 1876. A handbill was printed, optimistically declaring: 'The directors have little doubt that the general desire must be to properly discharge this just liability.' The experiment was a failure and the collector was withdrawn in May.[21]

Richmond continued to run its own water supply for nearly a century, though in 1883 it eventually conceded that it couldn't get enough water from its own wells and contracted with the Southwark & Vauxhall to supply extra water that – oh, the irony! – was cheaper than Richmond's own.[22] The Richmond Borough Waterworks was eventually taken over by the Metropolitan Water Board in 1965. By then most of the water it distributed was properly treated, and indeed much came in the form of a bulk supply from the board; but some still came unfiltered from the Thames, and was used for watering Kew Gardens.[23]

Engineering investigation

From first to last the affair was mishandled by the S&V as well as by the vestry. But perhaps the company's directors were distracted by the alarming discovery while all this was going on of an enormous black hole in their accounts.

In 1876 the S&V and the Grand Junction still shared a chairman and several directors and a chief engineer, Joseph Quick. As with the Simpsons and the Mylnes, Quick belonged to an engineering dynasty: his father (also called Joseph) had been engineer to the Southwark company, and on his father's death in 1844 he had succeeded him, shortly before the merger with the Vauxhall company. Six years later he became consulting engineer to the Grand Junction as well. Between them the two companies, in 1875, paid him the considerable salary of £2,200 a year, and he lived in style in a many roomed Georgian pile called Cross Deep House next to the Thames at Twickenham. He was highly experienced and a consultant to waterworks around Britain and the world – in Amsterdam, Antwerp, Beirut, St Petersburg and Odessa.[24]

Quick was talented and innovative. His achievements included several improvements to pumping engines, and, in 1845, he helped Charles Dickens's brother-in-law, the engineer Henry Austin, design and patent 'duplex-wheel' railway rolling stock so that locomotives and carriages could run on both standard gauge lines and Brunel's Great Western broad gauge. I have tracked down a photograph of him dating from 1880, when he was aged seventy-one, which shows a cheery-looking fellow with a bulbous nose, whiskers, plenty of grey hair above a receding forehead and a bluff demeanour.[25]

London's growth and the theoretical requirement to implement constant supply meant Quick was overseeing a huge programme of capital investment at the Grand Junction and S&V. Both companies had built new intakes with extensive facilities at Hampton in the 1850s, and had extended them since. In the mid-1870s the Grand Junction was building a new reservoir at Shoot-up Hill in Kilburn, installing new pumping engines at Kew Bridge and at its existing reservoir on Campden Hill, and new boilers at Hampton. The S&V was building new reservoirs and a pumping station at Nunhead in Peckham, and rebuilding its reservoirs and filter-beds at Battersea.

Both companies were paying thousands of pounds a month on account to contractors. All received regular payments, certified by Quick and authorised by the directors.[26]

The largest contracts had been awarded without competitive tender. Quick and the chairman would agree on the need for some extension to the works; the proposal would be approved by the board and, at the same meeting, Quick would then produce not only a plan and specification for the work but also the price he had already taken the precaution of getting from the contractor; all the directors needed to do was nod it through.[27] He would sometimes show the contractor's tender first to his friend John Hawkshaw, who we met in Chapter 11. 'It will be in every way desirable for the company to accept their offer,' Hawkshaw reassuringly said of one quote.[28]

But in 1875 this cosy state of affairs was disrupted after two men smelt a rat. One was a director of both companies called Henry Whiting, the other was the government auditor, Allen Stoneham. In July Whiting had started poking around in Quick's affairs. First he looked into the running of both engineering departments: how many staff did they have, and what were their duties? And then, apparently convinced there was something fishy about the contracts Quick had negotiated, he investigated the contractor's bills for work at Nunhead and Shoot-up Hill and compared them with the original specs.[29] He found nothing amiss, but nonetheless both companies' directors decided to alter their arrangements with Quick, a sign perhaps that they were losing confidence in him. He agreed to retire from the Grand Junction – where his assistant, Alexander Fraser, had in any case been doing most of the work – with a pension of £500 and an agreement to give the company the benefit of his advice and experience whenever they wanted it.[30] At the S&V, two senior staff in the engineer's department were let go and Quick's son, another Joseph, was also given notice 'in his present capacity' as assistant engineer, and instead the partnership of Messrs Joseph Quick & Son were appointed engineers to the company at £1,250, saving the S&V £600 a year.[31]

Whiting's interest in Quick may have been prompted by the fact that Stoneham had also become concerned about the engineer's financial management. The auditor's suspicions had been aroused when, in March 1875, he asked to see the Grand Junction's contracts with the pumping engine manufacturers Harvey's of Hayle, on the basis of which the payments authorised by Quick were made. The contracts, he was told, were not kept at the office but 'would be produced on the settlement of the balance with the contractors'. He was fobbed off again in September 1875, but, in March 1876, when he was told a further £10,000 was due to Harvey's, he refused to pass the accounts without seeing the contracts; at which point it emerged that no proper contracts existed. Worse, it seemed the company had paid out more to Harvey's for 'new works' than the original tenders specified. It was a similar story at the S&V. And Stoneham discovered that the Grand Junction was paying some of its suppliers – including at least one firm of which Joseph Quick was a director – 15 per cent more than other water companies.[32]

Capital confusion

As if all that weren't enough, Stoneham also realised that Quick had been wrongly classifying revenue expenditure as capital investment. That sounds arcane – who but an accountant would worry about it? – but in fact it was vitally important.

Harvey's – and to some extent other contractors – were doing two kinds of work. They were constructing new plant and machinery; and they were repairing and maintaining existing plant. The first represented long-term investment by the Southwark & Vauxhall and the Grand Junction; the second was part of the water companies' annual running costs. As in any business, long-term investments were defined as 'capital' expenditure, which contributed to the company's asset value; everything else was 'revenue' expenditure, which was set against trading profits.

Victorian investors had known the importance of correctly distinguishing the two at least since the days of George Hudson, the Railway King. This colossus of the railroads was the dominant figure in the railway mania of the 1840s, when hundreds of new railway companies were authorised and share prices soared in a classic stock market bubble. Hudson was immensely rich, an MP and a former Lord Mayor of York. At one point his companies controlled more than a quarter of all Britain's railways, most of them converging on York. Investors scrambled for shares, which paid first-rate dividends from the very beginning.

But he was also a swindler whose empire came crashing down at the end of the decade. Hudson's frauds and faults were many. He sold his shares back to his own companies at inflated prices. He put into his own pocket money intended for paying contractors. He used newly raised capital to pay existing shareholders' dividends.

And he also cooked the books. Running costs on Hudson's railways were lower than those of his rivals; profits and shareholders' dividends were correspondingly higher. How did he do it? By booking revenue expenses as capital expenditure, which did not show up as costs in the equivalent of the profit and loss account. It was, of course, unsustainable in the long run: if the real operating costs were much higher than appeared, and large amounts of cash were also leaving the business in the form of dividend payments, sooner or later the enterprise would run out of money: the gravy train would hit the buffers.

When his manipulations were revealed, Hudson was disgraced and effectively bankrupt. Many of his shareholders, meanwhile, lost large amounts of money. One consequence was the Companies Clauses Act of 1845, which made at least one of Hudson's abuses illegal by forbidding a company to use money raised for capital purposes to pay dividends. Another was that people like Stoneham – whose previous job had been in the Board of Trade's railway department – were on the lookout for similar dodges in other industries, including water. One of Stoneham's jobs was to certify each water company's share capital and the amount invested over the years in plant and equipment: the two figures needed to be roughly equal, to demonstrate that money raised as share capital had been properly spent on reservoirs and pumps and other good things, and not siphoned off.*

This principle had been established in 1852, as a document in the Grand Junction's files makes clear. That year, following the passage of the Metropolis Water Act, the company put before Parliament a private bill authorising it to raise the capital necessary to meet the obligations imposed by the new law. The bill was scrutinised (along with similar acts from the other companies) by a special committee of MPs, and the company had to produce detailed figures spelling out everything it had spent since its foundation.

'As the present committee seem to consider that their province is to protect the interest of the public [evidently still a novel idea in 1852] almost without considering the just rights of the companies,' counsel was told, 'they have adopted the idea of allowing to the companies as capital only such a sum as they can shew to be the cost of works as actually existing and in use.'[33]

Whether deliberately or inadvertently, Stoneham realised, Quick had been allocating spending on new plant *and* on repairs and renewals largely to the capital account at both companies. Much of the money he spent with Harvey's was not for new engines at all, but for refurbishing existing ones. As a result, both companies' profits were artificially inflated, thereby giving the directors more money, on paper at least, to pay out in dividends.

---

* Thus Stoneham certified the S&V's capital in March 1875 as £1.34 million in shares and £430,000 in loans, a total of £1.77 million. He also certified expenditure of £1.75 million on 'the works and undertaking' (LMA, ACC/2558/SV/1/182, 31 March 1875).

Quick's practice also exaggerated the value of the company's assets. In the financial world this kind of artificial inflation of a company's asset or capital value is known by an apt piece of jargon: it is called 'watering capital' or 'watering stock'. The term is supposed to have originated with an American cattle driver and financier called Daniel Drew, who made his cattle drink large amounts of water before they got to market to make them deceptively heavy. When he switched careers to Wall Street, he began defrauding investors in much the same way, by issuing stocks and shares in companies with a much larger nominal value than the value of their underlying assets.

Joseph Quick's faulty book-keeping at the Grand Junction and the S&V had the same effect as watering stock: as well as inflating profits, it made the value of the companies' physical assets appear greater than it really was. All in all it was very poor accounting practice. And it was criminal.

Did the directors of the Grand Junction and the Southwark & Vauxhall fully appreciate what Quick had been doing, and quite what a financial mess he had got them into? It seems from their reaction to a letter Stoneham wrote, alerting them to the issue, that they did not. It is just possible to discern their sense of shock beneath the customarily impersonal language of their board minutes. At the Grand Junction the letter was read out to the court of directors. 'Whereupon the court desire the attendance of Mr Quick the engineer,' the minutes say, 'and request him to give them information as to the state of Messrs Harvey & Co's accounts . . . to facilitate early consideration of this matter.' A week later they called a special meeting and 'had Mr Quick before them'. They concluded that 'very large sums included in these accounts have had reference not to the construction of new engines but to the repair of engine work generally'.[34] Equally unsettling, Quick produced additional invoices from Harvey's for more than £10,000 that the directors had not been told about and had not been expecting.

Eventually Stoneham concluded that £55,000 at the Grand Junction and £33,000 at the S&V had been wrongly allocated to capital and needed to be reassigned, which would have a dramatic effect on future profits. And the newly discovered liabilities to Harvey's (which eventually totalled £19,800 at the Grand Junction and £10,700 at the S&V) would also need to be booked as a charge against revenue. For companies like the Grand Junction and the S&V, these were very large sums indeed: the Grand Junction's turnover was only £115,000. Dividends would suffer badly.

Meanwhile, Stoneham was refusing to certify the accounts and neither company could pay a dividend. A week before the Grand Junction's half-yearly general meeting of shareholders, this was, at the very least, embarrassing – and Quick's position was now untenable. On 25 May 1876, he resigned from the Southwark & Vauxhall, and he resigned from the Grand Junction on 7 June, the day of the general meeting. The chairman of both companies, Arthur Clay, swiftly followed him out.[35]*

---

* Quick's S&V resignation letter was exceedingly brief and looks to have been hurriedly written. The company's formal reply notes that he has offered his resignation on account of 'the relations now existing between yourself and one of the members of this board': he must have conveyed that orally, for the phrase is not in his letter.

Feet of Clay

Why did Quick act as he did?

The most charitable explanation is that he was very busy building things and lost control of the details. After all, he wasn't getting any younger: he was sixty-seven, and may have been starting to show his age.

A less charitable and much more damaging explanation is that he conspired with successive chairmen to break the law in order to keep the companies' dividends artificially high. That's certainly what he told a committee of investigation set up by Grand Junction shareholders.

Quick had served three chairmen. The first, Sir William Clay, we have already met. He remained chairman of both companies until his death at the age of seventy-seven in 1869. He was described by Henry Whiting, who had served on the board with him, as 'virtually the dictator of the concern' whose 'confidential adviser' had been Quick and whose knowledge and standing in the company made it impossible for the other directors to oppose him.[36]

Sir William was succeeded by James Clay, his cousin and also an MP. James, in his youth, had been a dandy and notorious womaniser, who had voyaged in his yacht round the Mediterranean on a tour of reputedly spectacular debauchery accompanied by the young Benjamin Disraeli. His portrait, bejewelled and ringleted, hangs in the entrance hall at Disraeli's home at Hughenden. James

---

(cont.) The member of the board was almost certainly Whiting (LMA, ACC/2558/SV/1/192, Letter book Jelly to Quick, 31 May 1876).

Clay, too, died in harness at the Grand Junction and S&V in 1873: his feeble signature on the board minutes bears witness to his frailty and ill-health. Perhaps his youthful debauchery had finally caught up with him.[37]*

The successor to these two men, one old, the other ill, was Sir William Clay's thirty-one-year old younger son, Arthur Temple Felix Clay, an occasional barrister, a part-time painter and a man with no obvious qualifications (beyond his parentage) for running a water company. The National Portrait Gallery has a studio photograph of him taken in 1861, when he would have been nineteen. Tall and thin, he looks a rather languorous youth. A later chalk sketch by his artist friend Samuel Cockerell (whose father, the architect Samuel Pepys Cockerell, had been one of the Grand Junction's founding directors), shows him with a luxuriant full beard, sitting in a chair with his head resting on his hand, deep in thought.[38]

He matured into an unsuccessful businessman whose career was pretty much over before he turned forty, and a second-rate artist. Later still he became an inveterate writer of letters to newspapers on subjects ranging from the sanitary condition of Charterhouse School, where his sons were being educated, to the underfed children of the London poor. He was a champion of free school meals – though in a bracing Victorian way, he was very keen that they only went to children who were genuinely starving, believing as he did that many working-class parents were too idle or too irresponsible to feed their children properly and that the state should not encourage this behaviour.

* Despite his friendship with the Tory Disraeli, he was a political Liberal, as well as being an authority on whist.

In 1911 he wrote a book explaining why socialism was a bad idea.[39]

In his evidence to the shareholders' committee, Quick said the practice of charging the cost of Harvey's repairs to capital had been started by Sir William Clay – because the company could not afford both to account for Harvey's charges properly and to maintain its dividends. The policy had been confirmed by James Clay, and when James in turn died, Quick said, he 'brought the matter in August 1875 to the notice of the present chairman', Arthur Clay.

The committee of investigation commissioned a professional accountant to look at the Grand Junction's books. He confirmed that, even though the company enjoyed a gross profit margin after operating expenses and interest of 51 per cent of turnover and should have been awash with cash, it had indeed for several years been paying out more than it could afford in dividends to its shareholders.[40]

One man to whom this would not have come as a surprise was the Grand Junction's secretary, E. O. Coe. Ernest Coe (the O stood for Oswald) had been bred to the role. His father, W. M. Coe, had been the Grand Junction's secretary since 1813, shortly after the company was founded. Ernest succeeded him and held the post until his retirement at the age of eighty in 1888: it wasn't only chief engineers who established long-lived dynasties.

In his youth, Ernest had published a book of lithographs showing the gothic porches of four English cathedrals and sometimes described himself as an architect. But after his youthful dalliance with art, he matured into a hard-working Victorian who lived 'above the shop' at the Grand Junction's Mayfair offices.[41] Only late in life did he return to intellectual pursuits, publishing Victor Hugo's tragedy

Angelo, 'rendered into English blank verse with explanatory notes and some remarks on French dramatic poetry, past and present'.[42]

He was very good friends with his opposite number, Charles Robinson, at the S&V: they addressed one another as 'Dear Charles' and 'Dear Ernest' in their correspondence, whereas almost everyone else was 'Dear Sir' – a rare exception was their close colleague 'Dear Mr Quick'. Robinson was eventually sacked when it emerged that he had put his son on the company payroll as a junior clerk while the boy was still at school.[43]* It is hard to imagine Coe attracting such an accusation: he was far too clever.

Coe had shares in numerous gas and water companies, including the Southwark & Vauxhall. He also audited some of them: shareholders preferred one of their own to audit the company books rather than a professional accountant, because accountants' main business was dealing with bankruptcies, and if a firm engaged a professional, then observers might conclude it was about to go bust. He was something of a bully, and could be magnificently patronising when he chose. He was efficient and diplomatic in his dealings with his directors, but he treated the Grand Junction's customers with suppressed disdain

* Robinson claimed he had just been giving the boy handwriting lessons. In a world without typewriters or photocopiers, let alone computers, legible handwriting was an important accomplishment: many professional men expected to start out somewhere as junior clerks, copying letters and documents. Generally, they were well-trained. The Southwark & Vauxhall and Grand Junction papers are a pleasure to read, with the exception of minutes copied by one clerk at the S&V, whose spidery scrawl is virtually illegible. Perhaps that was Robinson Junior?

unless they had a title, in which case he was oily and sycophantic. He could be withering to errant employees.[44]

In April 1875, shortly before the Grand Junction was engulfed in crisis, he wrote a thirty-page memorandum on 'the duties of the chief officer'. It is a handbook of mid-Victorian management, which also amounts to a rather self-satisfied self-portrait. The chief officer, Coe wrote, must have 'a special aptitude for organization and control, a sound and rapid judgment and a power of resource for many sudden emergencies . . . great firmness united with mildness and equanimity of disposition, a strict sense of justice and above all a discriminative knowledge of that human nature with which the managing officer is being brought constantly into contact.'[45]

Coe – though he was wily enough to escape the censure levelled at Quick – knew perfectly well what had been going on. The evidence for this is in his own hand. In November 1875, he had scribbled a note to one of the Grand Junction's directors, William Higgins, who later became chairman. The note is a private letter, containing information that he asks should not yet be shared with the other directors.

'I merely jot these matters down for your consideration,' Coe observes blandly, before revealing to Higgins (and this is well before the shareholders' committee started to investigate) that between October 1870 and October 1873 the Grand Junction's dividend payments had been far higher than the company's profits could justify. His figures are different in detail to those of the shareholder committee's accountant but they tell the same story. Coe blames James Clay. 'And I must say,' he writes to Higgins, 'he persevered in the above course with his eyes open, for

I was time after time pointing out to him the evil [illegible]. I believe what he dreaded was rather the loss of popularity than the loss of dividend by pursuing a wiser course.[46]

Coe here sounds rather like Quick, protesting that none of it was his fault. But even if you think Quick and Coe's attempt to shift the blame on to a dead man was a dishonourable one, it does look very much as if James Clay, and probably Sir William Clay, had knowingly undermined the financial stability of both companies for fear of the backlash if they cut the dividend – and then colluded with the chief engineer and one of the company secretaries to cook the books. Their successor, Arthur Clay, did nothing to stop the practice.

Mad hatter

Once again, as with the East London company and the 1866 cholera outbreak, it is the failure of the company's directors to grasp what was going on or to challenge it that is especially striking. There are shades here of the prodigious fraudster Augustus Melmotte in Anthony Trollope's novel *The Way We Live Now*, which in 1876 had recently been published in serial form and which satirises the Victorian habit of appointing nonentities as company directors. They are mostly dupes, who understand nothing of the business for which they are supposedly responsible; the scheming Melmotte has no difficulty exploiting their ignorance and indolence.

The directors of the Grand Junction and the Southwark & Vauxhall were less idle than Melmotte's, but it's clear that at least some of them lacked diligence, and that both boards were asleep at the wheel. For the most part they simply rubber-stamped the decisions of the chairman and the chief engineer. That might have been fine when the 'dictatorial' and thoroughly competent Sir William was in charge. It was no good at all when other members of the Clay clan stepped into Sir William's shoes – particularly Arthur, who was way out of his depth from the very start.

Many of the companies' directors owed their seats to the fact that they were family. Arthur Clay's fellows on the boards of the Grand Junction, the S&V or both included at one time or another his older brother, his sister's husband, and his wife's brother Frederick (a member of the Barclay brewing family). There was also Frederick Wigan, a Southwark hop factor and railway director, whose father-in-law was Arthur's great-uncle and whose brother-in-law was the solicitor to both companies. And there were the brothers Noel and Henry Whiting, whose uncle Frank had also been a director of the Grand Junction.

Though both companies were joint-stock enterprises with publicly traded shares, they were still run much like the partnerships that predominated in British commerce and industry. Outside the railways, whose sheer size meant responsibility had to be devolved, many businesses were only just beginning to employ professional managers. Control was in the hands of small groups of men whose own practical experience of business – if they had any – was likely to be in partnerships, and who trusted one another, often because they were related.

The same names crop up elsewhere in businesses connected with the Clays. Henry Whiting, Arthur Clay, Frederick Wigan, the engineer Joseph Quick and Quick's favourite building contractor, John Aird, served on the boards of two gas companies in Brazil – one chaired by Sir William Clay – and a gas and water company in Sardinia.[47] And Arthur was also the founding chairman of the Odessa Waterworks in what was then Russia, a disastrous venture that began supplying water from the River Dniester in 1873 through a 26-mile pipeline. The company's directors may sound familiar: they included Arthur's brother; his brothers-in-law, Frederick and Robert Barclay; and Frederick Wigan. Joseph Quick & Son were the engineers. E. O. Coe was one of the auditors. In 1876 – the same year as he had to resign as chairman of the Grand Junction and Southwark & Vauxhall following the exposure of Quick's malfeasance – Arthur resigned as Odessa chairman after the board concluded that 'the enterprise can only be considered a dead failure'.[48]*

---

* When it was clear things were going wrong, Clay travelled to Odessa and St Petersburg in the autumn of 1874. We know he was there not only from a note to the secretary of the Southwark & Vauxhall excusing himself for five or six weeks, but also from the board minutes of the Grand Junction, which record his absence on urgent business in St Petersburg on 7 October, and because the public inspector's inquiry at Richmond had to be postponed as Clay was reportedly in Odessa (LMA, ACC/2558/SV/1/180, Clay to Robinson, 3 October 1874; ACC/2558/GJ/1/14/1, Court minutes, 7 October 1874). Once in Russia, he may have linked up with Robert Barclay, whose passport, preserved at the London Metropolitan Archives, shows he travelled out in September via Berlin, and also visited both Odessa and St Petersburg. The brewer Barclay, one of whose best-selling lines was Russian Imperial Stout, was given leave to remain in the country until 29 March 1875 (LMA, ACC/2305/1/1546).

The one director of the S&V and Grand Junction who emerges with credit is Henry Whiting.

*

The Whiting family lived scattered around Lavender Hill, then a semi-rural neighbourhood popular with other wealthy capitalists. They owned £45,000-worth of shares in the S&V, and others in the Grand Junction. The patriarch of the family was Matthew, a Justice of the Peace and the son of a Rotherhithe sugar refiner, 'living on dividends'. Old Matthew's son, Noel, unmarried and still living with his parents in 1871 at the age of forty-eight, was a 'colonial broker' – that too might mean a sugar importer. He inherited the family nest egg: when he died childless in 1903, the last survivor of his generation, he left the truly enormous sum of £650,000.[49]

His older brother, Henry, was described in 1861 as a merchant dealing in silk plush. This was the material they covered top hats with – it came from France and appears to have had no other use – and a top hat was an essential piece of Victorian gentlemen's equipment, so it was a good trade. Even so, Henry is unlikely to have accumulated a fortune of £143,000 by the time of his death in 1894 from importing hat stuffs alone. Much of his income must have come from his investments. He was also a notable philanthropist, who gave large sums to good causes, in particular brave and injured policemen and their families.[50]*

---

* For seventeen years, until his death, Whiting gave generously to the Metropolitan Police Orphanage Fund and was its 'first subscriber' (*The Times*, 9 August 1888; *Annual Report* 1894). He also gave to other police charities, sometimes secretly (*The Times*, 22 February

Given his connection with the hat business, he may have been the Henry Whiting, 'hatter's furrier' of Southwark Bridge Road, who in 1845 was granted a patent 'for certain improvements in machinery or apparatus for shaping the brims of hats'.[51]

Henry was assiduous and principled, if frequently tactless, with an obsessive's eye for detail. He later claimed to have spent three or four days a week on water company business, the only director to put in anything like that much time. After years making little impact, he suddenly 'woke up' around 1874 – perhaps he'd been reading Trollope and resolved to do better. He was determined to root out inefficiency and any hints of corruption, but, nerdy and wordy as he was, he sometimes tried his colleagues' patience by droning on too long at board meetings.[52]

It was Whiting who, in 1874, had discovered the S&V secretary Charles Robinson's wrongdoing. Then, in 1875, he forced the resignation of the solicitors to both companies because he thought they were overcharging. One ruse that especially incensed him had to do with a public

---

(cont.) 1895) and to the families of officers killed in the course of their duties, especially in Ireland (*The Times*, 16 September 1887). He also had a controlling streak. Before his death, he established a £30,000 trust fund to go to his youngest child, Juliette, on her marriage, and then to her children, provided she wed with the consent of her mother and two brothers. If they didn't approve, then the money was to go to police charities. In 1902, at the age of thirty-five, Juliette married the sixty-year old Major-General Sir Alfred Turner, a friend of her father, but her surviving brother refused consent; she went to court to try to overturn the terms of the trust but lost. The Metropolitan and City Police Orphanage got the money instead (*Daily Telegraph*, 30 November 1907).

inquiry the lawyers attended. In the past they had charged the S&V £7 a day for 'perusing' the minutes of hearings like this, and 10 shillings for making a copy. After Whiting's protests, they had agreed to abandon the perusing charge . . . but were now charging £7 for the copy.[53]

Whiting was a maverick, and when he became chairman of the S&V after Arthur Clay's resignation, the role didn't suit him at all. He got into furious rows with his fellow directors, and his conduct of company general meetings was little short of disastrous: he was commendably frank, but usually had to be publicly corrected by colleagues or shareholders, who often objected to something he said. He was idealistic, obsessive, and prone to imagining conspiracies. Maybe, if he really was a hatter, he had a touch of the madness that afflicted Lewis Carroll's character.

*

Victorian capitalism was often an intensely personal affair. In modern companies, many of the directors are also the concern's most senior managers; in Victorian water companies, all the directors were non-executives. They were also shareholders, answerable to their fellow 'proprietors', and, in Victorian Britain, proprietors expected to be left alone by government to do pretty much what they liked with their property. They had put their money to work and expected a decent return on it, and they resented anything that got in the way by adversely affecting their dividends. E. O. Coe was privately scathing about the 1871 water act, mainly because it meant the companies were obliged to spend money on expensive infrastructure that he thought would never make a profit.[54]

Proprietors were often suspicious not only of the government but also of their own directors, if they thought the board might be putting the long-term interests of the company ahead of its shareholders' pockets. Proprietors expected all available profits to be divided among them each year. They complained about money set aside in reserve funds or to cover contingencies, and some companies – such as the shipping firm P&O from the late 1870s – resorted to 'secret' reserve funds in which especially high profits were squirrelled away to avoid paying them out to shareholders. In the 1840s, the railways had begun to appreciate the good sense of setting money aside to cover the eventual replacement of worn-out assets, such as locomotives and rolling stock; but in 1851 none of the London water companies had a depreciation reserve.[55]*

All this helps to explain the cavalier callousness with which the S&V directors acted in Richmond when they thought their interests were threatened, and why the Clays and their colleagues had no inhibitions about accounting shortcuts that allowed them to keep the dividends up. It is significant that the shareholders' committee

---

* One shareholder in the Bombay Gas Company in 1869 complained that setting up depreciation funds was 'robbing' shareholders. Another in the immensely profitable Imperial Continental Gas Association complained, in 1866, that the company's depreciation fund 'was benefiting shareholders *in posse* at the expense of those *in esse*', and another, in 1868, said: 'The principle seems to be to place, half year by half year, a large portion of the profits to some fund which possibly may benefit the grandchildren of the gentlemen who are now present' – a reminder that mid-Victorian capitalism was often a family affair (*JGL*, XVIII, pp. 345–6, 11 May 1869, XVII, pp. 872–3, 8 December 1868, XIX, pp. 876–7, 6 December 1870).

that investigated the financial skulduggery at the Grand Junction did not condemn it: condemnation would have meant admitting that a policy from which they had themselves benefited was flawed.

What Joseph Quick had done was not just poor accounting practice. Thanks to him, money raised over several years in the form of new share capital had not all been spent on fixed plant, as it should have been, but had been diverted into keeping profits and therefore dividends artificially high. In effect, the company had been paying dividends out of capital, and as Allen Stoneham pointed out, that was in breach of the Companies Clauses Act. Yet despite both companies' disregard for the law, no punitive action was taken, just as no action had been taken against the East London in 1866 or the Southwark & Vauxhall in 1870 for allowing unfiltered water into their mains.

Stoneham allowed both companies to spread the repayments from capital to revenue over five years, and they were suitably grateful. The Grand Junction directors believed this would give them 'ample time for setting matters right without undue pressure on the shareholders' – in other words, there would still be some money available to pay out in dividends, albeit reduced (at the S&V at one point the dividend fell to just 2 per cent).[56]

But there seems to have been little political appetite for tougher action. The 1852 act for instance gave the government power to fine companies £200 for a failure to supply clean and wholesome water, and £100 a month thereafter if they persisted. No fine had ever been imposed.[57] The government had tools at its disposal, but chose not to use them.

Why? In this case it may have been unwilling to jeopardise the financial health of companies with such a vital infrastructure role. But it may also have been a question of class solidarity. MPs were themselves overwhelmingly members of the investing class, and would be predisposed to cut fellow share-owners some slack.

In time the finances of both companies improved, though it was touch and go for a while. The Grand Junction transformed its position by the simple expedient of collecting the water rates in advance. It meant a tremendous boost to cash flow, as well as reducing bad debts and losses from absconding tenants, but the S&V didn't think it would be possible in the poorer district south of the river.[58]

As for legal action – though the authorities didn't act, the S&V did. It decided to sue Quick. The problem was what to sue for: it could not accuse him of false accounting, since that might open a can of worms best kept tightly shut. In the end it decided to claim back more than £8,000, which it said had been wrongly paid to both Quicks, father and son, over many years. The hearing was disastrous, the case effectively collapsed, and after a year of wrangling over costs, a humiliated and no doubt frustrated S&V ended up paying Quick & Son £1,235, including 17 guineas unpaid salary.[59]

19

The Triumph of Vestrydom

For eighty years the question of what to do about London's water was bedevilled by the shortcomings of London local government, and by a failure to agree on the answer to two fundamental questions. What was 'London'? And who – if anyone – was responsible for it?

There were, in fact, two Londons. There was the ancient City of London; and there was the wider built-up area. Victorians often called this wider London 'the Metropolis', a term in use since at least 1698, when the author of *The London Spy Compleat* first arrived in 'our metropolis' determined to expose the vanities and vices of the town.[1] He had used the word in the sense defined by Samuel Johnson in his dictionary: 'The mother city; the chief city of any country or district.' But by the nineteenth century it meant London above all, the largest city in the world.

Throughout the century acts were passed establishing the Metropolitan Police and the Metropolitan Board of Works, and regulating the metropolitan gas and water supplies and the 'construction of buildings in the metropolis and its neighbourhood'. Yet much of this legislation specifically excluded the City, or was obliged to make special provision for it. Even today there is a City police force, quite distinct from the Met (it specialises in investigating fraud). Nor is the modern City formally part of Greater London, but a ceremonial county in its own right.

There was a reason for this distinction: the City Corporation wanted nothing to do with the rest of the capital, if that could possibly be arranged. It was controlled by the City's livery companies: they were rich, and dedicated to spending their money on good dinners and good works, as they still are. They feared – and they were probably right – that their wealth would quickly dissipate if the Corporation took on responsibility for London as a whole; nor were they prepared to subordinate themselves to any London-wide authority that might raid their coffers and curb their privileges. The City had powerful friends: one of its four MPs, Lord John Russell, was Prime Minister from 1846 to 1852 and again in the 1860s, and many City liverymen also sat in Parliament. And it was prepared to go to pretty well any lengths to preserve its independence: when, in 1884, the government introduced a bill that would have transformed the Corporation into a municipality for the whole of London, the City spent £20,000, an enormous amount, on opposing the legislation, deploying tactics that included bribery, intimidation and violence at public meetings.

This City exceptionalism had consequences whenever any London-wide initiative was contemplated. Generally it was a nuisance, though sometimes there were benefits. When Joseph Bazalgette designed his northern low-level sewer, he had to do it in conjunction with William Haywood, the City's engineer, because it ran through the City; happily, Haywood was extremely competent. And when its independence was threatened by the 1848 public health bill, the City promptly got its own bill through Parliament and appointed its first medical officer, the equally competent John Simon, who worked with Haywood to improve the Square Mile's sewers and turned the City into a beacon of good sanitary practice.

But the City did not and would not speak for London. In which case, who did?

London local government in the 1840s was chaotic. Outside the City lived a million and a half people whose local affairs were supervised by a bewildering array of overlapping bodies. There were seven sewer commissions (an eighth served the City). There were nearly 100 different boards in charge of paving or lighting or cleansing the streets: responsibility for a three-quarter-mile-long stretch of the Strand was split between nine of them. There were nineteen paving and/or lighting boards in the parish of St Pancras according to one historian (twenty-one according to another), on which sat some 900 commissioners, mostly self-selected or appointed by landowners.[2]

And, most importantly, there were more than ninety vestries, whose districts ranged from the tiny – the Liberty of the Old Artillery Ground near Bishopsgate, for instance, with a population of 1,500 – to the enormous – like St George's Hanover Square, with a population of over 60,000. The ratepayers met in the church vestry to elect local officials and manage their affairs, which included keeping the peace, relieving the poor – a function carried out from the 1830s through 'boards of guardians of the poor' – and, in some cases, paving the streets. Some of the vestries were 'open', meaning that every ratepayer with property above a certain value had a say in their running; others were 'close' or 'select', which meant that at some point an act of Parliament had limited their membership to a self-perpetuating oligarchy of the principal inhabitants; still others had started out as select vestries but switched in the 1830s to a system in which the vestry members were elected annually by a majority of the ratepayers. As we have seen, vestries were notoriously reluctant to spend money and notoriously corrupt when they did. They were dominated in London by local tradesmen, and by the owners of slum properties, who resisted measures to make them improve their properties on the grounds that neither they nor their tenants could afford it. When vestries were given powers to enforce sanitary legislation, they often neglected to exercise them; the *Pall Mall Gazette* observed, as late as 1884, that giving them the job was akin to asking poachers to enforce the game laws.

In all, there were places on all these vestries, paving boards and the rest for over 10,000 commissioners, guardians and vestrymen – a formidable phalanx, most of whom were opposed to any reform, and alive to the manifold opportunities for graft and corruption.

As well as the vestries, there were the county magistrates or justices of the peace, whose responsibilities included bridges and licensing as well as dealing with offenders, and who nominally served unpaid. Appointing prominent local citizens as magistrates might work tolerably well in the shires, where the obvious candidates for the job were members of the local gentry with independent incomes and some sense of noblesse oblige. But in Middlesex, which housed the majority of London's burgeoning suburbs, the gentry had departed, and their place had been filled by men from a lower social class. These 'trading justices' saw the post as an opportunity for personal wealth-creation and were effectively for sale to the highest bidder.

The shortcomings of the vestries, whether open or select, were not limited to London, and vestrydom held sway across the country until in 1835 a Municipal Corporations Act allowed larger towns and cities to establish the forerunners of modern city and district councils. But London was exempted from the act. A royal commission in 1837 recommended a single unified system of government for the metropolis, but left open the question of whether it should be one of the new provincial-style municipalities or whether central government should be responsible. Either way, nothing happened. In 1851 John Stuart Mill observed that water supplies should be in the hands of local government, but 'in the case of London, unfortunately, this question is not a practical one. There is no local government of London.'[3]

It was not until 1855 that Big Ben, Sir Benjamin Hall, finally grasped the nettle of metropolitan municipal reform. The paving and lighting commissions were swept away, as the sewer commissions already had been, and the vestries were restructured. The smaller ones were grouped together in what were called district boards or 'unions'. And to preside over the interests of London as a whole – and in particular to undertake the grand project of building the main drainage – the Metropolitan Board of Works was created.

Hall was MP for Marylebone, and had a deep understanding of the politics of London. He knew that many vestrymen were deeply opposed to change, jealous of their lucrative privileges and status, profoundly suspicious of centralisation and committed to the idea of local self-government. The vestries viewed him as their man. Only someone they thought was on their side could have persuaded them to accept his changes, but he also knew how far he could push them. His masterstroke was to put the London-wide authority – a potential rival to the vestries as a source of influence and money – under their control: it was the vestries and the new district boards who selected the Metropolitan Board of Works' forty-six members (including three representing the City).[4]

So here, at last, was a public body that might be capable of taking responsibility for London's water: not a municipality, exactly, and only indirectly representative of Londoners, but more than a mere sewer commission. Its other tasks at the outset included street naming and numbering, building regulation and the creation of broad new thoroughfares across the congested city. As time went by a ragbag of additional responsibilities was foisted on to it: for parks and open spaces, for the fire brigade, for inspecting the gas supply, for suppressing cattle plague . . . So why not water too?

To begin with that question was academic. The board had quite enough to do building Bazalgette's sewers and the Embankment. But, by 1869, when Lord Richmond's commission came down unambiguously in favour of public ownership of water – 'a sufficiency of water supply is too important a matter to all classes of the community to be made dependent on the profit of an association'[5] – the main drainage was largely complete. Two years later the government introduced a bill to make the board of works the water companies' regulator, and to give it the power to buy them up.

The companies predictably opposed the bill. So, less predictably, did some of those who supported the idea of public ownership. The problem for them lay with the board, which for all its achievements had acquired a reputation as a talking shop dominated by small-minded vestrymen. There was a feeling that it was a merely provisional body, not a 'proper' municipality. The select committee that considered the bill concluded: 'The supply of water to this great and growing city cannot be placed upon a proper footing until Parliament shall have determined upon the proper municipal administration of the metropolis.' The home secretary agreed. The government withdrew the purchase proposal and the 1871 act reached the statute book with no mention of public ownership.

When, in 1877, the board proposed its own legislation to buy the companies, the government wasn't impressed and the proposal got nowhere. The *Journal of Gas Lighting* was dismissive. Was the board of works 'a body fit to be trusted with the management of the water supply?' it asked. 'We say, emphatically, "No".' The *Journal* explained why nothing would happen: 'It is the want of an authority enjoying public confidence that stands in the way of the purchase of the water companies', combined with the London water companies' 'exceedingly strong' parliamentary influence.[6]

The board failed to take the hint. Three times more during the 1880s it sought authorisation to buy the companies, but each time it was rebuffed. By now it was widely seen as unaccountable, prone to empire-building and corrupt, 'the board of perks'. Some of the allegations levelled at it were fanciful but others were not.* Either way, its

---

* One allegation involved Joseph Bazalgette and the contract to build the Embankment, awarded to George Furness. Bazalgette had earlier recommended Furness as a suitable contractor to build

political capital had been eroded and its proposals were effectively ignored.

So campaigners came up with another alternative, a specially created body, a 'Water Trust', which would buy up the companies and be answerable to national government. The idea had been around since 1851 but now it received support from both main political parties. In 1880 the government introduced a bill to put the proposal into practice.

Way back in 1821, James Weale had been if not a lone voice then in a decided minority in calling for public ownership, and the political establishment had dismissed his idea. In 1851, the possibility of public ownership was being widely canvassed, but there were too many practical difficulties. By 1881, the political establishment had embraced the prospect. In sixty years the 'Overton window' – the range of policies acceptable to the political mainstream – had shifted decisively. The arguments in principle had largely been won. The remaining political arguments were largely about the means, and about the cost. And it was the cost that stymied the 1880 proposal: both political

---

(cont.) a sewer system for the Russian city of Odessa, where Sir John Rennie was a consultant engineer. In return, Bazalgette got a slice of Rennie's commission. When this emerged, it looked, to some, distinctly fishy. In fact, Furness had not been Bazalgette's first choice for the Embankment job and he went to some lengths to try to prevent Furness from getting it. But the allegations damaged both Bazalgette's reputation and the board's. The board's reputation suffered further – and with justification – towards the end of its life when details of widespread corruption in the architects' department emerged (Stephen Halliday, *The Great Stink*, pp. 90–91, and David Owen, *The Government of Victorian London*, pp. 169–92).

parties took fright when told they would have to spend around £33 million.

Communism in water

Then, in 1889, the Metropolitan Board of Works was abolished and London finally got a fully-fledged municipality. Or almost fully-fledged. In a sweeping modernisation of all local government, new directly elected county councils were created, and London got one too. And almost everyone assumed that, in due course, this new London County Council would take over the water.

It turned out not to be that simple. Firstly, the LCC hadn't been given the powers. Unlike the other county councils, it had to submit a budget every year to Parliament and it had no innate authority to purchase and operate public utilities. National government may have set up the council but it was suspicious of this alternative source of democratic legitimacy on its own doorstep, and sought to keep it on a tight rein. Before it could even spend money on researching a possible water purchase, the council had to get an additional act of Parliament.

Secondly, the legislation that brought the LCC into being also created new county councils for Middlesex, Surrey and the other ancient counties round the capital. 'Water London' – the area served by the water companies – extended well beyond the new County of London; the surrounding counties made it very clear they weren't prepared to let the LCC run their taps.

Then, three years after the LCC was established, new elections returned a council with a markedly different political complexion. The first LCC had been nominally non-partisan, under the chairmanship of a Liberal, Lord Rosebery, soon to become prime minister. The new council was much more radical: the Progressive alliance of Liberals and labour-movement representatives had 100 seats, the Moderate opposition of the Conservatives had thirty-seven. And the Progressives' platform had been largely drawn up not by Liberals but by socialists, members of the Fabian Society under the leadership of Sydney Webb, who became the LCC member for Deptford.

To the Fabians, London's water companies were just capitalist rentiers, exploiting the working class: not landlords but 'water lords'. In one of his Fabian tracts, *London's Water Tribute*, Webb maintained these water lords charged Londoners over £2 million for water that cost only £900,000 a year to supply, and enjoyed returns of 9½ per cent a year on their capital – capital that was in any case much larger than it needed to be. Plenty of municipalities had shown they could deliver water just as effectively and a good deal more cheaply than private companies, but, for Webb and the Fabians, an LCC takeover of water was about more than saving money: it was merely the first step towards taking over pretty much everything else as well. Webb foresaw a city in which citizens would enjoy not just publicly owned and democratically controlled water, but public housing, public health and welfare and public transport. The gas supply would be municipalised. So would key industries and employers, such as the docks. What Webb called 'communism in water' was a Trojan horse through which 'a complete revolution in the administration of nearly every department of municipal affairs' could be achieved: it was the lubricant that would ease the ship of socialism down the slipway.

Unsurprisingly, the Conservative government of Lord Salisbury was horrified. Almost a century later, Margaret Thatcher, faced with a radical left-wing Greater London Council at odds with everything she believed in, simply abolished it. Since Salisbury had only just created the LCC, that wasn't really an option; instead he did all he could to frustrate it. Eventually, in 1899, the vestries and district boards were transformed into metropolitan borough councils, which, it was hoped, would act as a counterbalance to what the Conservatives saw as the LCC's wilder excesses.

The LCC, meanwhile, had pressed ahead with its plans for water. It set its chief engineer to work devising a grand plan for bringing water from Wales, reviving J. F. Bateman's proposal of 1866, and pressed for another royal commission, which it hoped would show that the companies didn't have enough water and that continuing to take it from the Thames was a threat to health. The commission, chaired by Lord Balfour, reported in 1893, having decided, as the Richmond commission had done, that there *was* enough water and that the Thames *was* safe. The LCC, undaunted by this rebuff, launched a plan to take over two of the companies, the Lambeth and the Southwark & Vauxhall, as a first step towards taking over the lot.

Between 1892 and 1895, Salisbury was in opposition, which meant the LCC's proposals got a favourable hearing from Rosebery's Liberal government. But once back in power, Salisbury quickly killed off the LCC's initiative. Stalemate threatened, until nature intervened, rather as it had done in the Great Stink of 1858. The summers of 1895–99 were the warmest for forty years and the driest in thirty, and London's water supplies started drying up as well. In 1898 the East London company, worst hit, had to introduce rationing, turning the water on for just three hours twice a day – much as it had in the bad old days of intermittent supply. The LCC's Progressives seized the opportunity to renew the campaign for municipalisation, and won widespread support. As one historian put it, 'The water companies watched their political vulnerability rise as the levels in their reservoirs dropped.'[7] The Conservative government played for time and, in 1897, appointed yet another royal commission, chaired by Lord Llandaff.

Llandaff and his commissioners spent a leisurely two years considering whether and how the water companies should be purchased by a public authority. At the end of it they brought in the now obligatory verdict that the water should indeed be in public hands, but offered a new/old solution to the question of whose hands those should be. Not the national government; not the LCC; but a water trust or water board on which the new metropolitan boroughs and the new county councils would also be represented – with the red-in-tooth-and-claw socialists of the LCC comfortably outvoted.

And that, with some modifications, was what London finally got. The Metropolis Water Act of 1902 established the Metropolitan Water Board, only fourteen of whose sixty-seven members were nominated by the LCC. Another eighteen were nominated by local authorities outside the County of London, one each came from the Thames and Lea Conservancies, two came from the City, and the remaining twenty-nine from the vestries – or, at least, their descendants, the metropolitan boroughs. It was a posthumous triumph for vestrydom.

Public versus private interest

The companies had been defeated – although their shareholders were handsomely compensated in the subsequent
buy-out. Those same shareholders had also done extremely
well during the dying years of the old regime: in 1895, Parliament was told, four of the eight companies were paying
the maximum permitted dividend of 10 per cent a year,
and all but one of the rest were paying close to that.
(The exception was the still-troubled Southwark & Vauxhall, which could manage only 6 per cent, though by 1903
its dividend too had reached 10 per cent.)[8]

To their credit, they had also continued to invest. One
of the questions the Llandaff commission considered was
(of course) whether the Thames remained a suitable source,
or whether the new water board should look to Wales for a
new supply, as the LCC wanted. And just as with every
other inquiry since 1869, Llandaff opted for the Thames.

Money was one consideration: the LCC had costed its
Welsh scheme at £38.8 million at a time when, as the historian John Broich has helpfully pointed out, the annual
cost of the entire Royal Navy was only £28.5 million.[9]
But the clinching argument for Llandaff and his commission seems to have been the response from three of the
companies to the problem of periodic water shortages,
with which they had been battling even before the droughts
of the late 1890s. Their solution – first presented to the
Balfour Commission in 1893 – was to increase the storage
capacity of their reservoirs, which could be filled up when
rainfall was copious and used to tide them over the dry
periods.[10] In 1896 the three companies, the New River,

Grand Junction and West Middlesex, formed a joint venture to build two vast water holding pens on flat land at Stanwell, to the south west of what is now Heathrow airport. They were known as the Staines reservoirs, and drew their water from a new intake at Hythe End, immediately to the west of the modern M25 and opposite Runnymede. They were costly, but a good deal cheaper than the Welsh proposal, and the scheme could easily be expanded – as it has been. Four further reservoirs, even more gigantic, have since been built in this noisy neighbourhood in London's drab suburban outskirts, the last in the 1970s, along with others south of the river and still more in the Lea Valley. Storage is now the name of the game.

By the 1890s, the companies and other opponents of public ownership were unquestionably on the back foot, reduced to little more than procedural arguments and delaying tactics. In the parliamentary debate on the LCC's proposals in 1895, Joseph Chamberlain, who as a radical reforming mayor in the 1870s had successfully municipalised Birmingham's water supply, articulated a view that by now had the status of a truism, at least outside London: 'It is not, after all, in the public interest that an enterprise which is of necessity in the nature of a monopoly should remain in private hands. We may give every credit to the public spirit of the directors of a private company; but still it is true, after all, that their first duty is to their shareholders, and that the interest and convenience of the public are likely to suffer if they are at any time antagonistic to the interests of the shareholders.'[11]* By 1895 Chamberlain's

* Chamberlain is reputed to have said something similar in 1894: 'It is difficult and indeed almost impossible to reconcile the rights

radicalism had softened markedly, and he was soon to go into government as colonial secretary in a coalition between his Liberal Unionists and the Conservatives. That he was nevertheless still arguing that it was impossible to reconcile the public interest with private gain is a mark of how deep-rooted that notion had become.

In Chamberlain's speech and in Sidney Webb's critique of the water companies, we can see the seeds of the post-1945 Labour government's policy of nationalising not just utilities but also industries like coal and rail, which were deemed to be of 'strategic' importance, and which Labour believed should be managed in the wider interests of society at large. Indeed, you could argue that the London water buy-out was the first such 'nationalisation', partly because it was so big and partly because it was undertaken by an appointed board representing wider interests than just a single municipality.

But there is also, in these late nineteenth-century stirrings, a hint of something more far-reaching still: a sense that the vehicle that lay at the heart of capitalist private enterprise, the joint-stock corporation, was simply not capable of fulfilling some of the tasks it was being given. In the century and a quarter since, corporations in general and

---

(cont.) and interests of the public with the claims of an individual company seeking as its natural and legitimate object the largest private gain.' This quotation was used by trade unions opposed to water privatisation in the 1980s in a pamphlet, *Water Down the Drain*. I have been unable to find the original source and, though Chamberlain may well have said the same thing twice in the space of a year, it seems equally likely that the 1980s' campaigners were using a garbled or misremembered version of Chamberlain's authenticated speech to Parliament.

the corporation as an idea have come under attack from many quarters. An especially penetrating onslaught came in 2004, when a Canadian law professor, Joel Bakan, published a book in which he argued that corporations are 'pathological' institutions. They possess great power, which makes them formidable; but they are also profoundly self-ish, and that makes them dangerous: 'The corporation's legally defined mandate is to pursue, relentlessly and without exception, its own self-interest, regardless of the often harmful consequences it might cause to others,' he wrote.[12] A corporation's directors as people may wish to act in the wider public interest, but their hands are tied by their duty under the law to act in the best interests of their shareholders. Bakan's contention is that this, combined with the legal 'personality' independent of their directors or employees which corporations enjoy, permits, nay encourages, outright criminal behaviour of the sort that would brand a real person a psychopath. He summons a parade of pharmaceutical companies, tobacco companies, oil companies, car companies, fast food companies and tech companies to make his point.

If Joel Bakan is right, Hugh Myddelton and the founders of the New River Company have an awful lot to answer for.

20

Takeover to Today

In July 1904, almost 300 years after critics had lamented
the City's transfer of its water to Hugh Myddelton, 'by
which means that which was intended for a public good
shall be converted into a private gain', and more than
eighty years after James Weale had suggested the supply of
water 'ought not to be the subject of free trade, nor any kind
of trade', London's water finally became public property.

The companies handed over their customers, their pipe
networks and their pumping stations, lock, stock and
smoking chimneys, to the Metropolitan Water Board, and
melted away – all except for the New River, whose extensive property holdings around New River Head were
exempt from the takeover, and which continued in being.
Today the New River Company Ltd, incorporated in 1905
and with assets worth more than £400 million, still trades
as a subsidiary of a commercial property firm.

The old companies' shareholders were generously
compensated – too generously, some said. After lengthy
arbitration hearings in front of a three-man panel, the
companies were awarded a total of over £47 million. It was
less than they had asked for; nonetheless the buy-out laid a
heavy financial burden on the new water board, since the

payment was made in the form of 'water stock', which carried a guaranteed dividend of 3 per cent, for which the board was responsible. In 1913 the board's chairman complained that, out of its £3 million annual income, it was paying out more than half in interest and annuities.[1]

The board also had to meet a ragbag of financial obligations inherited from the New River, including the Crown Clog (which no longer went to the Crown but to 'private persons whose property it has become' and had somewhere along the line been reduced from £500 to £400 a year), plus annuities of £3,750 a year to former shareholders in the London Bridge Waterworks, payable until October 2082 (so far as I know, they're still being paid by the board's successor, Thames Water). The old companies' charges had varied from 3 per cent to 7½ per cent of the rateable value of a property; the board was allowed to charge a maximum of 5 per cent, but it wasn't enough. In 1922 the rules had to be changed to allow it to charge up to 10 per cent.[2]

Some of the companies' most senior staff were let go, but the East London's chief engineer, W. B. Bryan, got the equivalent job at the board and the S&V's James Restler became his deputy and then successor when Bryan died at his desk in 1914.

In 1905 the board ran a series of articles in the first few issues of its staff magazine recounting the history of the water companies. The series had a title, 'The Rate-payers' Bargain': one aim, evidently, was to demonstrate what the board's customers had got for their money when the companies were taken over at such huge expense. But it was also an exercise in team-building: the board had to weld staff inherited from eight separate and sometimes competing organisations, each with its own geographical area and distinctive culture, into a single harmonious whole, and understanding their respective histories probably helped.

Later, old hands would sometimes contribute reminiscences to the magazine. In 1925 F. W. Drake, a one-time New River employee, recalled the attendance money paid to New River directors: like ill-organised children struggling with punctuality, they only qualified if they managed to get in before a board meeting started. By 1850 there was a fixed sum of £300 a year 'for division among those in the boardroom at 11 o'clock'. A local watchmaker was employed to check the accuracy of the boardroom clock each week, and the company's auditor acted as schoolroom monitor, writing down the names of those attending and drawing a line to establish who was on time and eligible for that week's pay out. Drake remembered watching millionaire directors sprinting across the yard to the Board Room to get in before the clock struck so as to qualify for their pay out.[3]

The offices at New River Head, Drake said, were 'very secluded', with a bar across the road to prevent vehicles passing (this was before Rosebery Avenue was opened in 1892, a major tram and later bus route that destroyed the seclusion for ever). On the north side the collectors' offices looked out on to the Round Pond. When it froze, staff were allowed to scramble through the office window and go skating. Migrating water fowl used to visit. There were water lilies and enormous goldfish in the warm water of the condensing pond next to the engine house – until both lilies and fish were killed in a single night by the use of a 'poisonous lubricant' and never replaced.[4]

In another article, H. F. Rutter, who had been the West Middlesex engineer at the time of the takeover, described his old company's paternalistic management style in an era before old-age pensions and routine trade union recognition, calling it benevolent despotism: 'Both salaries and wages were on a modest scale, but every man knew that if he behaved himself his position was secure, and his old age provided for . . . On Saturdays both officers and men had the privilege of knocking off work at four o'clock instead of working on till half-past five.'[5]

'ECW' contributed his memories of the East London Waterworks, a company he first joined in 1885. It was something of a family affair. The accountant, with the apt name of Josiah Purser, brought two of his sons into the business, who went out to work as collectors. The inspector also introduced his son to the business, as did six of the seventeen collectors. The chief clerk's uncle was a collector – a man called J. T. Jones, who collected Bethnal Green and whom ECW likens to Dickens's Mr Lillyvick, the collector of water rates in *Nicholas Nickleby*, whose wealth makes him a figure of supreme importance to his poorer relatives and who marries an actress. The days when Jones and his colleagues drew their half-yearly balance 'were fete days at the office, in which the younger members participated'.[6]

The old companies' collectors were evidently formidable as well as affluent men (senior collectors earned up to £1,000 or £1,200 a year, a more than comfortable middle-class salary), and they make several appearances in reminiscences published in *Aquarius*. One reputedly carried a loaded revolver with him to deal with awkward customers. The water board paid them more modestly than the companies had done and they were gradually phased out as the board shifted to collecting water rates by post. No more were appointed after 1936.[7]

*

For the best part of seventy years, the Metropolitan Water Board did an effective job. As with other municipal waterworks, it was run by professional water managers answerable to board members, who in turn answered to ratepayers: appointed by local councils, they were focused on keeping the customers sweet rather than on profits and dividends. The success of these municipal ventures gave the lie to those who suggested that anything run by local authorities must necessarily be wasteful and inefficient. At the start and at the end, the board was starved of investment, but in between it flourished: its eventual abolition owed less to its own failings and more to the government's desire for a more joined-up, 'strategic' approach to water management based on river catchments.

Once its early financial problems had been overcome, the board built new intakes and enormous new reservoirs in the Thames and Lea valleys, durable safeguards against future water shortages: between 1911 and 1953 it increased its storage capacity for unfiltered water from 8.9 billion to 27.3 billion gallons. In the late 1950s, it built the Thames–Lea Tunnel, at 19 miles the longest artificial tunnel in the world when it was constructed, a twentieth-century New River, which transfers 120 million gallons a day from the Thames at Hampton to the reservoirs in the Lea Valley.[8]

Purification techniques were also improved. In 1916, shortly after the armies fighting on the Western Front began killing one another with chlorine gas, the board started using chlorine for more benign purposes, to disinfect drinking water. It had first been used in this way at Maidstone after typhoid appeared in 1897, and Alexander Houston, who was to become the board's top scientist, had used it in 1905 during another typhoid outbreak at Lincoln. In London the trigger wasn't disease but the need to save coal during wartime: chlorinating the water meant it didn't need to be pumped in and out of subsiding reservoirs; instead the raw water, with chlorine added, could go direct from a river intake to the sand filters. The board later developed rapid high-pressure filters, which removed matter held in suspension: it meant the slow sand filters through which it passed afterwards needed cleaning far less often. During the 1920s and 30s, a series of appealing art deco buildings sprang up at the board's waterworks to house these 'primary filters'.[9] By 1921 London's water was so good the government deemed it safe to abolish Frank Bolton's old post of metropolitan water examiner.

In time, the board began to find its inheritance from the old companies an embarrassment. It wanted to demolish London's oldest surviving steam engine house, built at New River Head in 1789, only to find that it was a listed building. Apart from its age, the board's engineer complained, it had no virtues whatsoever: 'It is ugly, outdated, and a serious obstacle to redevelopment,' and he had planned to replace it with 60,000 square feet of offices and a basement carpark.[10] The building stood forlornly empty for another forty years, until a plan was announced to convert it into the Quentin Blake Centre for Illustration, opening in 2023. The board took an equally dim view of the old New River pumping station in Green Lanes, Stoke

Newington, a Scottish baronial extravaganza, which was also listed in 1972. 'This pumping station is completely useless for any purpose connected with the water industry,' the board's clerk complained. 'It constitutes at the moment an expensive lavatory for pigeons.'[11] In the 1990s the building became the Castle indoor climbing centre.

In 1974 the board itself floated off into history, subsumed into the Thames Water Authority, one of the ten new regional bodies in England and Wales set up by the Conservative government of Edward Heath to combine water supply, sewage treatment, river management and pollution control. Edwin Chadwick would have been delighted that at last the mains and the drains were under one management, though there were exceptions. Twenty-eight commercial operations, known as 'statutory water companies' and responsible only for water supply, survived under the umbrella of the new authorities; around London they included three companies that served the Colne Valley, Rickmansworth and Lea Valley.

The new dispensation didn't last. The authorities' investment plans fell foul of the Treasury's determination in the 1980s to keep the public sector borrowing requirement down. So in 1989, casting around for more publicly owned assets to privatise in the wake of British Telecom and British Gas, Margaret Thatcher's government hit upon the water industry.

Initially the Prime Minister had her doubts: 'The water authorities are natural monopolies for many of their functions and we need to be particularly careful when considering replacing a public monopoly with a private one,' she said in 1985.[12] But the water industry's physical assets were in a woeful state, and the need for investment to replace ageing water mains and sewage treatment plants concentrated minds. No government – and certainly not Mrs Thatcher's – was likely to come up with the money, but private sector shareholders might, attracted by the reliable income streams that utilities produce. The dangers of a privatised monopoly would be mitigated by the establishment of a plethora of regulators. Ofwat (the Office of Water Services) would have the power to cap prices and issue fines. There would be a Drinking Water Inspectorate to monitor quality. And a new National Rivers Authority (later to become part of the Environment Agency) would be responsible for pollution control and environmental regulation.

Opponents thought this a bad idea. You might have expected their arguments to be laid out in *Water Down the Drain*, a leaflet produced by the water industry trade unions: 'Despite the overwhelming evidence that public service and private gain cannot work together in harmony in the water industry,' it said, 'the government appears determined to press ahead with its privatisation proposals.'[13] Yet the 'overwhelming evidence' was missing from the pamphlet itself, which went into considerable detail about matters that had little to do with privatisation – why proposals to introduce water metering, for instance, would hit the neediest hardest, or why separating pollution monitoring from water supply and sewage treatment was a recipe for conflict – but did not explain specifically why public service and private gain were incompatible. The Overton window had shifted again, but the anti-privatisation folk had failed to notice. Like Joseph Chamberlain in the 1890s, they took it as axiomatic that private ownership of a public service was a bad idea, and that it was therefore unnecessary to make the case. Mrs Thatcher disagreed.

Private interests

The privatised water industry started well. The government wrote off some £5 billion-worth of water authority debt, the new companies were floated with a nationwide marketing campaign ('You too can be an H_2 owner'), the shares were oversubscribed and the Treasury raised £5.23 billion to make up for the debt write-off. And investment flooded in: in the first five years after privatisation, £13.5 billion was spent on plugging leaks, cutting pollution and improving water standards, much of it driven by the need to meet new regulations imposed by the European Community.[14]

At the same time prices rose 'astronomically'. So did water company profits, water company dividends and top executives' salaries: 'The figures are an investor's dream,' wrote the *Observer* in 1994. And despite all the money the companies were spending, ageing mains kept on bursting, elderly sewers kept on collapsing and up to a fifth of the country's water was lost to leaks. So consumer complaints went up as well.[15] A decade later it was clear the new system wasn't working.

The regulatory regime had been designed to reward the new companies if they became more efficient and for spending more on new and updated plant, while putting limits on how much they could increase prices to the customer, thus limiting their shareholders' potential returns. Big profits early on came about because Ofwat, which had the job of setting the level of prices and returns every year, had significantly underestimated the scope for cost cuts and improvements in efficiency.

But worse was to come. A new type of shareholder started buying into the industry. The privatised companies had started out as publicly quoted enterprises with widely-held shares, and the government kept a 'golden share', allowing it to retain ultimate control. But, in the mid-1990s, the golden shares expired. One by one the companies were bought out and taken over, until, by 2021, just three retained their stock market listing. The fate of the rest was to be parcelled up and sold on periodically to new owners – initially to other utility companies, but later to 'infrastructure investment' consortiums of banks and private equity and sovereign wealth funds. Some of these new proprietors showed precious little interest in meeting the standards set by Ofwat and the EC (and later the EU). They were more interested in cash flow than water flow, and knew more about financial engineering than the hydraulic kind. They were distant and unaccountable. This was not the popular capitalism the original architects of privatisation had hoped for, and it was not something with which the regulator was equipped to grapple.

Thames Water PLC, successor to the Thames Water Authority, was bought after ten years by the German power station company RWE for £4.3 billion. Six years later, RWE sold it again, having repeatedly failed to meet the targets set by Ofwat for reducing leaks, and complaining that its foray into the water business had not been a success. As failures went, it was remarkably lucrative: RWE sold Thames for almost twice what it paid.[16]

The purchaser was a consortium led by an Australian infrastructure investment bank, Macquarie, reputedly dubbed the 'vampire kangaroo' by Australian newspapers for its ruthless focus on profits and tax minimisation. Macquarie kept Thames in its portfolio for another decade until the water company was once more sold. In those ten years, investigations by the *Financial Times* and the BBC later showed, Macquarie paid itself and fellow investors £1.6 billion in dividends and loaded Thames with £10.6 billion in debt, ran up a £260 million pension deficit and paid no UK corporation tax.* It had invested £1 billion a year in Thames's ageing infrastructure but had still enjoyed twice the investment returns that would normally be expected from a privatised utility company, suggesting it could have invested a good deal more. Much of the money it had borrowed to buy Thames was repaid with new loans contracted by Thames itself through a subsidiary in the Cayman Islands.

Meanwhile, in its last year under Macquarie's control, Thames was fined a record £20.3 million for dumping raw sewage: people living near one sewage plant dubbed the effluent that came from it 'crappucino', and a judge considered one breach of pollution regulations had been

---

* One of the first steps Macquarie took was to pay itself and other shareholders a special one-off dividend of £500 million, taking the dividend total in the fifteen months to March 2007 to £656 million, against £155 million in the previous twelve months, thus taking out of the business cash that might have been spent on improving infrastructure and services (Thames Water Utilities report and accounts, period ended 31 March 2007).

'borderline deliberate'. The company was fined another £8.55 million for missing its leak reduction targets.[17]*

English water companies had become licences to print money. A study by Greenwich University showed that, between 1989 and 2018, the companies – which, remember, had next to no debt at the moment of privatisation – took on borrowings of £51 billion. Most of that went to the shareholders: between them the companies paid out £56 billion in dividends to investors. Three of the companies, Anglian, Severn Trent and Yorkshire, actually paid out more in dividends in the ten years to 2017 than their pre-tax profit totals.[18]

Corporate structures became fiendishly convoluted, as though designed to maximise shareholders' freedom of manoeuvre and minimise scrutiny by regulators, investors or journalists. Shell companies were routinely established, some in offshore tax havens. Until it promised to improve the simplicity and transparency of its structure, Thames had nine main group companies, two registered in the Cayman Islands and a number of other subsidiaries, including

---

* In July 2021 Southern Water was fined an even more enormous sum, £90 million, for repeatedly, deliberately and illegally dumping millions of litres of untreated sewage into the sea and rivers over several years. The deliberate nature of the offences suggested water companies had yet to get the message that this sort of behaviour was unacceptable. The following month Macquarie returned to the UK water business by injecting more than £1 billion of additional equity into Southern. Macquarie told Ofwat the new investment would be spent on upgrading treatment plants and other infrastructure – money Southern could not otherwise afford to spend – and that it would limit its dividend yield from the investment to under 4 per cent over the next four years.

one in Guernsey.[19] In 2021, Thames told me that all the companies in the group were now registered in the UK; an 'abridged version' of its structure listed six holding companies between the ultimate shareholders and Thames Water Utilities Ltd, the company that actually delivers the water.

Affinity Water, which now owns those three statutory water companies serving the Colne Valley, Rickmansworth and the Lea, has (at the time of writing) an even more labyrinthine structure and a similar history of being bought and sold. Today Affinity serves a wide arc round London, from the south-west to the north-east, along with parts of Essex and a stretch of the Kent coast from Deal to Dungeness. First, the original three companies merged as Three Valleys Water. Then, in 1987, Three Valleys was bought by the French multinational Veolia. In 2012 Veolia sold the company, which by then included several other water companies and had been renamed Affinity. The buyer was an infrastructure investment consortium led by two leading City institutions, who in turn sold it in 2017 to another consortium of three investors, one German, one Dutch and one British. An organogram on the company's website shows the three partners jointly control a vehicle called Daiwater Investment Ltd. From there on, the chart reads like an Old Testament genealogy, with 'owns' in place of the 'begats'.

Daiwater owns Affinity Water Acquisitions (Investments) Ltd, which owns Affinity Water Acquisitions (HoldCo) Ltd, which owns Affinity Water Acquisitions (MidCo) Ltd, which owns Affinity Water Acquisitions Ltd, which owns Affinity Water Capital Funds Ltd, which begat six subsidiaries, one of which, Affinity Water Holdco Finance, owns Affinity Water Holdings Ltd, which in turn owns the Ofwat-regulated company that actually delivers the water, Affinity Water Ltd.[20] You don't have to understand the purpose of this maze of companies to know it has nothing to do with the efficient delivery of potable water.

One purpose is, in fact, to raise debt, either from shareholders or from outside lenders, such as banks and insurance companies, and to render the regulated water business 'insolvency-remote' – that is, to protect lenders and the business itself from any attempt by the shareholders to default on their debt repayments. As interest rates plummeted, shareholders enthusiastically swapped debt for equity: borrowing was cheap, and spreading the same dividend totals over fewer shares made for higher returns per share. The availability of cheap money might also, of course, have been an opportunity to improve things for customers by further increasing investment; it was an opportunity the new breed of shareholders did not take, preferring to enrich themselves instead. You might call it asset stripping; it certainly wasn't asset improvement.

This kind of behaviour outraged even those one might expect to be supporters of private enterprise. The *Financial Times*, the house newspaper of the investment community, concluded in September 2017 that water regulation had failed. 'Water is a local service that should be accountable to the people it serves,' its columnist wrote, echoing the arguments put to inquiry after inquiry in the nineteenth century. In a leader in 2019, the paper told the water companies they still had to prove the case for private ownership. Ofwat's first director-general, Sir Ian Byatt, wrote (long after he'd retired): 'Customers have been overcharged; dividends have been excessive.' Financial engineering had become more important than providing a service; the companies were gaming the system. 'Nearly everyone on the [Thames Water] board are investors and one cannot resist the idea that they are more concerned with money than with serving the public,' he said.[21]

Even the Conservative environment secretary Michael Gove added his voice to the chorus, accusing the water companies of undermining trust by their use of tax havens and 'opaque financial structures'. Thames really ought to have paid some tax, he suggested.[22]

The regulator, Ofwat, seemed powerless to prevent all this, and often reluctant to confront the companies directly, preferring to try to talk them into changing their behaviour. Much of the time they took no notice. One problem was that, while Ofwat's powers were clear enough when it came to setting prices and levels of return, it had only 'soft' powers to change the way managements and shareholders behaved. It might urge greater transparency, but it could not enforce it: one critical weakness was that any changes to the terms of a company's licence required the company's agreement.

What leverage Ofwat does have it doesn't always use. When the extent of shareholders' predations became clear, the regulator resolved to act, only to pull its punches at the next price and investment review, which coincided with the fall-out from the financial crash of 2008: it was worried that too stringent an approach might destabilise the companies.

In fact, the companies may have destabilised themselves by taking on so much debt. It makes them alarmingly vulnerable to interest rate rises. What happens if rates rise and several of Britain's monopoly water suppliers run into financial difficulties as a consequence, all at the same time? It's almost impossible for them to go bust – in the event of possible bankruptcy, they become subject to a 'special administrative regime' designed to safeguard the water supply and water treatment business and to find a buyer. But buyers may be thin on the ground in such circumstances.

Meanwhile, Ofwat's credibility was undermined when four water companies successfully played it off against another regulator, the Competition and Markets Authority. Ofwat's 2019 price review set a new and extremely tough limit of 2.96 per cent return on the cost of capital, the lowest ever imposed on a regulated utility and much less than the previous 4.67 per cent. The companies (not including Thames) appealed to the CMA, which in March 2021 accepted their arguments that they would have too little money both for investment and for operating costs under Ofwat's proposal, and increased the rate of return to 3.2 per cent.

Some critics fear there is another reason why the companies' levels of debt are imprudent. The more capital investment they make, the more tax they are allowed to defer on any profits they make – one reason why their tax bills have been low or non-existent. They can also set against tax the interest payments on the money they borrow for investment. There is a temptation to go on borrowing and investing at high levels in order to keep dividend payments up. The snag is that the tax deferred must be paid eventually. The consequences of this can be likened to what happens in a pyramid investment scheme, such as the South Sea Bubble or George Hudson's railway empire.

Each successive year sees higher interest payments as the loans accumulate, and a higher level of deferred tax payments. In order to go on paying dividends, the company has to borrow still more and claim more tax relief on still more new purchases of fixed assets. Somewhere down the track the companies will face a cash crunch (especially if interest rates rise), when there is no longer enough money both to invest and to repay loans, and the deferred tax becomes due. At that point dividends may crash. The trick is to sell out before that stage is reached so that new shareholders, who have played no part in these exploitative financial manoeuvrings, have to deal with the financial fall-out.

That's what Macquarie seems to have done at Thames, saddling its new owners with the consequences of its rapacity. The company's ten external shareholders in 2021 included two Canadian public employees' pension funds, the UK universities' pension scheme and sovereign wealth funds in Abu Dhabi, Kuwait and China. Faced with the reality of Thames's financial position, they agreed to forego all dividends for the three years up until 2020 – not such a hardship for those who had been shareholders back in the Macquarie era, perhaps, who had already banked considerable gains, but a significant hit for the university pension scheme and one of the Canadian pension funds, which only bought their shares in 2017 and 2018. They must have known the company's financial state, but presumably hoped that in due course their shares would nevertheless produce a steady flow of cash to pay their pensioners. Thames's operating company was still making considerable profits on supplying water and treating sewage, and paying dividends to companies higher up the ownership chain; but those dividends went to pay interest on debts, not to the ultimate shareholders.

Much of this behaviour is reminiscent of the bad old days of Victorian capitalism – not just of George Hudson but of the Grand Junction and the Southwark & Vauxhall in the 1870s, borrowing to pay dividends which were much higher than their trading position could justify. There is much to be said for capitalism as a way of getting things done, of channelling investment and using assets productively for the good of both shareholders and society at large. But left to their own devices, shareholders will enrich themselves and let society go hang. As the Victorians slowly discovered, it is up to governments and regulators to see that doesn't happen.

Little wonder, in view of all this, that the opposition Labour party went into the 2019 general election pledged to renationalise water – though that is far from a guaranteed panacea. Nationalised industries are often inefficient. And shareholders would need to be compensated. Taking water back into public ownership may involve a price tag just as 'eye-watering' as that paid for the London water companies in 1904, if the interests of legitimate investors in the industry such as pension funds are to be protected.[23]

Britain's water companies now say they have mended their ways. But it seems Joel Bakan's pathological corporation is alive and well and was, until recently, rampaging through Britain's water industry.

Putting water in the pipes

It's not only the modern water industry's accounting practices that call the nineteenth century to mind. So do the holes in the road.

In 2016 a water main burst in Upper Street, Islington, near the Angel and just north of New River Head. A fountain erupted in the small hours on a corner between an antiques shop and an estate agent. One of the city's water arteries had begun haemorrhaging torrents into nearby homes and businesses, flooding basements and closing a main route south into the City. Hundreds of thousands of litres must have run to waste. It was one of eight 'high profile trunk main burst events' across London in the space of under two months, and it was the worst – the 36-inch cast iron main was the biggest of the eight pipes involved, and the fact that it happened on a busy bus route and shopping street in an affluent neighbourhood guaranteed the flooding got wide coverage.

Thames Water was so concerned that it commissioned a review, which found the Upper Street pipe 'to be in very poor condition with large areas of external and through-wall corrosion'. The review doesn't say how old it was, but one newspaper report suggested 160 years, which, if true, would mean the New River Company must have first laid it back in the 1850s. It needed wholesale renewal, and for much of the next two years traffic through the Angel was badly disrupted by the work.[24]

Even Victorian cast iron has a finite life and Thames Water and its predecessors have been struggling for decades with the seemingly endless task of replacing their ageing pipes, ideally before they fracture. Thames is making progress. In 2018, it lost 645.6 million litres a day from leaks. In 2020, that was down to 543 million litres – but that's still nearly a fifth of the water entering the pipes. 'The most effective way to reduce leakage is asset replacement,' the company says. But wholesale replacement is expensive: it's cheaper to adopt a piecemeal policy of replacement that the company calls 'find and fix'.[25]

Then there's the war on waste – another problem the Clays and Coes and Quicks would recognise. Thames customers today use 146 litres a day each; Affinity's customers use more, 152 litres – perhaps it's because they have all those suburban gardens to water – and reducing consumption is a priority. The companies have a programme of 'household water audits' by staff who visit customers, advise on ways to cut consumption and drop plastic bags full of water into their lavatory cisterns to reduce the capacity and cut the amount of water per flush: toilets account for a third of domestic water use, but I can testify that the plastic bags can be counterproductive because the flush is no longer as effective, so you end up pulling the chain a second time. This is the work of Victorian-style water police, though it sounds more benign. More important still is the introduction of household meters, which encourage customers to use less water.

All this is because London risks running out of water. The population is still expanding. Climate change is bringing hotter, drier summers. And there are environmental pressures that the Victorians did not face: for instance, to reduce extraction from aquifers in order to safeguard the unique ecology of the chalk streams which are abundant in southern and eastern England – this is a particular challenge for Affinity, which gets two-thirds of its supplies from underground sources.

Thames predicts a shortfall of 1 billion litres a day by 2050. The smaller Affinity expects to be 108 million litres a day short by 2045 in the areas it serves round London. Many of their proposed solutions to this looming crisis would sound familiar to a Victorian or even a Regency water engineer. One is to tap the canals. The Grand Junction began life distributing canal water to households; now Affinity has a plan to bring additional water from the Midlands along the Grand Union canal. The idea of bringing water from Wales has been revived, yet again, with a scheme to release more water into the headwaters of the Severn around Lake Vyrnwy and then pump it from downstream near Tewksbury to Culham, south of Abingdon on the Thames. A version of the idea was first suggested in the early 1970s, revived by the National Rivers Authority in 1994 and again by Thames in 2006, and was the subject of a public inquiry in 2010. The scheme is still under active consideration. A rather charming but much more expensive version of the plan suggested pumping the water up the disused Thames and Severn Canal and through the Sapperton tunnel, which was built in 1789 and would need restoration. Either version of the scheme would be costly and might have significant environmental implications.[26]

And then there's increased storage – building more reservoirs on the upstream Thames. As early as 1908, the Metropolitan Water Board surveyed land in the valley of the river Enborne between Reading and Newbury as a possible site for a reservoir, though it was never built. In 2006, Thames Water announced a plan to build a vast new water storage pen, holding 150 billion litres, on flat land just south west of Abingdon. This 'south-east strategic reservoir' would fill gradually – perhaps with water from the Severn– Thames transfer – allowing Thames and Affinity to release up to 294 million litres a day back into the river for abstraction downstream in dry spells. Thames Water's latest plans envisage bringing the reservoir on stream by 2038.[27]

There are other ruses for increasing water supply, however, which were not available to the Victorians. One is desalination – though it's expensive and Affinity has rejected it as 'excessively costly'. Thames Water built a desalination plant at Beckton in 2012, powered by renewable energy produced by the sewage works next door. It was intended to supply up to 150 million litres a day as a back-up for use in periods of drought, but only operated for part of the year and was out of action completely in 2019. Following this 'long-term outage', the plant's maximum output was cut to 100 million litres, for reasons that are unclear.[28] Another source of extra water is effluent reuse – Thames is exploring ideas for recycling up to 300 million litres a day of wastewater from its Mogden sewage treatment works in Isleworth back into the system, and extra water brought by canal from the Midlands would come from a sewage treatment plant near Sutton Coldfield.

A third way to increase supply is pumping water back into the chalk aquifers under London. In the 1980s and 90s, an 'artificial recharge scheme' was instituted along the route of the New River and alongside the Lea Valley reservoirs, and expanded in the 2000s. Small brick blockhouses were built, housing boreholes and pumps to complement the older wells and pumping stations constructed as far back as the mid-nineteenth century. They extract water from the chalk to supplement the flow in the New River and into the reservoirs during periods of drought. But around thirty of them are also equipped to pump water back *down*, to top up the aquifer when there's a water surplus. Mike Jones, one of Thames's water resource specialists, says the scheme makes use of the purpose-built boreholes, the New River and the existing reservoirs, but if suggested today, would not go ahead because it would be hugely disruptive and vastly expensive. He also told me the water in the New River itself is too turbid to be pumped back down into the chalk – the sediment would simply clog the borehole and the aquifer around it – so the boreholes are fed with treated drinking water.

Water legacy

Not only the artificial recharge scheme but the New River itself is an expensive indulgence. Thames Water's engineers would much rather replace it with a pipe – far easier and cheaper to maintain. The southernmost stretch is especially hard to justify in economic terms: since 1988, most of the water has been diverted at Turkey Street (near Freezy Water, south of Enfield) and sent to a treatment plant at Coppermills in the Lea valley. The remainder is allowed to run on to Stoke Newington but then has to be brought back again to Coppermills (part of the way in a pipe running in the reverse direction under the river bed).[29] The river survives because of its 'amenity value': it is picturesque, and a good excuse for an invigorating tramp through the suburbs. South from Stoke Newington the river has disappeared. By the nineteenth century, what had once been a picturesque ornament to the landscape had become a nuisance, hemmed in by houses, attracting dirt: bit by bit it vanished into pipes and culverts. One indirect result was a wartime tragedy: in October 1940, more than 100 people died when a German parachute bomb hit Dame Alice Owen's school in Islington, a short step from New River Head. They had been sheltering in the basement: the bomb not only destroyed the school buildings but fractured the iron pipe in which the New River ran; most of the dead drowned.[30]

Other relics of London's water industry survive because they too have amenity value, though most, unlike the New River, have long since been taken out of service. I have visited many of these sometimes numinous places while researching this book. The old West Middlesex filter beds at Barnes have become the London Wetlands Centre, where you can spot over 200 bird species and where three-storey hides like prison watchtowers loom over the winding paths. But the bulldozers have obliterated all traces of the previous layout: it is a place to delight bird nerds but not water nerds. The wetlands in the Lea Valley are more rewarding. At Lea Bridge, the East London's old filter beds are clearly visible. Some have been left to run wild and have filled with reeds and scrub: the unwary could tumble in. Further south by the Olympic Park at Old Ford, the East London's pipes lie strewn across the Lea like a giant's abandoned game of Pik-a-stik.

At Kempton, still a Thames Water operational site, they have occasional open days, when you can visit Henry Stilgoe's extravagant machine hall beside the flyover leading to the M3, standing amid a wasteland of empty concrete. It rained on the day they celebrated the ninetieth birthday in 2019 of their huge Worthington-Simpson engines; it was made wetter still by a restored Metropolitan Fire Brigade steam fire engine, which threw a jet high over the parked cars.

*

In October 2018, I went to Peckham, in south London, and walked to the reservoirs at Nunhead, taking a picture of a rare Southwark & Vauxhall street cover on the way. (Yes, I confess, I am that man: the one who suddenly stops in front of you to photograph the pavement.) The reservoirs were built by Joseph Quick and occupy a steep hilltop site next to Nunhead Cemetery and there is little to see: this, too, is an operational site and a fence topped with razor wire runs alongside the footpath between the cemetery and Thames Water's ground. Back in 1875, a landslip during construction damaged the brickwork of one of the reservoirs and for several years they stood unfilled: an independent engineer declared them not fit for use. A group of concerned local residents, led by the rector of St Antholin's, Nunhead, wrote to the company and to the newspapers, describing what they called 'a species of panic' in the neighbourhood at the perceived danger. 'No less than 18,000,000 gallons of water, weighing 72,000 tons (or more than the weight of the ten heaviest ironclad ships in the navy), will be pent up within the walls of these reservoirs, so that in the event of any part giving way, not only our houses will all inevitably be swept away, but our lives and those of our children will be endangered,' they told *The Times*. The S&V's secretary wrote a reassuring reply – accompanied by another, less emollient letter to the rector personally, calling his letter to the newspapers libellous and threatening legal action if his allegations were repeated.[31]

Covered service reservoirs such as these at Nunhead are situated at high points all around inner London, hiding in plain sight on the edge of open spaces or among residential streets, and still in use. The Lambeth company's reservoirs are in Streatham and on Brixton Hill, next to the Brixton windmill. The old West Middlesex reservoirs are on Primrose Hill and in West Hampstead, where the water shares a site with the West Heath Lawn Tennis Club. There is a former Chelsea Waterworks reservoir next to The Telegraph pub on Putney Heath, and a well-disguised East London Waterworks reservoir under Finsbury Park.

Harder to miss are the works at Hampton, the second London water intake established in the 1850s on the non-tidal Thames. The handsome engine houses designed by Joseph Quick and James Restler and their colleagues are being repurposed as a base for biotech start-ups and homes for affluent commuters, but mostly Hampton, too, is still a sprawling operational site. The intake there is one of around ten on the Thames between Datchet and Sunbury managed by Thames Water or Affinity. The figure is derived from Thames's and Affinity's water resources management plans, though I have been unable to confirm it: Thames told me that the number and location of intakes, like the location of service reservoirs, 'isn't information we share publicly'. No one wants to make it too easy for bad actors to tamper with London's water supply.

The river's flow now branches off into a man-made delta that projects the river basin out beyond its natural contours and over the hills north and south of the city, through a myriad channels and 13,000 miles of pipes, only to gather in the flow once more and deliver it back to the parent river at Barking and Crossness. The old companies and their engineers took tremendous pride in these networks and all their accompanying infrastructure. Critics accused them of wasteful duplication, but this Victorian spider's web below ground remains the backbone of London's modern water supply, bolstered by later developments, such as the Thames water ring main, a giant pipe that shuttles clean water from treatment plants to local mains and acts as an additional service reservoir.

A message in oak

One sunny morning in the summer of 2019, I met a friend of a friend on the wide flight of steps leading up from Rosebery Avenue to what was once the headquarters of the Metropolitan Water Board at New River Head. The building is a piece of Edwardian bombast, boilerplate public architecture, completed in 1920 but designed before the First World War and intended to convey a sense of solidity, stability and safety: an organisation headquartered thus could be trusted with the responsible job of watering the Empire's capital.*

The board itself, of course, is long gone and the building is now posh flats; I had come to meet one of the residents. She had kindly agreed to show me a rare survival from the early days of London's water industry, normally inaccessible to the public. She led me through the main entrance into a vast top-lit space, now empty and echoing but once the 'rental ledger hall', where the board's clerks totted up water bills. And then we went upstairs to the Oak Room.

To make way for its new offices, the water board, in 1911, demolished the complex of buildings that had grown up around Hugh Myddelton's first reservoir and modest water house, a distinctive but utilitarian structure.

---

* A building next door constructed in 1938 to house the board's laboratories is architecturally even more striking, a many-windowed modern sweep of red brick, terminating in a rotunda bearing a flagpole and the board's crest. The rotunda contains a staircase lit by windows of glazing blocks three storeys high. It was cutting-edge modern architecture built to house cutting-edge scientific analysis.

This original building had soon acquired architectural airs, when, about 1693, it was extensively remodelled by John Grene, the New River Company's clerk, who had married Hugh Myddelton's granddaughter and decided to make the water house his home, but evidently thought it insufficiently grand (perhaps he was looking to spend the dividends from his wife's shares?). The centrepiece of his refurbishment was a spectacular interior known originally as the Court Room.

When the old water house went, the Court Room was dismantled, preserved and then reconstructed in the water board's new building and renamed the Oak Room, on account of the panelling on the walls, which feature decorative swags carved in high relief by the famed wood carver Grinling Gibbons, or by someone Gibbons taught.

The room is a testament to the New River Company's sense of its own importance, but also to the wealth and power of London's water industry as a whole. When the company chairmen met together in the nineteenth century to discuss issues of common interest (often the latest government scheme to take them over), it was to New River Head that they repaired, and there, no doubt, they assembled in this room, from which the affairs of London's largest and richest and most senior water company were directed. This was where the 'mercenary river' was guided into ever more elaborate, ever more extensive and ever more lucrative channels. To those privileged, then and now, to gain access, it is a space that speaks of wealth and power and status.

On the ceiling is an oval portrait of William III, the reigning monarch when the room was fitted out; its plaster frame is a riot of fruits and foliage, birds and trees, trident-wielding mermen and bucolic landscapes full of cottages, five-bar gates and anglers. At the four corners are roundels in which plaster swans glide serenely and sea monsters writhe. Above the fireplace are the arms of the royal Dutch House of Orange, with their motto *Je maintiendra* ('I shall maintain'), and on either side are Grinling-like swags full of aquatic symbols: fish, crabs, lobsters (perhaps someone forgot to tell the artist that the New River dealt in fresh water, not the salt variety). In the centre is an oval boardroom table and a dozen elegant wooden chairs. It is a formal interior, though today rather sterile: a stage set awaiting performers who will never come, the grandees of London's water industry having long since abandoned the place.

Though the Oak Room ceiling boasts William III's motto, the New River's own motto was different: *Et plui super unam civitatem*, a line from the Latin Vulgate Bible, usually translated as 'And I rained upon one city'. When, in due course, the New River and the rest were taken over, the Metropolitan Water Board co-opted the motto, along with the most striking visual element in the New River Company's seal: an image of the hand of Providence sprinkling water drops from the sky.

Modern water companies don't flaunt seals or coats of arms, so the New River's iconography effectively disappeared with the water privatisation of the 1980s. But the seal (and motto) survive on two bridges across an ornamental water on the line of the old New River in Stoke Newington's Clissold Park. During the eerie, empty months of the Covid-crisis lockdowns in 2020 and 2021, when I was writing this book, I often crossed them during my government-sanctioned daily exercise. So did hundreds of other ordinary Londoners, most of them oblivious to their significance, just as most of us never think about how the water in our taps gets there or where it ultimately goes.

Yet they serve as a monument, more accessible and a good deal more modest than the Oak Room, to one of the world's first and most profitable business corporations, and also to the men and the institutions, and the costly paraphernalia, the clever engineering and the careful science, and the greed and the skill, which for more than 400 years have kept one of the world's greatest cities watered and alive.

Notes

Introduction

1 *Journal of Gas Lighting, Water Supply and Sanitary Reform* (N.B.: hereafter *JGL*), XXIX, p. 126, 23 January 1877, and pp. 978–81, 19 June 1877. For full details of the Richmond fiasco, see Chapter 19.
2 'The Rolling English Road', G. K. Chesterton's famous poem, can be found here: https://www.poetryfoundation.org/poems/48212/the-rolling-english-road.

1. Conduits and Cobs

1 Campion's story is told in Frederick Clifford, *A History of Private Bill Legislation*, vol. II (London: Butterworth, 1885 and 1887), p. 48. Clifford's book is one of the principle sources for the history of London's medieval and early modern water supply, along with Roberta J. Magnusson, *Water Technology in the Middle Ages: Cities, Monasteries and Waterworks after the Roman Empire* (Baltimore and London: Johns Hopkins University Press, 2001); H. W. Dickinson, *Water Supply of Greater London* (Leamington Spa and London: Newcomen Society, 1954); Leslie Tomory, *The History of London's Water Industry 1580–1820* (Baltimore: Johns Hopkins University Press, 2017); and Ted Flaxman and Ted Jackson, *Sweet & Wholesome Water: Five centuries of history of Water-bearers in the City of London* (London: privately printed, 2004).
2 Clifford, *A History of Private Bill Legislation*, vol. II, p. 36.
3 John Stow, *The Survey of London* (1603 edition; London: Everyman, 1908), pp. 12–13.

4 British Museum, https://www.britishmuseum.org/collection/object/P_1880-1113-3517.

5 Clifford, *A History of Private Bill Legislation*, vol. II, p. 44; Flaxman and Jackson, *Sweet & Wholesome Water*, p. 14.

6 Ben Jonson, *Every Man in His Humour, Plays* I (London: Everyman, 1964), pp. 9 and 33.

7 Ruth Goodman, *The Domestic Revolution: How the Introduction of Coal into our Homes Changed Everything* (London: Michael O'Mara, 2020), p. 92. Goodman's book, and her earlier *How To Be a Tudor: A Dawn-to-Dusk Guide to Everyday Life* (London: Penguin 2015), are an entertaining mine of information on early modern water use in London, along with Lawrence Wright's *Clean and Decent: The History of the Bathroom and the WC* (London: Routledge and Kegan Paul, 1966).

8 Goodman, *The Domestic Revolution*, p. 247.

9 Wright, *Clean and Decent*, p. 68.

10 Goodman, *How To Be a Tudor*, p. 17.

11 Samuel Pepys, *Diary*, 21 February 1665.

12 Ibid., 23 February 1665.

13 Goodman, *How To Be a Tudor*, p. 19.

14 Ibid., pp. 23–4.

15 Clifford, *A History of Private Bill Legislation*, vol. II, pp. 62–3.

16 Ben Jonson, *Poems* (London; Routledge and Kegan Paul, 1971), pp. 69–75.

17 Pepys, *Diary*, 20 October 1660.

18 *Minutes of Evidence taken before the Select Committee on the Supply of Water to the Metropolis 1821*, p. 16.

19 In his sequel to Shakespeare's *Taming of the Shrew, The Woman's Prize or the Tamer Tamed,* quoted in Tomory, *The History of the London Water Industry*, p. 13. Ned Ward, in *The London Spy Compleat*, eds Allison Muri and Benjamin Neudorf (London, 1703), p. 47, wrote: 'We now turn'd down to the Thames-side, where the frightful roaring of the Bridge Water-falls so astonish'd my Eyes, and terrified my Ears, that, like Roger in his Mill, or the Inhabitants near the Cataracts of Nile, I could hear no Voice softer than a Speaking Trump.' Somewhat counterintuitively, the waterworks caught fire three times, in 1633, during the Great Fire of 1666 and again in 1779: on the last two occasions much of the works burned down.

20 Tomory, *The History of the London Water Industry*, p. 38.

21 Clifford, *A History of Private Bill Legislation*, vol. II, pp. 54–5.

Notes

2. The Purchas'd Wave

1 My account of the New River's genesis and construction is based on J. W. Gough, *Sir Hugh Myddelton: Entrepreneur and Engineer* (Oxford: Clarendon Press, 1964), pp. 1–73; Robert Ward, *London's New River* (London: Historical Publications, 2003), pp. 19–46; Bernard Rudden, *The New River: A Legal History* (Oxford: Clarendon Press, 1985), Chapters 1–4; G. F. Stringer, *Some Descriptive Notes on the New River Head* (1927; reprinted London: Amwell Society and Thames Water, 2012); and Leslie Tomory, *The History of the London Water Industry 1580–1820* (Baltimore: Johns Hopkins University Press, 2017), pp. 50–8.

2 Ward, *London's New River*, pp. 19–20.

3 Gough, *Sir Hugh Myddelton*, p. 46.

4 Ibid., p. 44.

5 Rosemary Weinstein, 'Who Hid the Cheapside Hoard? A Goldsmith's Row Mystery Resolved', *London Topographical Record*, vol XXXII, London, 2021, pp. 151–201.

6 Gough, *Sir Hugh Myddelton*, p. 12.

7 Ibid., p. 99.

8 Ibid., p. 20.

9 Stringer, *Some Descriptive Notes on the New River Head*, pp. 17–20.

10 For the Cathay venture, see Stephen Alford, *London's Triumph: Merchant Adventurers and the Tudor City* (London: Penguin, 2018), pp. 39–44. For Antwerp, see C. G. A. Clay, *Economic Expansion and Social Change: England 1500–1700* (Cambridge: CUP, 1984), vol. II, pp. 111–9.

11 Alford, *London's Triumph*, p. 72.

12 William Dalrymple, *The Anarchy: The Relentless Rise of the East India Company* (London: Bloomsbury, 2019), p. 11.

13 Tomory, *The History of the London Water Industry*, p. 53.

14 Rudden, *The New River: A Legal History*, p. 30.

15 Ward, *London's New River*, p. 62.

16 Rudden, *The New River: A Legal History*, pp. 48–9, 57, 126.

17 Gough, *Sir Hugh Myddelton*, p. 56; Ward, *London's New River*, pp. 31–2.

18 Ward, *London's New River*, p. 26.

19 Derek Ingram, 'The First Caian Engineer and the First Caian Pirate', *The Caius Engineer*, 13 (1), 2001; Tomory, *The History of the London Water Industry*, p. 40.

20 Ward, *London's New River*, pp. 80–1

21 Stow, *The Survey of London* (1633 edition), pp. 12–13.

22 Samuel Lewis, *The History and Topography of the Parish of Saint Mary, Islington* (London: 1842), p. 430.

23 Gough, *Sir Hugh Myddelton*, p. 86.

24 Samuel Smiles, *Lives of the Engineers*, vol. 1 (London: John Murray, 1862), p. 109.

25 Sir Alexander Houston, *The Romance of the New River* (reprinted from 'Sir Alexander Houston's Twentieth Annual Report to the Metropolitan Water Board', London: MWB, 1926), p. 3.

26 John Hollingshead, *Underground London* (London: 1862; reprinted using optical character recognition software, Memphis, 2012), Chapter 13; Houston, *The Romance of the New River*, p. 3.

27 Houston, *The Romance of the New River*, p. 3; Stringer, *Some Descriptive Notes on the New River Head*, pp. 16–7; Gough, *Sir Hugh Myddelton*, p. 87.

28 Michael Essex-Lopresti, *Exploring the New River* (Studley: Brewin Books, 1997), p. 6.

3. The River Runs

1 I have used Ward, *London's New River*, along with Rudden, *The New River: A Legal History*, and Tomory, *The History of the London Water Industry*, as my principal sources for this chapter.

2 See LMA, ACC/2558/MW/C/15/111/01, a 1691 agreement between the 'Governour and Company of the New River' and Stephen Morris of Stanhop Street, demising and granting 'One Water-course, conveniently furnished with Water running in and through one small Branch or Pipe of Lead containing half an Inch of water or thereabouts, and in and through one small Cock of Brass souldred and set unto the same, and placed in the Yard of the new dwelling-house of the said Stephen Morris and in manner hereafter expressed, for the only proper use and service of the said Lessees Family inhabiting and dwelling in the house aforesaid'. Agreement to run for two years for 26s 8d, payable at the New River Water House. The company warrants to turn the water on at least three days a week, subject to the right of inspecting the householder's cock, pipe and branches. The tenant is not to sell the water or let it run to waste and to maintain the cock and the pipe on his land. There are fines for non-payment of rent or letting the water run to waste, and the company warrant to give a quarter's water free if

there is a break in service of more than fourteen days (except in case of frost).

3 J. T. Smith, *Book for a Rainy Day* (London, 1845), quoted in *Aquarius*, XV, 1925, pp. 438–42.

4 H. W. Dickinson, *Water Supply of Greater London* (Leamington Spa and London: Newcomen Society, 1954), plate VI.

5 Ward, *London's New River*, p. 54.

6 Ibid., p. 60.

7 *Aquarius*, I, 1905, pp. 3–5.

8 Tomory, *The History of the London Water Industry*, p. 61.

9 LMA, ACC/2558/MW/C/15/314 – A Proclamation for the Carefull Custody & Well Ordering of the New River.

10 Metropolitan Water Board, *London's Water Supply 1903–1953*, appendix E, pp. 356–7.

11 Samuel Rolle, *Account of the Burning of London* (1667), quoted in William Matthews, *Hydraulia: An Historical and Descriptive Account of the Water Works of London and the Contrivances for Supplying Other Great Cities in Different Ages and Countries* (London, 1835), pp. 21–2.

12 Rudden, *The New River: A Legal History*, pp. 96.

13 The York Buildings' extraordinary history is told at length in David Murray, *The York Buildings Company* (Glasgow: James Maclehose, 1883), https://www.electricscotland.com/business/york.pdf.

14 Ward, *London's New River*, p. 110.

15 Pepys, *Diary*, 16 August 1667.

16 Peter Earle, 'The Making of the English Middle Class', *Business, Society and Family Life in London 1660–1730* (London: Methuen, 1989), pp. 68–9, 138

17 Rudden, *The New River: A Legal History*, p. 67.

4. Froth and Bubble

1 Pepys, *Diary*, 26 October 1663, 4 April 1666.

2 For the history of soap, see Goodman, *The Domestic Revolution*; Doreen Yarwood, *The British Kitchen*; Lawrence Wright, *Clean and Decent*.

3 Goodman, *The Domestic Revolution*, p. 273.

4 Ibid., p. 278.

5 Ibid., p. 278; Mary Collier, *The Woman's Labour: An Epistle to Mr Stephen Duck* (London: 1739), via https://www.usask.ca/english/barbauld/related_texts/collier.html.

6 Goodman, *The Domestic Revolution*, p. 275.

7 Peter Earle, *The Making of the English Middle Class: Business, Society and Family Life in London, 1660–1730* (London: Methuen, 1989), pp. 298–9.

8 For the history of business at this time and the South Sea Bubble, I have drawn on Earle, *The Making of the English Middle Class*; John Carswell, *The South Sea Bubble* (Stroud: Alan Sutton, 1993); and Malcolm Balen, *A Very English Deceit: The South Sea Bubble and the world's first great financial scandal* (London: Fourth Estate, 2003).

9 LMA, ACC/2558/MW/C/15/193, Chelsea Waterworks warrants for St James's Park and Hyde Park. For details of London's water industry in the eighteenth century in this and the following chapter, I am indebted especially to Tomory, *The History of the London Water Industry* and Carry van Lieshout, *London's Changing Waterscapes: the Management of Water in Eighteenth-Century London* (unpublished PhD thesis, King's College London, 2012), https://kclpure.kcl.ac.uk/portal/.

10 Hugh Barty-King, *Water – The Book* (London: Quiller Press, 1992), p. 61.

11 https://www.britishmuseum.org/collection/object/P_1862-1213-51.

12 LMA, ACC/2558/MW/C/15/199, New River, Sorocold proposals.

13 Ward, *London's New River*, pp. 129–141. Further details of Sorocold's career can be found in F. Williamson, 'George Sorrocold of Derby – a Pioneer of Water Supply', reprinted from the *Journal of the Derbyshire Archaeological and Natural History Society*, NS 10, no. 57, 1936, in *Studies in the History of Civil Engineering, Vol 5, Water Supply and Public Health Engineering*, ed. Denis Smith (Ashford Variorum, 1999).

14 LMA, ACC/2558/NR/13/10/2-10, Reports by Ashfordby, Leeson and Garnault to the Governor and other gentlemen 1741–2.

5. Here Be Dragons

1 *The York-Buildings Dragons* (London, 1726), pp. 5–6.

2 Pat Rogers, 'The York Buildings Dragons: Desaguliers, Arbuthnot and attitudes towards the scientific community', *Notes and Records, Royal Society*, December 20, 71(4), 335–360 (London, 2017), https://www.ncbi.nlm.nih.gov/pmc/articles/PMC5906434/.

3 *Survey of London*, xvii, Chapter 5, Hungerford Market, https://www. british-history.ac.uk/survey-london/vol18/pt2/pp40-50.

4 LMA, ACC/2558/MW/C/46/32-35, Papers of G. C. Berry; Murray, *The York Buildings Company*, pp. 55, 108

5 For more on Savery and the pioneers of steam, see Smiles, *Lives of Boulton and Watt*; H. W. Dickinson, *Sir Samuel Morland: Diplomat and Inventor, 1625–1695* (Cambridge: Newcomen Society, 1970).

6 Dickinson, *Water Supply of Greater London*, p. 60.

7 London Picture Archive, https://www.londonpicturearchive.org.uk/ view-item?i=21732&WINID=1616416417410.

8 Erasmus Darwin, *The Botanic Garden*, part 1, lines 289–96.

9 Dickinson, *Water Supply of Greater London*, p. 58.

10 Tomory, *The History of the London Water Industry*, pp. 102–3.

11 van Lieshout, *London's Changing Waterscapes*, p. 215

12 Ibid., pp. 190–2.

13 Ibid., p. 189.

14 LMA, ACC/MW/C/15/291 has the 1783 agreement together with a New River collector's complaint from 1746 about 'Thames water' (i.e. London Bridge) collectors poaching customers, and a 1788 letter from the London Bridge superintendent complaining that New River turncocks have offered his customers an emergency supply during a severe frost only if they agree to switch suppliers permanently. In both cases the expectation was clearly that the complaint would be acted upon and the poaching stopped.

15 van Lieshout, *London's Changing Waterscapes*, pp. 212–13.

16 I have drawn freely on Robert Ward's book *The Man Who Buried Nelson: The Surprising Life of Robert Mylne* (London: Tempus, 2007) in this section, along with Tomory, *The History of the London Water Industry*; G. M. Binnie, *Early Victorian Water Engineers* (London: Thomas Telford, 1981); Gwilym Roberts, *Chelsea to Cairo: Taylor-made Water Through Eleven Reigns and in Six Continents* (London: Thomas Telford, 2006); and the invaluable *Grace's Guide to British Industrial History*, https://gracesguide.co.uk/.

17 Ward, *The Man Who Buried* Nelson, pp. 99–100.

18 Sir John Rennie, *Autobiography* (London and New York, 1875), pp. 429–32.

19 Information from documents in the London Metropolitan Archives
    dated 7 June 1771, 29 August 1782, 25 September 1782, kindly
    supplied by Bob Phillips.

6. Water Wars

1 LMA, ACC/2558/MW/C/15/12, Ralph Dodds, *Observations on Water.*
2 Much of the information in this chapter is drawn from John
   Graham-Leigh's invaluable little book, *London's Water Wars: The
   Competition for London's Water Supply in the 19th century* (London: Francis
   Boutle, 2000), and from the *Minutes* of the 1821 select committee.
   Graham-Leigh worked for the Metropolitan Water Board and then
   for its successor Thames Water until his retirement in 2000, latterly
   as regulation and policy manager, so had ample opportunity to see
   first-hand how difficult it is to mix water and private capital.
3 Gary M. Anderson and Robert D. Tollison, 'Adam Smith's Analysis
   of Joint-Stock Companies', *Journal of Political Economy*, vol. 90, no. 6,
   pp. 1237–56, December 1982.
4 Graham-Leigh, *London's Water Wars*, pp. 25–6.
5 Ibid., pp. 28–9.
6 Ibid., pp. 28–33.
7 *Minutes 1821*, p. 74
8 Graham-Leigh, *London's Water Wars*, p. 42.
9 For the sorry story of the Stone Pipe Company, see Upper Windrush
   Local History Society, 'Stone Pipe Company', http://www.uwlhs.
   uk/prj_spc.html; David Ellis, 'The Stone Pipe Company Scandal in
   the early 19th Century – Incompetence or Fraud?', *Hurstbourne
   Tarrant Historical Society*, 2016, http://www.hbthistoricalsociety.org.
   uk/. The West Middlesex started out with stone pipes but
   abandoned them after a year (Col. Sir Francis Bolton, *London Water
   Supply* (London, 1884), pp. 124–5).
10 LMA, ACC/2558/MW/C/15/19-22, Grand Junction handbills;
   Minutes 1821, p. 80.
11 LMA, ACC/2558/GJ/01/0001, Grand Junction court minutes,
   26 June and 3 July 1812, 29 January and 5 March 1813; Matthews,
   Hydraulia, p. 106.
12 LMA, ACC/2558/GJ/01/0001, Grand Junction court minutes,
   especially 3 July 1812, 20 November 1812, 28 December 1812, 15
   January 1813, 26 February 1813, 12 March 1813, 4 May 1813.

13 For Merceron's extraordinary and reprehensible career, see Julian
    Woodford, *The Boss of Bethnal Green: Joseph Merceron, the Godfather of
    Regency London* (London: Spitalfields Life Books, 2016).

14 *Minutes 1821*, pp. 174–6.

15 https://www.britishmuseum.org/collection/object/P_1862-
    0614-308.

16 https://www.britishmuseum.org/collection/object/P_1880-1113-
    2052.

17 https://manchesterartgallery.org/news/unlocking-work-by-ford-
    madox-brown/.

18 LMA, ACC/2558/MW/C/15/24.

19 Sir William Clay, *Remarks on the Water Supply of London* (London,
    1849; second edition, preface dated 15 December 1849), p. 65.

20 *The Times*, 'The History of the Water Monopoly', 1849, 10-part
    series reprinted in *Aquarius*, III and IV, 1907–8.

21 Ward, *London's New River*, p. 167.

22 See, for instance, Clay, *Remarks on the Water Supply of London*, pp. 64–5.

7. Heavy Duty

1 LMA, ACC/2558/MW/C/15/283 'Experiments on fire engines at
   New River Head, Islington'.

2 W. Tregoning Hooper, 'The Cornish Pumping Engine', *The Engineer*,
   28 August 1953.

3 Zerah Colburn and William H. Maw, *The Waterworks of London*,
   reprinted from *Engineering* (London, 1867), p. 17.

4 Details of the engines in the collection at Kew Bridge are on the
   museum's website, https://waterandsteam.org.uk/our-engines/.

5 Erasmus Darwin, *The Botanic Garden*, part 1, lines 262–3.

6 Thomas Wicksteed, *An Experimental Inquiry Concerning the Relative
   Power Produced by the Cornish and Boulton and Watt Pumping Engines*
   (London, 1841), pp. 1–3.

7 LMA, ACC/2558/EL/A/01/027, Court minutes, 27 August 1835
   (N.B.: there are two volumes of East London court minutes
   catalogued in error with the same number, ACC/2558/
   EL/A/01/027; I have used material from both).

8 LMA, ACC/2558/EL/A/01/027, Court minutes, 8 October 1835.

9 Wicksteed, *An Experimental Inquiry*, pp. 1–3; LMA, ACC/2558/
   EL/A/01/027, Court minutes, 5 and 19 March 1836, 23 March and

8 June 1837; see ACC/2558/MW/C/15/124 for the contract of sale and associated correspondence.

10 H. W. Dickinson, 'How the Cornish Engine Came to London', *Engineering*, 510, 31 May 1946.

11 East Cornwall Silver Mine, https://www.aditnow.co.uk/

12 John Bennett, 'John Connell Delarue Bevan and the East Cornwall Silver Mining Company, *British Mining*, 43, Sheffield, 1991, https://www.nmrs.org.uk/assets/pdf/BM43/BM43-5-8-bevan.pdf

13 LMA, ACC/2558/GJ/8/028, Grand Junction engineer's report, 11 November 1835; ACC/2558/GJ/1/37/1-9, Grand Junction court minutes, 13 July 1836.

14 LMA, ACC/2558/EL/A/01/027, East London court minutes, 21 and 28 July 1836.

15 LMA, ACC/2558/GJ/1/9/1, Grand Junction court minutes 1843–46; ACC/2558/GJ/1/10/1, Court minutes, September 1846-August 1850; ACC/2558/GJ/08/29, Wicksteed's report of 12 November 1844.

16 A. Guthrie, *Cornwall in the Age of Steam* (Padstow: Tabb House, 1994), p. 121; Caroline Fox, *Memories of Old Friends: Extracts from the Journals and Letters 1835–1871* (London, 1882), 13 February 1840, p. 54.

17 Private communication from John Porter.

8. Consumer Affairs

1 The cartoon is reproduced in Graham-Leigh's *London's Water Wars*, p. 73.

2 *Minutes 1821*, appendix.

3 LMA, ACC/2558/MW/C/15/24, New River notice to parishes; ACC/2558/MW/C/15/27, Notice of protest meeting: ACC/2558/MW/C/15/6, West Middlesex handbill.

4 *Minutes 1821*, p. 97.

5 *Minutes 1821*, pp. 3–8.

6 *Minutes 1821*, pp. 11, 14–15.

7 Ibid., p. 10.

8 Ibid., p. 57.

9 Ibid., p. 38.

10 Ibid., p. 37.

11 Ibid., p. 71.

12 Ibid., p. 138.

13 Ibid., pp. 126–7.

14 Ibid., p. 108.

15 Ibid., p. 95.

16 Ibid., p. 114.

17 Ibid., pp. 146–7.

18 Ibid., p. 147.

19 Ibid., pp. 152–8.

20 Ibid., pp. 97–8.

21 Graham-Leigh, *London's Water Wars*, pp. 80–81.

9. The Dolphin

1 https://www.poetryfoundation.org/poems/50578/a-description-of-a-city-shower.

2 *The York-Buildings Dragons*, p. 8.

3 Barty-King, *Water – The Book*, p. 69.

4 John Wright, *The Dolphin or Grand Junction Nuisance* (London, 1827 – published anonymously), pp. 6–7.

5 Ibid., p. 49.

6 Ibid., p. 61.

7 LMA, ACC/2558/MW/C/15/172, John Rennie Report to directors of the Grand Junction on the intake at Chelsea; ACC/2558/MW/C/15/264 'Facts relative to the Impurity and Insalubrity of the Water Supplied from the Thames'.

8 *Report from the Select Committee of the House of Lords 1840*, pp. 99–100.

9 *Morning Chronicle*, 4 September 1827.

10 Matthews, *Hydraulia*, p. 351.

11 *The Times*, 'History of the Water Monopoly', reprinted in *Aquarius*, 1908; Bill Luckin *Pollution and Control: A Social History of the Thames in the Nineteenth Century* (Bristol: Adam Hilger, 1986), pp. 12–13; LMA, ACC/2558/MW/C/15/264 'Facts Relative to the Impurity and Insalubrity of the Water Supplied from the Thames'.

12 Daniel E Lipschutz, 'The Water Question in London, 1827–1831', *Bulletin of the History of Medicine*, vol. 42, no. 6, 1968, pp. 521–3.

13 LMA, ACC/2558/MW/C/15/347, Letter from Robert Peel to the West Middlesex Waterworks, 22 June 1829; ACC/2558/GJ/01/35 Grand Junction directors' report to proprietors, 12 June 1828.

14 Clay, *Sir William Clay and his family*, pp. 15–16.

15 *The Times*, 27 December 1849.

16 *The Times*, 27 December 1849.

17 Clay, *Sir William Clay and his Family*, gives full details of the saga.

18 LMA, ACC/2558/GJ/1/38, Grand Junction court record book,
    April 1837 to April 1841.
19 LMA, ACC/2558/GJ/01/0007/1, Grand Junction court minute
    book, 1836–9.
20 Clay, *Remarks on the Water Supply of London*, p. 9.
21 https://www.britishmuseum.org/collection/object/P_1862-
    1217-517.
22 John Edwards Vaughan, *History of Parliament* (https://www.
    historyofparliamentonline.org/volume/1820-1832/member/
    edwards-vaughan-john-1772-1833).
23 https://www.britishmuseum.org/collection/object/P_1862-
    1217-517.
24 Clay, *Sir William Clay and his Family*, p. 25.
25 LMA, ACC/2558/MW/C/15/5, Lambeth company handbills.
26 S. E. Finer, *Life and Times of Sir Edwin Chadwick* (London: Methuen,
    1952), p. 391.
27 Dickinson, *Water Supply of Greater London*, pp. 95–8.
28 LMA, ACC/2558/MW/C/15/164, Arthur Hill Hassall, *A
    Microscopic Examination*, pp. 11–12

10. Boiling, Toiling and Baths

 1 *Aquarius*, 1934, pp. 164–5, which also reproduces a photograph of
    the original.
 2 Susan Palmer, *At Home with the Soanes* (London: Pimpernel Press,
    2015), pp. 21.
 3 *Minutes 1851*, p. 668.
 4 Kew Bridge Museum, *Wash Day Blues: an Exhibition about Laundering
    through the Ages* (London, 1999).
 5 Ruth Goodman, *How To Be a Victorian* (London: Penguin, 2014),
    p. 262.
 6 General Board of Health, *Report 1850*, pp. 71–5.
 7 Amanda Vickery, *Behind Closed Doors* (London: Yale, 2010), p. 122.
 8 Roy and Leslie Adkins, *Eavesdropping on Jane Austen's England*
    (London: Abacus, 2014), p. 97.
 9 Kew Bridge Museum, *Wash Day Blues*.
10 Dorothy Hartley, *Water in England* (London: Macdonald, 1964),
    pp. 332–3.
11 Ibid., p. 306.

12 Anthony S. Wohl, *Endangered Lives: Public Health in Victorian Britain* (London: Dent, 1983), p. 64.

13 Adkins, *Eavesdropping on Jane Austen's England*, p. 140. Much of the material in this section is drawn from the Adkins' book, from David J. Eveleigh's *Bogs, Baths and Basins: the Story of Domestic Sanitation* (Stroud: History Press, 2011), from Lawrence Wright's *Clean and Decent*, and from Dorothy Hartley's *Water in England*.

14 Adkins, *Eavesdropping on Jane Austen's England*, pp. 139–40.

15 John Tyre (pseud), *Free Like Conduit Water: The New River, its Moral and Immoral Economies* (London: Past Tense, 2013), pp. 11–12.

16 Eveleigh, *Bogs, Baths and Basins*, p. 63.

17 Wright, *Clean and Decent*, p. 138.

18 Ibid., p. 169.

19 Eveleigh, *Bogs, Baths and Basins*, p. 74.

20 Ibid., p. 65.

21 Hartley, *Water in England*, p. 220.

22 Ibid., pp. 218–19.

23 Wright, *Clean and Decent*, p. 228.

24 Hartley, *Water in England*, pp. 244–7.

11. The Age of Engineers

1 *JGL*, XI, p. 37, 28 January 1862.

2 Finer, *The Life and Times of Sir Edwin Chadwick*, pp. 439–4.

3 Smiles, *Lives of the Engineers* (Folio edition), p. xvii.

4 For James Simpson's career, see Gwilym Roberts *Chelsea to Cairo: Taylor-made Water through Eleven Reigns and in Six Continents* (London: Thomas Telford, 2006) and Binnie, *Early Victorian Water Engineers*.

5 Roberts, *Chelsea to Cairo*, pp. 103, 129

6 Institution of Civil Engineers obituary in *Grace's Guide*.

7 Presidential address to the Institution of Civil Engineers 1853, quoted in Binnie, *Early Victorian Water Engineers*, p. 71.

8 LMA, ACC/2558/GJ/08/029, J. F. Bateman report for the Grand Junction re alterations to Kew Works.

9 LMA, ACC/2588/LA/01/0008, Lambeth board minutes, 9 December 1845; ACC/2558/MW/C/15/36, Lambeth Waterworks papers re Ditton works, 27 July, 23 August 1847.

10 LMA, ACC/2558/MW/C/15/36, Lambeth re Ditton Works.

11 Binnie, *Early Victorian Water Engineers*, p. 172.

12. The Invention of Sanitation

1 Stephen Halliday, *The Great Stink: Sir Joseph Bazalgette and the Cleansing of the Victorian Metropolis* (London: History Press, 2001), p. 40.

2 Pepys, *Diary*, 29 July 1663.

3 Henry Mayhew, *London Labour and the London Poor*, vol. II (London, 1864), pp. 511–12.

4 Wohl, *Endangered Lives*, p. 86.

5 *Minutes 1851*, p. 715.

6 Halliday, *The Great Stink*, p. 35; Charles Dickens, *Little Dorrit* (London: Penguin, 1967), p. 68; Michelle Allen, *Cleansing the City: Sanitary Geographies in Victorian London* (Athens: Ohio University Press, 2008), p. 56.

7 For Chadwick's career, see Finer, *The Life and Times of Sir Edwin Chadwick*. For Victorian sanitary reform generally, see Lee Jackson, *Dirty Old London: The Victorian Fight Against Filth* (London: Yale, 2014), Wohl, *Endangered Lives*, and Allen, *Cleansing the City*.

8 David Owen, *The Government of Victorian London* (Harvard University Press, 1982), p. 26

9 Allen, *Cleansing the City*, p. 38.

10 Charles Dickens, *Dombey and Son* (Ware: Wordsworth Classics, 1995), pp. 598–9.

11 LMA, ACC/2558/MW/C/15/166, Dean of Westminster, *The Removal of the Cholera*.

12 Allen, *Cleansing the City*, p. 13.

13 *Minutes 1851*, pp. 215–16.

14 *The Use of Pure Water* (London: Ladies' Sanitary Association, undated), p. 20.

15 *Minutes 1851*, pp. 305, 313.

16 Allen, *Cleansing the City*, p. 38.

17 Finer, *The Life and Times of Sir Edwin Chadwick*, pp. 356–80.

13. Science Applied

1 Christopher Hamlin, *A Science of Impurity: Water Analysis in Nineteenth Century Britain* (Bristol: Adam Hilger, 1990), p. 76. I have drawn widely on Hamlin's book in this chapter, and on Bill Luckin, *Pollution and Control: A social history of the Thames in the Nineteenth Century* (Bristol: Adam Hilger, 1986), and Steven Johnson, *The Ghost Map:*

A Street, a City, an Epidemic and the Hidden Power of Urban Networks
(London: Penguin, 2008).

2 Hamlin, *A Science of Impurity*, p. 277.

3 Wright, *The Dolphin*, p. 68.

4 Hamlin, *A Science of Impurity*, p. 89.

5 Clay, *Remarks on the Water Supply of London*, pp. 95–6.

6 Hamlin, *A Science of Impurity*, p. 87.

7 Ibid., p. 139.

8 Ibid., p. 142.

9 LMA, ACC/2558/EL/A/28/001, Unidentified newspaper cutting,
   August 1866. Also quoted in Hamlin, *A Science of Impurity*, p. 158.

10 Luckin, *Pollution and Control*, pp. 61–2.

11 https://wellcomecollection.org/works/pw7fqzb9.

12 Reproduced in Halliday, *The Great Stink*, p. 24.

13 Arthur Hill Hassall, *A Microscopic Examination of the Water Supplied to
   the Inhabitants of London and the Suburban Districts* (London, 1850), pp.
   7–9, 57–8.

14 *Minutes 1851*, p. 236.

15 Hassall, *A Microscopic Examination*, p. 32.

16 *Minutes 1851*, p. 221.

17 Ibid., p. 699.

18 Ibid., p. 696.

19 Luckin, *Pollution and Control*, p. 82.

20 Johnson, *The Ghost Map*, p. 114.

21 Finer, *The Life and Times of Sir Edwin Chadwick*, pp. 297–8.

22 For an account of John Snow's early life and career, see Johnson,
   The Ghost Map, pp. 58–70.

23 Wohl, *Endangered Lives*, p. 118.

24 Johnson, *The Ghost Map*, p. 66–7.

25 Daniel E. Lilienfeld, 'John Snow: The First Hired Gun?', *American
   Journal of Epidemiology*, vol. 152, issue 1, pp. 4–9, July 2000.

26 *Minutes 1851*, p. 292.

27 *The Times*, quoted in *Minutes 1851*, p. 356.

28 *Minutes 1851*, pp. 376–7.

29 Johnson, *The Ghost Map*, p. 128.

30 Ibid., p. 205.

31 John Simon, 'Report on the Last Two Cholera Epidemics', https://
   johnsnow.matrix.msu.edu/work.php?id=15-78-7F.

32 Dickinson, *Water Supply of Greater London*, p. 106

33 Halliday, *The Great Stink*, p. 131.

34 John Broich, *London: Water and the Making of the Modern City* (Pittsburgh University Press, 2013), pp. 50–51.

35 Halliday, *The Great Stink*, pp. 140, 141.

36 Hamlin, A *Science of Impurity*, p. 241.

37 Ibid., p. 244; *The Engineer*, 13 November 1896; Wohl, *Endangered Lives*, p. 131.

38 Percy and Grace Frankland, *Micro-organisms in Water* (London, 1894), p. 119ff.

39 *Aquarius*, X, January 1934, p. 12.

14. Regulating the Flow

1 *Morning Chronicle*, 24 September 1849.

2 Clay, *Remarks on the Water Supply of London*, p. 89; General Board of Health, *Report 1850*, p. 8; Anne Hardy ,'Parish Pump to Private Pipes: London's Water Supply in the Nineteenth Century', *Medical History*, supplement no. 11, 1991, p. 80.

3 *Minutes 1851*, pp. 215–16.

4 General Board, *Report 1850*, pp. 25–8.

5 *Minutes 1851*, pp. 26–38.

6 Ralph Turvey, 'Constant Water Supply', unpublished MS in the author's possession, undated (from now defunct website via John Porter), pp. 3, 8; Binnie, *Early Victorian Water Engineers*, p. 10.

7 Binnie, *Early Victorian Water Victorian Engineers*, p. 12; Roberts, *Chelsea to Cairo*, p. 198.

8 *JGL*, XIV, pp. 628, 22 August 1865.

9 *JGL*, XIV, p. 715, 3 October 1865, pp. 746–8, 17 October 1865, pp. 777–8, 31 October 1865.

10 *JGL*, XIV, pp. 628, 22 August 1865; General Board, *Report 1850*, p. 153

11 Clay, *Remarks on the Water Supply of London*, pp. 46ff and 107.

12 Rudden, *The New River: A Legal History*, pp. 306–10

13 LMA, ACC/2588/MW/C/15/298, Address to occupiers; Ward, *London's New River*, p. 73.

14 LMA, ACC/2558/NR/13/304, History of the New River; ACC/2558/NR/02/166-9, New River board papers, 1844–5; Ward, *London's New River*, p. 72.

15 Clifford, *A History of Private Bill Legislation,* vol. ii, p. 155n; Clay, *Sir William Clay and his family,* pp. 7–8, 5–6; Clay, *Remarks on the Water Supply of* London, pp. 73–4, 76.

16 Finer, *The Life and Times of Sir Edwin Chadwick,* p. 387; Clifford, *A History of Private Bill Legislation,* vol. ii, pp. 156–7.

17 Clay, *Remarks on the Water Supply of* London, p. 76.

18 LMA, ACC/2558/GJ/08/001-3, ACC/2558/GJ/1/13/1&2 Grand Junction court minutes, 20 February 1867, 4 June 1868.

19 LMA, ACC/2558/EL/A/01/025, East London court minutes, 9 January 1834.

20 Matthews, *Hydraulia,* pp. 343–7; LMA, ACC/2558/ MW/C/43/029, John Martin 1828 plan for the West End.

21 Glasgow Water Supply, https://www.ice.org.uk/what-is-civil-engineering/what-do-civil-engineers-do/glasgow-water-supply/.

22 Clifford, *A History of Private Bill Legislation,* vol. ii, pp. 166–7.

15. Volcanoes of Filth

1 https://www.britishmuseum.org/collection/object/P_1909-0406-4.

2 https://artcollection.culture.gov.uk/artwork/3297/.

3 Allen, *Cleansing the City,* pp. 74, 70.

4 Gustave Doré and Blanchard Jerrold, *London: A Pilgrimage* (New York: Dover, 1970). See for instance illustrations on pp. xxxiv, 49, 179, 185 and plates opposite pp. 4, 18, 26, 30, 40, 58, 114, 136 and 150.

5 Halliday, *The Great Stink,* p. 11.

6 Ibid., p. x.

7 Henry Jephson, *The Sanitary Evolution of London* (Brooklyn, 1907), p. 77.

8 This account of the Great Stink and its consequences is based on Rosemary Ashton, *One Hot Summer: Dickens, Darwin, Disraeli and the Great Stink of 1858* (London: Yale, 2017), Allen, *Cleansing the City,* and Halliday, *The Great Stink.* The quotations in this paragraph can be found at Ashton, pp. 118, 124, and Allen, *Cleansing the City,* p. 57.

9 Ashton, *One Hot Summer,* pp. 205, 107, 131, 229.

10 Ibid., p. 18.

11 *The Times,* 21 July 1858.

12 Ashton, *One Hot Summer,* p. 184.

13 Luckin, *Pollution and Control,* pp. 17–19.

14 John Hollingshead, *Underground London,* p. 24.

15 Jackson, *Dirty Old London,* p. 5.

16 Hollingshead, *Underground London*, pp. 15–18.

17 Allen, *Cleansing the City*, pp. 82, 84. The historian was Donald J. Olsen.

16. Choleraic Poison

1 For a narrative of the outbreak, see Halliday, *The Great Stink*, pp. 137–40, and Luckin, *Pollution and Control*, pp. 86–95.

2 LMA, ACC/2558/EL/A/28/001, *East London Observer*, 8 December 1866. The East London Waterworks kept a scrapbook of press cuttings, which has been preserved in the London Metropolitan Archives: I have drawn on it freely.

3 LMA, ACC/2558/EL/A/28/001, *East London Observer*, 6 Sep 1866; ACC/2558/EL/A/01/038, East London court minutes, 19 November 1863.

4 *Minutes 1851*, p. 667.

5 *The Times*, 5 September 1866.

6 LMA, ACC/2558/EL/A/01/039, Court minutes, 2 August, 9 August, 16 August 1866.

7 For the Ouse scheme, see LMA, ACC/2558/EL/A/01/039, Court minutes, 8 September, 29 September, 6 October, 13 October 1864.

8 *The Times*, 2 August 1866; LMA, ACC/2558/MW/C/15/01/008, Court minutes, 20 September 1866.

9 LMA, ACC/2558/EL/A/01/039, Court minutes, 13 September 1866; ACC/2558/MW/C/15/01/008, East London engineer's reports, 20 September 1866.

10 LMA, ACC/2558/EL/A/01/038, Court minutes, 6 December 1860, 7 February 1861, 4 August 1864; ACC/2558/MW/C/15/01/008, Engineer's reports, 9 August 1866.

11 *Evening Standard*, 11 December 1866.

12 LMA, ACC/2558/EL/A/01/038, Court minutes, 4 August 1866.

13 Halliday, *The Great Stink*, p. 139.

14 LMA, ACC/2558/EL/A/28/001, *The Globe*, 16 September 1870, *Illustrated Times*, 24 September 1870.

15 Luckin, *Pollution and Control*, pp. 91–2.

16 LMA, ACC/2558/EL/A/28/001, *Evening Standard*, 14 August 1866.

17 Institute of Civil Engineers obituary in *Grace's Guide*.

18 LMA, ACC/2558/EL/A/28/001, *South London Chronicle*, 20 July 1872; *JGL*, XXI, p. 657, 30 July 1872, XXI, pp. 702, 854, 13

August 1872; Vanessa Taylor and Frank Trentmann, 'Liquid Politics: Water and the Politics of Everyday Life in the Modern City', *Past & Present*, vol. 211 (1), pp. 199–241, May 2011, https://doi.org/10.1093/pastj/gtq068.

19 For changing notions of 'the consumer' and the Dobbs case, see Taylor and Trentmann, 'Liquid Politics'.

20 *JGL*, XXI, p. 295, 9 April 1872.

21 *Balfour Commission*, p. 16; *Minutes 1851*, pp. 759–60. And see Hardy, 'Parish Pump to Private Pipes: London's Water Supply in the Nineteenth Century' *Medical History*, supplement no. 11, 76–93, 1991: she credits Whitechapel's medical officer, John Liddle, for pushing the East London to introduce constant supply.

22 *Minutes 1852*, East London, p. 18.

23 Turvey, 'Constant Water Supply'.

24 *Balfour Commission*, p. 33.

25 Bolton, *London's Water Supply*, p. 163.

26 *Balfour Commission*, p. 66.

17. Cow-keepers and Firefighters

1 *Minutes 1851*, pp. 774–7.

2 *Minutes 1821*, pp. 141–2

3 Ibid., pp. 120–6

4 *Report 1840*, pp. 62–77.

5 LMA, ACC/2558/EL/A/01/025, East London court minutes, 17 February 1834; *JGL*, XXVII, p. 506, April 1876.

6 *Minutes 1821*, p. 160; *Minutes 1821*, p. 140; LMA, ACC/2558/SV/01/183, Southwark & Vauxhall letter book, 24 December 1875, 3 January 1876, 11 February 1876; ACC/2558/GJ/1/176, GJ letter book, 26 May 1875; ACC/2558/GJ/1/1/178, GJ letter book, 19 February 1877.

7 LMA, ACC/2558/SV/1/28, S&V court minutes, 16 January 1879.

8 LMA, ACC/2558/GJ/1/14/1, GJ court minutes, 22 July 1874.

9 Shotter Boys, https://www.britishmuseum.org/collection/object/P_1880-1113-2809; Scharf, https://www.britishmuseum.org/collection/object/P_1862-0614-270.

10 LMA, ACC/2558/MW/C/15/42, Grand Junction handbill.

11 van Lieshout, 'The most valuable means of extinguishing fires': Fire-fighting and the London water companies in the long

eighteenth century', *London Journal, 42* (1), pp. 53–69, 2017, https://doi.org/10.1080/03058034.2017.1279869.

12 LMA, ACC/2558/MW/C/15/24.

13 For Braidwood, Shaw and the history of fire-fighting, I have relied on Judith Flanders, *The Victorian City: Everyday Life in Dickens' London* (London: Atlantic, 2012), pp. 111-21, Susan Holloway, *Courage High: A History of Firefighting in London* (London: HMSO, 1992) and David Owen, *The Government of Victorian London, 1855–1889*, ed. Roy McLeod (Harvard University Press, 1982).

14 LMA, ACC/2558/GJ/1/14/1, GJ court minutes, 6 January and 17 February 1875.

18. Watering Capital

1 *Daily Telegraph*, 30 July 1874.

2 *JGL*, XXIX, p. 658, 1 May 1877.

3 LMA, ACC/2558/MW/C/15/240, Report to the Richmond Vestry of the Committee appointed to enquire into the Water Supply.

4 Ron Berryman, 'Charles Burt and Richmond's Water War', *Richmond History* 24, 2004, p. 67–71.

5 LMA, ACC/2558/MW/C/15/240, Report to the Richmond Vestry.

6 LMA, ACC/2558/SV/1/192, S&V letter book Robinson to Hargrove's, 30 October 1874; ACC/2558/SV/1/180, S&V letter book Senior to S&V, 12 May 1874.

7 *Windsor and Eton Express*, 9 January 1875; LMA, ACC/2558/SV/1/181, Hargrove's to S&V, 6 January 1875.

8 LMA, ACC/2558/SV/1/123, Minutes of general meeting, 9 December 1875, ACC/2558/SV/1/192, Undated table of annual collections in Richmond, October 1875.

9 *JGL*, XXIX, pp. 978–81, 19 June 1877, XXIX, p. 91, 16 January 1877.

10 *JGL*, XXVII, 26 December 1876.

11 LMA, ACC/2558/SV/1/23, Minutes of general meeting, 14 December 1877, ACC/2558/SV/1/14/1, Court minutes, 14 December 1876; ACC/2558/SV/1/14/1, Draft letter, 14 December 1876.

12 LMA, ACC/2558/SV/1/14/1, Court minutes, 1 February 1877; *Surrey Advertiser*, 4 December 1875; *Surrey Comet*, 4 December 1875; Berryman, 'Charles Burt and Richmond's Water War'.

13 Reproduced in Berryman 'Charles Burt and Richmond's Water War'.

14 *JGL*, XXIX, p. 91, 16 Jan 1877, *Evening Standard*, 19 January 1877.

15 *JGL*, XXIX, pp. 118–9, 126, 23 January 1877.

16 *JGL*, XXIX, pp. 154–5, 159–60, 30 January 1877, *Evening Standard*, 27 January 1877.

17 *JGL*, XXIX, pp. 262, 20 February 1877.

18 LMA, ACC/2558/SV/1/14/1, Court minutes, 3 April 1877, *Windsor & Eton Gazette*, 14 April 1877.

19 *Daily News*, 21 December 1876, *Pall Mall Gazette*, 30 January 1877.

20 *Surrey Advertiser*, 12 January 1878.

21 LMA, ACC/2558/SV/1/27, Court minutes, 7 February 1878, 20 March 1878, 16 May 1878.

22 Ron Berryman ,'Richmond's Waterworks', *Richmond History* 37, pp. 56–63, 2016.

23 LMA, ACC/2558/MW/C/45/014, Notes on the Richmond supply 1967.

24 Quick's GJ salary, LMA, ACC/2558/GJ/1/166, 1 April 1874, S&V salary, *JGL*, XXVII, pp. 878–9, 19 December 1876; ACC/2558/GJ/1/176, letter book Coe to R. H. Wyatt, 27 April 1875.

25 Sally Potts kindly supplied the photograph, plus information on the Quicks' occupancy of Cross Deep House.

26 LMA, ACC/2558/SV/1/14/1, Court minutes, 9 January 1873, offers a typical example.

27 See, for example the decision to rebuild the Grand Junction standpipe at Kew Bridge, taken at a meeting on 23 January 1867 (LMA, ACC/2558/GJ/1/13/1&2) .

28 LMA, ACC/2558/SV/1/14/1, Court minutes, 7 November 1872. For other examples of contracts accepted without tender, see ACC/2558/GJ/1/14/1, Court minutes, 6 November 1872, ACC/2558/GJ/1/14/1, Court minutes, 23 July 1873, ACC/2558/SV/1/191/1, Letter book Robinson to Harvey's and Robinson to Aird's, 13 November 1872.

29 LMA, ACC/2558/SV/1/14/1, Court minutes, 2 March 1876, ACC/2558/GJ/1/14/1, Court minutes, 24 May 1876, ACC/2558/GJ/1/377, undated note from Whiting.

30 LMA, ACC/2558/GJ/1/14/1, Court minutes, 16 February 1876, 1 March 1876.

31 LMA, ACC/2558/SV/1/14/1, Court minutes, 14 October 1875, 28 October 1875; ACC/2558/SV/1/193, Letter book Jelley to Coome, Jelley to Layton, 29 September 1875.

32 *JGL*, XXX, p. 757, 13 November 1877.

33 LMA, ACC/2558/GJ/01/0743, Case for the promoters.

34 LMA, ACC/2558/GJ/1/14/1, Court minutes, 1 June 1876, ACC/2558/GJ/1/178, Letter book Coe to Harvey's, 7 February 1877.

35 LMA, ACC/2558/ SV/1/14/1, Court minutes, 25 May 1876, ACC/2558/GJ/1/14/1, Court minutes, 7 Jun 1876.

36 *JGL*, XXIX, pp. 978–81, 19 June 1877.

37 National Trust Collections via artuk.org; James Clay's death reported LMA, ACC/2558/GJ/1/14/1, Court minutes, 1 October 1873.

38 https://www.npg.org.uk/collections/search/portrait/mw281285. Christopher Clay kindly supplied the sketch by Cockerell.

39 *The Times* obituary, 20 March 1928. See also letters and articles in *The Times* of 15 July 1886 (Charterhouse), 5 May 1890 (a Clay painting reviewed with faint praise), 26 November 1901 and 18 December 1901 (underfed children), 17 September 1906 (socialism). *Syndicalism and Labour* was published in 1912.

40 LMA, ACC/2558/GJ/1/755, Committee of investigation report. The professional accountant was Robert McLean.

41 *The Times*, 30 November 1830, 4 September 1843.

42 *The Times*, 10 March 1880.

43 Robinson's dismissal can be tracked in LMA, ACC/2558/ SV/1/14/1, Court minutes, 3 December, 8 December, 10 December, 21 December 1874; ACC/2558/SV/1/181, Letter book Robinson to Clay, 4 December 1874.

44 See, for instance, his letters to Robinson's successor at the S&V, Alfred Jelley, in LMA, ACC/2558/GJ/1/176, Letter book 17, 19 and 21 October 1875.

45 LMA, ACC/2558/GJ/1/896, Report of duties of chief officer, 21 April 1875.

46 LMA, ACC/2558/ GJ/1/176, Letter book, 12 November 1875.

47 See for instance *JGL*, XII, p. 796, 29 December 1863, XIV, p. 16, 10 January 1865, XVI, pp. 14–15, 8 January 1867, XVII, p. 909, 22 December 1868, XIX, pp. 54–55, 18 January 1870.

48 *JGL*, XXVII, pp. 695–6, 9 May 1876.

49 *Survey of London: Battersea*, Chapter 10, p. 3, Chapter 11 p. 14; Census 1871; Noel Whiting's will via probatesearch.service.gov.uk.

50 Census 1861; Henry Whiting's will via probatesearch.service.org.uk.

51 *Repertory of Patent Inventions*, vi, p. 35

52 LMA, ACC/2558/SV/1/14/1, Court minutes, 4 May and 11 May 1876, ACC/2558/GJ 1/14/1, Court minutes, 5 Apr 1876.

53 LMA, ACC/2558/SV/1/182, Whiting to board, 20 July 1875.

54 LMA, ACC/2558/GJ/1/167, GJ letter book Coe to Ellice, 24 April 1876.

55 C. J. Napier, 'Fixed Asset Accounting in Shipping', pp. 343–73, in R. H. Parker and B. S. Yamey (eds), *Accounting History: Some British Contributions* (Oxford: Clarendon Press, 1994).

56 LMA, ACC/2558/GJ/1/167, Coe to Stoneham, 29 July 1876, ACC/2558/ SV/1/183, Stoneham to directors, 18 October 1876, ACC/2558/SV/1/14/1, Court minutes, 19 October 1876.

57 *JGL*, XXV, pp. 321–2, 9 March 1875.

58 LMA, ACC/2558/GJ/1/167, Coe report, 7 March 1877; *JGL*, XXIX, pp. 978–81, 19 June 1877.

59 LMA, ACC/2558/SV/1/34/1, Court minutes, 17 December 1879, ACC/2558/SV/1/15/1, Court minutes, 8 January 1880.

19. The Triumph of Vestrydom

1 Edward Ward, *The London Spy Compleat*. Ned Ward's scabrous, scurrilous satire is an entertaining introduction to London at the turn of the seventeenth and eighteenth centuries, but for this chapter's account of London water politics in the nineteenth century I have drawn chiefly on William Robson, *The Government and Misgovernment of London* (London: George Allen & Unwin, 1939), David Owen, *The Government of Victorian London 1855–1889*, ed. Roy McLeod (Harvard University Press, 1982) and John Broich, *London: Water and the Making of the Modern City* (Pittsburgh University Press, 2013).

2 Robson, *The Government and Misgovernment of London*, p. 23, Owen, *The Government of Victorian London*, p. 32–3.

3 Broich, *London*, p. 43.

4 See Jackson, *Dirty Old London*, pp. 91–7, for Hall and his role in the establishment of the MBW.

5 Robson, *The Government and Misgovernment of London*, p. 107.

6 *JGL*, XXIX, pp. 298–9, 20 February 1877, XXIX, pp. 338–9, 6 March 1877.

7 Broich, *London*, p. 97. The drought increased demand for water by up to 28 per cent.

8 Sir John Lubbock, *Hansard*, 22 February 1895; *Aquarius*, I, 1905, pp. 48–50.

9 Broich, *London*, p. 110.

10 *Balfour Commission*, pp. 33ff.

11 Joseph Chamberlain, *Hansard*, 22 February 1895.

12 Joel Bakan *The Corporation: The pathological pursuit of profit and power* (New York: Free Press, 2004), pp. 1–2.

20. Takeover to Today

1 *Aquarius*, VIII, 1913, pp. 142–4.

2 Dickinson, *Water Supply of Greater London*, p. 126.

3 *Aquarius*, XV, 1925, p. 393.

4 Ibid., pp. 415–18.

5 Ibid., 1924, p. 244–5.

6 Ibid., pp. 286–7. 'ECW' also threw in some gratuitous anti-Semitism aimed at the 'Jew landlords' in the East End.

7 Aquarius, undated, pp. 129–30, XLVII–XLIX, November 1960, p. 255.

8 Metropolitan Water Board, *London's Water Supply*, p. 160; *Aquarius*, October 1960, pp. 216–18.

9 *The Engineer*, 22 June 1917, 22 June 1928.

10 Ward, *London's New River*, p. 210.

11 Ibid., p. 184.

12 Barty-King, *Water – The Book*, p. 174.

13 *Water Down the Drain*, p. 18

14 John Dickens, 'Privatisation and Water', *Policy Making in Britain*, ed. Maurice Mullard (London: Routledge, 1995), pp. 159–79.

15 John Hassan, *A History of Water in Modern England and Wales* (Manchester University Press, 1998), pp. 193–6.

16 *Financial Times*, 17 October 2006. I have relied heavily in what follows on the *FT*, whose coverage of this issue has been consistently exemplary.

17 *FT*, 4 May, 10 September, 12 October, 5 November, 23 November 2017.

18 *FT*, 12 October 2018; Kate Bayliss and David Hall, 'Bringing Water into Public Ownership'.

19 *FT*, 23 November 2017, 19 October 2020.

20 https://www.affinitywater.co.uk/docs/Group-structure-from-April-2020.jpg.

21 *FT*, 4 May 2017, 17 December 2019, 6 January 2020.

22 *FT*, 31 January, 1 March 2018.

23 Bayliss and Hall, 'Public Ownership'; Water UK news item 'Bad for the Environment, Bad for Customers, and Bad for the Economy', 21 November 2019.

24 Thames Water, *Trunk Mains Forensic Review Final Findings Report*, 24 March 2017.

25 Statistics on water use today and details of proposals to increase supplies are derived from Thames Water and Affinity Water's *Water Resources Management Plans*, revised in April 2020.

26 John Lawson, 'The Proposed Severn to Thames Transfer', October 2013.

27 *Aquarius*, 1948, pp. 124–5; *BBC News*, 14 September 2006; GARD Group Against Reservoir Development, http://www.abingdonreservoir.org.uk/.

28 Thames Water, *Water Resources Management Plan annual review 2019-20*; *Londonist* 'The Place That Will Save Us When There's a Drought', https://londonist.com/2015/10/london-s-desalination-plant.

29 Michael Essex-Lopresti, *Exploring the New River*, pp. 21–7.

30 https://damealiceowens.herts.sch.uk/about-us/our-history/war-memorials/.

31 LMA, ACC/2558/SV/01/193, S&V letter book Jelley to Drew, 12 November 1875, *Evening Standard*, 13 November 1875.

Bibliography

Ackroyd, Peter, *London: The Biography* (London: Chatto & Windus, 2000)

Aditnow.co.uk, Mine exploration, photographs and mining history, https://www.aditnow.co.uk/

Adkins, Roy and Leslie, *Eavesdropping on Jane Austen's England* (London: Abacus, 2014)

Affinity Water, *Water Resources Management Plan*, https://www.affinitywater.co.uk/docs/Affinity_Water_Final_WRMP19_April_2020.pdf April 2020

Alford, Stephen, *London's Triumph: Merchant Adventurers and the Tudor City* (London: Penguin, 2018)

Allen, Eleanor, *Wash & Brush Up* (London: A & C Black, 1976)

Allen, Michelle, *Cleansing the City: Sanitary Geographies in Victorian London* (Athens: Ohio University Press, 2008)

Almeroth-Williams, Thomas, *City of Beasts: How Animals Shaped Georgian London* (Manchester University Press, 2019)

Alsford, Stephen, *Florilegium Urbanum*, http://users.trytel.com/~tristan/towns/florilegium/community/cmfabr24.html

Anderson, Gary M., and Robert D. Tollison, 'Adam Smith's Analysis of Joint-Stock Companies', *Journal of Political Economy*, vol. 90, no. 6 1237–1256, December 1982

Bibliography

Anon., *Supply of Water to London by means of the Henley and London Waterworks and Navigation* (London, 1848)

Aquarius, staff newspaper of the Metropolitan Water Board (in collection of the London Metropolitan Archives)

Ashton, Rosemary, *One Hot Summer: Dickens, Darwin, Disraeli and the Great Stink of 1858* (London: Yale, 2017)

Atkins, P. J., 'The Retail Milk Trade in London *c.* 1790–1914', Economic History Review new series, vol. 33, no. 4, 522–37, November 1980

Bakan, Joel, *The Corporation: The pathological pursuit of profit and power* (New York: Free Press, 2004)

Balen, Malcolm, *A Very English Deceit: The South Sea Bubble and the world's first great financial scandal* (London: Fourth Estate, 2003)

Barratt, Nick, *Greater London: The Story of the Suburbs* (London: Random House, 2012)

Barton, D. B., *The Cornish Beam Engine* (Cornwall Books, 1989)

Barton, Nicholas, *The Lost Rivers of London* (London: Historical Publications, 1982)

Barty-King, Hugh, *Water – The Book: An Illustrated History of Water Supply and Wastewater in the United Kingdom* (London: Quiller Press, 1992)

Bateman, J. F., *On the Supply of Water to London from the sources of the River Severn* (London, 1865)

Bayliss, Kate, and David Hall, 'Bringing Water into Public Ownership: Costs and Benefits', Greenwich Academic Literature Archive, 2017

Bennett, John, 'John Connell Delarue Bevan and the East Cornwall Silver Mining Company', *British Mining*, 43, Sheffield, 1991, https://www.nmrs.org.uk/assets/pdf/BM43/BM43-5-8-bevan.pdf

Berryman, Ron, 'Charles Burt and Richmond's Water
     War', *Richmond History* 24, 2004

——'Richmond's Waterworks', *Richmond History* 37, 2016

Binnie, G. M., *Early Victorian Water Engineers* (London:
     Thomas Telford, 1981)

Bolton, Col. Sir Francis, *London Water Supply* (London, 1884)

Bowman, John, *Water Supply Today* (Oxford University Press,
     1950)

Briggs, Asa, *Victorian Cities* (London: Pelican Books, 1968)

Broich, John, *London: Water and the Making of the Modern City*
     (Pittsburgh University Press, 2013)

Bromehead, C. E. N., 'The Early History of Water-Supply',
     The Geographical Journal, XCIX, nos 3 and 4, March
     and April 1942

Brooke, Jill, *A Green Finger into London*, unpublished MS,
     London, 2004 (at London Museum of Water and
     Steam, Kew Bridge)

Burton, Anthony, *The Railway Builders* (London: John
     Murray, 1992)

Carswell, John, *The South Sea Bubble* (Stroud: Alan Sutton,
     1993)

Chatfield, Michael, and Richard Vangermeersch (eds),
     The History of Accounting: An International Encyclopedia
     (London: Routledge, 1996)

Clay, C. G. A. (Christopher), *Economic Expansion and Social
     Change: England 1500–1700*, vol. 2, Industry, trade and
     government (Cambridge: CUP, 1984)

Clay, Christopher, *Sir William Clay and his Family*,
     unpublished MS, courtesy of the author

Clay, Sir William, *Remarks on the Water Supply of London*,
     second edition, preface dated 15 December 1849
     (London, 1849)

Clifford, Frederick, *A History of Private Bill Legislation*, 2 vols (London: Butterworth, 1885 and 1887)

Colburn, Zerah, and William H. Maw, *The Waterworks of London*, reprinted from *Engineering*, London, 1867

Collier, Mary, *The Woman's Labour: An Epistle to Mr Stephen Duck* (London, 1739), via https://www.usask.ca/english/barbauld/related_texts/collier.html

Cosh, Mary, *A History of Islington* (London: Historical Publications, 2005)

——*An Historical Walk along the New River* (London: Islington Archaeology & History Society, 1988)

Cummins, John, *Francis Drake* (New York: St Martin's Press, 1995)

Dalrymple, William, *The Anarchy: The Relentless Rise of the East India Company* (London: Bloomsbury, 2019)

Darcy, Jane, 'Promiscuous Throng: the "Indecent" Manner of Sea-bathing in the Nineteenth Century,' *TLS*, 3 July 2020

Darwin, Erasmus, *The Botanic Garden*, part 1, The Economy of Vegetation, 1788

Dickens, Charles, *Dombey and Son* (Ware: Wordsworth Classics, 1995)

——*Great Expectations* (Oxford: World's Classics, 1998)

——*Little Dorrit* (London: Penguin, 1967)

——*Our Mutual Friend* (London: Penguin Classics, 1997)

Dickens, John, 'Privatisation and Water', *Policy Making in Britain*, Maurice Mullard (ed) (London: Routledge, pp. 159–79, 1995)

Dickinson, H. W., 'How the Cornish Engine Came to London', *Engineering*, 510, 31 May 1946

——*Sir Samuel Morland: Diplomat and Inventor, 1625–1695* (Cambridge: Newcomen Society, 1970)

Dickinson, H. W., *Water Supply of Greater London* (Leamington Spa and London: Newcomen Society, 1954)

Doré, Gustave, and Blanchard Jerrold, *London: A Pilgrimage* (New York: Dover, 1970)

Dyos, H. J., and Michael Wolff, *The Victorian City: Images and Realities*, 2 vols (London: Routledge & Keegan Paul, 1973)

Earle, Peter, *The Making of the English Middle Class: Business, Society and Family Life in London 1660–1730* (London: Methuen, 1989)

Ellis, David, 'The Stone Pipe Company Scandal in the early 19th Century – Incompetence or Fraud?', *Hurstbourne Tarrant Historical Society*, 2016, http://www.hbthistoricalsociety.org.uk/

Emerson, George Rose, *London: How the Great City Grew* (London: Routledge, Warne and Routledge, 1862)

Essex-Lopresti, Michael, *Exploring the New River* (Studley: Brewin Books, 1997)

Evans, R. J., *The Victorian Age 1815–1914* (London: Edward Arnold, 1969)

Eveleigh, David J., *Bogs, Baths and Basins: the Story of Domestic Sanitation* (Stroud: History Press, 2011)

Finer, S. E., *The Life and Times of Sir Edwin Chadwick* (London: Methuen, 1952)

Flanders, Judith, *The Victorian City: Everyday Life in Dickens' London* (London: Atlantic, 2012)

Flaxman, Ted, and Ted Jackson, *Sweet & Wholesome Water: Five Centuries of History of Water-bearers in the City of London* (London: privately printed, 2004)

Forsyth, Hazel, *The Cheapside Hoard: London's Lost Jewels* (London: Museum of London, 2013)

Fox, Caroline, *Memories of Old Friends: Extracts from the Journals and Letters 1835–1871* (London, 1882)

Frankland, Edward, 'On the Proposed Water Supply of the Metropolis: a Lecture at the Royal Institution of Great Britain', reprinted from the *Journal of Gas Lighting* (London, 1868)

Frankland, Percy, and Mrs Percy Frankland (Grace), *Micro-organisms in Water* (London, 1894)

Frederic, Harold, *The Market Place* (London, 1899)

General Board of Health, *Report on the Supply of Water to the Metropolis* (London: HMSO, 1850)

Gerhold, Dorian, *London Plotted: Plans of London Buildings c. 1450–1720* (London Topographical Society, 2016)

Glasse, Hannah, *First Catch Your Hare: The Art of Cookery Made Plain and Easy*, 1747 edition (London: Prospect, 2012)

Goodman, Ruth, *How To Be a Tudor: A Dawn-to-Dusk Guide to Everyday Life* (London: Penguin 2015)

——, *How To Be a Victorian* (London: Penguin 2014)

——, *The Domestic Revolution: How the Introduction of Coal into our Homes Changed Everything* (London: Michael O'Mara, 2020)

Gough, J. W., *Sir Hugh Myddelton: Entrepreneur and Engineer* (Oxford: Clarendon Press, 1964)

Grace's Guide to British Industrial History, https://gracesguide.co.uk/

Graham-Leigh, John, *London's Water Wars: The Competition for London's Water Supply in the 19th century* (London: Francis Boutle, 2000)

Grenade, L., *The Singularities of London*, 1578, (eds) Derek Keene and Ian W. Archer (London Topographical Society, 2014)

Guthrie, A., *Cornwall in the Age of Steam* (Padstow: Tabb House, 1994)

Halliday, Stephen, *The Great Stink: Sir Joseph Bazalgette and the Cleansing of the Victorian Metropolis* (London: History Press, 2001)

Hamlin, Christopher, *A Science of Impurity: Water Analysis in Nineteenth Century Britain* (Bristol: Adam Hilger, 1990)

Hansard, via https://api.parliament.uk/historic-hansard

Hardy, Anne, 'Parish Pump to Private Pipes: London's Water Supply in the Nineteenth Century' *Medical History*, supplement no 11, 76–93, 1991

——, 'Water and the Search for Public Health in London in the Eighteenth and Nineteenth Centuries', *Medical History*, 28, 250–282, 1984

Hartley, Dorothy, *Water in England* (London: Macdonald, 1964)

Hassall, Arthur Hill, *A Microscopic Examination of the Water Supplied to the Inhabitants of London and the Suburban Districts* (London, 1850)

Hassan, John, *A History of Water in Modern England and Wales* (Manchester University Press, 1998)

Hassan, John, 'The Impact and Development of the Water Supply in Manchester, 1568–1882, *Journal of the Historic Society of Lancashire and Cheshire*, vol. 133, 25–45, 1983, https://www.hslc.org.uk/wp-content/uploads/2017/05/133-3-Hassan.pdf

Higham, Nick, 'Watering the Capital: an Untold Story of Fraud in the Victorian Water Industry', unpublished MS, 2019 (at London Museum of Water and Steam, Kew Bridge)

History of Parliament, http://www.histparl.ac.uk/

Hollingshead, John, *Underground London* (London, 1862; reprinted using optical character recognition software, Memphis, 2012)

House of Commons, *Minutes of Evidence Taken before the Select Committee on the Supply of Water to the Metropolis* (London, 1821)

——, *Minutes of Evidence taken before the Select Committee on the Metropolis Water Bill* (London, 1851)

——, *Minutes of Evidence taken before the Select Committee on the Metropolis Water Bills* (London, 1852)

House of Lords, *Report from the Select Committee of the House of Lords Appointed to Inquire into the Supply of Water to the Metropolis, with the Minutes of Evidence*, London, 1840

Houston, Alexander, *Rivers as Sources of Water Supply* (London, 1917)

——, *The Romance of the New River*, reprinted from Sir Alexander Houston's Twentieth Annual Report to the Metropolitan Water Board (London: MWB, 1926)

Hubbard, Kate, *Devices and Desires: Bess of Hardwick and the Building of Elizabethan England* (London: Chatto & Windus, 2018)

Hughes, Molly, *A London Child of the 1870s* (1934) (London: Persephone Books, 2005)

Inglis, Lucy, *Georgian London: Into the Streets* (London: Penguin, 2014)

Ingram, Derek, 'The First Caian Engineer and the First Caian Pirate', *The Caius Engineer*, 13 (1), 2001, https://web.archive.org/web/20070902112021/http://www.cai.cam.ac.uk/students/study/engineering/engineer01/cepirate.htm

Institution of Civil Engineers (ICE), *Proceedings*, London

Jackson, Lee, *Dirty Old London: The Victorian Fight Against Filth* (London: Yale, 2014)

Jephson, Henry, *The Sanitary Evolution of London* (Brooklyn, 1907)

John Snow Archive and Research Companion, https://johnsnow.matrix.msu.edu/

Johnson, Steven, *The Ghost Map: A Street, a City, an Epidemic and the Hidden Power of Urban Networks* (London: Penguin, 2008)

Jonson, Ben, 'Every Man in His Humour', *Plays* I (London: Everyman, 1964)

——, *Poems* (London; Routledge and Kegan Paul, 1971)

Journal of Gas Lighting, Water Supply and Sanitary Reform

Kempton Steam Museum, *90 Years of the Kempton Engines 1929–2019* (London, 2019)

Kensey, Michael F., *London's New River in Maps*, privately printed, 2013

Kew Bridge Engines, *How a Cornish Pumping Engine Works* (London, nd)

Kew Bridge Museum, *Wash Day Blues: an Exhibition about Laundering through the Ages* (London, 1999)

Kirkwood, James P., *Report on the Filtration of River Waters for the Supply of Cities* (St Louis, 1869)

Kynaston, David, *The City of London*, vol. 1, 'A World of Its Own 1815–1890' (London: Chatto & Windus, 1994)

Latham, Frank, *The Construction of Roads, Paths and Sea Defences* (Cambridge, 1903)

Laws, Bill, *Fifty Railways that Changed the Course of History* (London: New Burlington Books, 2018)

Lawson, John, 'The Proposed Severn to Thames Transfer', presentation, Royal Academy of Engineering, 25 October 2011

Legacies of British slave-ownership, https://www.ucl.ac.uk/lbs/

Lilienfeld, David E., 'John Snow: The First Hired Gun?',
    American Journal of Epidemiology, Vol 152, Issue 1, 4–9,
    July 2000

Lipschutz, Daniel E., 'The Water Question in London,
    1827-1831', *Bulletin of the History of Medicine*, vol. 42,
    no. 6, 510–26, 1968

Luckin, Bill, *Pollution and Control: A Social History of the Thames
    in the Nineteenth Century* (Bristol: Adam Hilger, 1986)

Magnusson, Roberta J., *Water Technology in the Middle Ages:
    Cities, Monasteries and Waterworks after the Roman Empire*
    (Baltimore and London: Johns Hopkins University
    Press, 2001)

Martin, John, *Thames and Metropolis Improvement Plan*
    (London, 1849)

Matthews, William, *Hydraulia: An Historical and Descriptive
    Account of the Water Works of London and the Contrivances
    for Supplying Other Great Cities in Different Ages and
    Countries* (London, 1835)

Mayhew, Henry, *London Labour and the London Poor*, vol.
    2 (London, 1864)

McGuire, Michael J., *The Chlorine Revolution: Water
    Disinfection and the Fight to Save Lives* (Denver:
    American Water Works Association, 2013)

Metropolitan Water Board, *London's Water Supply, 1903–1953*
    (London: Staples Press, 1953)

Michaels, David, *The Triumph of Doubt: Dark Money and the
    Science of Deception* (Oxford University Press, 2020)

Mithen, Steven, *Thirst: Water and Power in the Ancient World*
    (London: Weidenfeld and Nicolson, 2012)

Moore, Rowan, *Slow Burn City: London in the 21st century*
    (London: Picador, 2016)

Morris, R. E., *History of the New River*, unpublished MS, 1934 (London Museum of Water and Steam, Kew Bridge)

Mr Pepys' Small Change, 'The Three Tuns Tavern against the Great Conduit in Cheapside', https://c17thlondon tokens.com/2016/07/19/the-three-tuns-tavern-against-the-great-conduit-in-cheapside/

Murray, David, *The York Buildings Company* (Glasgow: James Maclehose, 1883), https://www.electricscotland. com/business/york.pdf

Newman, Jon, *River Effra: South London's Secret Spine* (London: Signal, 2016)

O'Connell, Sheila, *London 1753* (London: British Museum Press, 2003)

Odlyzko, Andrew, 'Bubbles and Gullibility', Digital Technology Centre, University of Minnesota, Winter 2020, http://www.dtc.umn.edu/~odlyzko/doc/mania17.pdf

Owen, David, *The Government of Victorian London, 1855–1889*, ed. Roy McLeod (Harvard University Press, 1982)

Oxford Dictionary of National Biography, https://www. oxforddnb.com/

Palmer, Susan, *At Home with the Soanes* (London: Pimpernel Press, 2015)

Parker, R. H., and B. S. Yamey (eds), *Accounting History: Some British Contributions* (Oxford: Clarendon Press, 1994)

Parker, R. H., *Management Accounting: an Historical Perspective* (New York: Augustus M Kelley, 1969)

Pearce, Fred, *When the Rivers Run Dry: Water, the Defining Crisis of the Twenty-First Century* (Boston: Beacon Press, 2018)

Peck, Alan S., *The Great Western at Swindon Works* (Royston: Heathfield Railway Publications, 2009)

Pepys, Samuel, *The Diary of Samuel Pepys*, https://www.pepysdiary.com/diary

——, *The Shorter Pepys*, ed. Robert Latham (London: Bell & Hyman, 1985)

Picard, Liza, *Restoration London: Everyday Life in London 1660-1670* (London: Phoenix, 2003)

——, *Victorian London: The Life of a City, 1840–1870* (London: Weidenfeld & Nicolson, 2005)

Old Bailey Online, https://www.oldbaileyonline.org

Poor Law Commission, *An Inquiry into the Sanitary Condition of the Labouring Population of Great Britain* (London, 1842)

Porter, Roy, *London: A Social History* (London: Penguin, 1996)

Pugh, Edwin, *The City of the World: A Book about London and the Londoner* (London: Thomas Nelson)

Report of the royal commission on Metropolitan Water Supply, the Balfour Commission (London, 1893)

Rennie, Sir John, *Autobiography* (London and New York, 1875)

Richardson, John, *Islington Past*, revised edition (London: Historical Publications, 2000)

Roberts, Gwilym, *Chelsea to Cairo: Taylor-made Water Through Eleven Reigns and Six Continents* (London: Thomas Telford, 2006)

Robson, William, *The Government and Misgovernment of London* (London: George Allen & Unwin, 1939)

Rogers, Pat, 'The York Buildings Dragons: Desaguliers, Arbuthnot and Attitudes towards the Scientific Community', *Notes and Records, Royal Society*, December 20, 71(4), 335–60 (London, 2017), https://www.ncbi.nlm.nih.gov/pmc/articles/PMC5906434/

Rose, Martin, *Henry Winstanley, 1644–1703: The Last Renaissance Engineer* (London: Cygnet Press, in press)

Rowlandson, Thomas, and A. C. Pugin, *The Microcosm of London*, with text by John Summerson (London: Penguin, 1943)

Rudden, Bernard, *The New River: A Legal History* (Oxford: Clarendon Press, 1985)

Saul, G. M., *London's Water Supply, 1580–1880: A Commentary on the Exhibition at Brunel University*, unpublished MS, 1979 (at London Museum of Water and Steam, Kew Bridge)

Schoenwald, Richard L., 'Training Urban Man' in Dyos and Wolff (eds) *The Victorian City: Images and Realities*, vol. 2, 669–92, 1973

Shadwell, Arthur, *The London Water Supply* (London, 1899)

Simon, John, 'Report on the Last Two Cholera Epidemics', https://johnsnow.matrix.msu.edu/work.php?id=15-78-7F

Smiles, Samuel, *Lives of Boulton and Watt* (London: John Murray, 1865)

——, *Lives of the Engineers*, vol. 1 (London: John Murray 1862)

Smith, Alan, 'Steam and the City: The Committee of Proprietors of the Invention for Raising Water by Fire, 1715–1735', MS of a paper read to the Newcomen Society, London, 9 November 1977 (at London Museum of Water and Steam, Kew Bridge)

Smith, Stephen, *Underground London: Travels Beneath the City Streets* (London: Abacus, 2005)

Steele, Jess, and Mike Steele (eds), *The Streets of London: The Booth Notebooks – East* (London: Deptford Forum Publishing, 2018)

Stilgoe, Henry, 'Some Features of the London Water Supply' in *Transactions of the Institute of Water Engineers*, vol. XXX, London, pp. 190–200, 1925

Stewart, Rick, *Notes on East Cornwall Silver Mines*, unpublished MS, 2016

Stow, John, *The Survey of London*, 1603 edition (London: Everyman, 1908)

——, *The Survey of London*, updated by Anthony Munday and others (London, 1633)

Stringer, G. F., *Some Descriptive Notes on the New River Head*. (1927; reprinted London: Amwell Society and Thames Water, 2012)

Sunderland, David, '"Disgusting to the Imagination and Destructive to the Health?" The Metropolitan Supply of Water, 1820–52', *Urban History*, 30, 3, pp. 359–80, 2003

Survey of London (via British History Online)

Talling, Paul, *London's Lost Rivers* (London: R H Books, 2011)

Taylor, Vanessa, and Frank Trentmann, 'Liquid Politics: Water and the Politics of Everyday Life in the Modern City', *Past & Present*, vol. 211 (1) pp. 199–241, May 2011, https://doi.org/10.1093/pastj/gtq068

Tellem, Geraint, *The Thames* (Andover: Jarrold, 2003)

Thames Water, *Water Resources Management Plan*, https://www.thameswater.co.uk/media-library/home/about-us/regulation/water-resources/technical-report/executive-summary.pdf April 2020

Thompson, E. P., *The Making of the English Working Class* (London: Penguin, 2013)

The Times, 'The History of the Water Monopoly', 1849, 10-part series reprinted in *Aquarius*, 46ff, 1908

The Use of Pure Water (London: Ladies' Sanitary Assocation, nd)

Tobacco Explained: The Truth about the Tobacco Industry . . . in its Own Words, https://escholarship.org/uc/item/9fp6566b

Tomory, Leslie, *The History of the London Water Industry 1580-1820* (Baltimore: Johns Hopkins University Press, 2017)

Tregoning Hooper, W., 'The Cornish Pumping Engine', *The Engineer*, 28 August 1953

Trench, Richard, and Ellis Hillman, *London Under London: A Subterranean Guide* (London: John Murray, 1984)

Trollope, Anthony, *The Way We Live Now* (London: Penguin Classics, 1994)

Turvey, Ralph, 'Constant Water Supply', turvey.demon. co.uk, undated, from now defunct website via John Porter

Tyas, G. F., *Old Pumping Machinery*, MS notes, now in the Science Museum, Berry Collection 4/7.1, 1948

Tyre, John (pseud), *Free Like Conduit Water: The New River, its Moral and Immoral Economies* (London: Past Tense, 2013)

UK Census Online

Upper Windrush Local History Society, 'Stone Pipe Company', http://www.uwlhs.uk/prj_spc.html

Vale, Edmund, *The Harveys of Hale* (Truro: D Bradford Barton, 1966)

van Lieshout, Carry, *London's Changing Waterscapes: the Management of Water in Eighteenth-Century London*, unpublished PhD thesis (King's College London, 2012), https://kclpure.kcl.ac.uk/portal/

Van Lieshout, Carry, '"The Most Valuable Means of Extinguishing the Destroying Fires": Fire Fighting and the London Water Companies in the Long Eighteenth Century', *London Journal*, 4 (1), pp. 53-69, 2017, https://doi.org/10.1080/03058034.2017.1279869

Vickery, Amanda, *Behind Closed Doors* (London: Yale, 2010)

Wagner, Tamara S., *Financial Speculation in Victorian Fiction: Plotting Money and the Novel Genre, 1815–1904* (Ohio State University Press, 2010)

Walling, Philip, *Till the Cows Come Home: The Story of Our Eternal Dependence* (London: Atlantic Books, 2018)

Ward, Edward, *The London Spy Compleat*, eds Allison Muri and Benjamin Neudorf (London, 1703)

Ward, Peter, *The Clean Body* (Montreal: McGill-Queen's University Press, 2019)

Ward, Robert, *London's New River* (London: Historical Publications, 2003)

——, *The Man Who Buried Nelson: The Surprising Life of Robert Mylne* (London: Tempus, 2007)

Warner, Malcolm (ed), *The Image of London: Views by Travellers and Emigrés, 1550–1920* (London: Barbican Art Gallery, 1987)

Water Down the Drain, produced for the Joint Trade Union Water Anti-Privatisation Campaign, *c.* 1988

Waterworks Clauses Act, 1847 (10 & 11 Vict c17)

Weinreb, Ben, and Christopher Hibbert, *The London Encyclopedia* (London: Macmillan, 1983)

Weinstein, Rosemary, 'Feeding the City: London's Market Gardens in the Early Modern Period', in Mireille Galinou (ed), *London's Pride: The Glorious History of The Capital's Gardens* (London: Anaya Publishers, pp. 80–99, 1990)

——, 'Who Hid the Cheapside Hoard? A Goldsmith's Row Mystery Resolved', *London Topographical Record*, vol XXXII, London, pp. 151–201, 2021

Wicksteed, Thomas, *An Experimental Inquiry Concerning the Relative Power of and Useful Effect Produced by the Cornish and Boulton and Watt Pumping Engines* (London, 1841)

Williamson, F., 'George Sorrocold of Derby – a Pioneer of Water Supply', reprinted from the *Journal of the Derbyshire Archaeological and Natural History Society* NS 10 no. 57, 1936, *Studies in the History of Civil Engineering, Vol 5, Water Supply and Public Health Engineering*, ed Denis Smith, Ashford Variorum, 1999.

Wilson, John F., *British Business History, 1720–1994* (Manchester University Press, 1995)

Wise, Sarah, *The Blackest Streets: The Life and Death of a Victorian Slum* (London: Vintage, 2009)

Wohl, Anthony S., *Endangered Lives: Public Health in Victorian Britain* (London: Dent, 1983)

——, 'Unfit for Human Habitation' in Dyos and Wolff (eds) *The Victorian City: Images and Realities*, vol. 2, 603–24, 1973

Woodford, Julian, *The Boss of Bethnal Green: Joseph Merceron, the Godfather of Regency London* (London: Spitalfields Life Books, 2016)

Woolrych, Edmund Humphrey (ed), *Metropolis Local Management Acts* (London, 1863)

Wright, John, *The Dolphin, or Grand Junction Nuisance* (London, 1827, published anonymously)

——, *Memoir* submitted to the royal commission (London, 1828)

Wright, Lawrence, *Clean and Decent: The History of the Bathroom and the WC* (London: Routledge and Kegan Paul, 1966)

Yarwood, Doreen, *The British Kitchen: Housewifery since Roman Times* (London: Batsford, 1981)

The York-Buildings Dragons (London, 1726)

Picture Credits

1a *The North Prospect of London taken from The Bowling Green at Islington.*
Coloured engraving by Thomas Bowles, 1752. (Historic Images/Alamy)

1b Round Pond, New River Head, 1914. (Courtesy of Thames Water
Archives)

2a *Old London Bridge.* Engraving from Harrison's *History of London*, 1776.
(Antiqua Print Gallery/Alamy)

2b York Watergate, Westminster. Engraving by Thomas Malton,
*c.*1790. (Image © London Metropolitan Archives/City of London)

3a Frontispiece to 'The Dolphin; or, Grand Junction Nuisance'
published in 1827. (© British Library Board. All rights reserved/
Bridgeman Images)

3b *Monster Soup.* Coloured etching by Paul Pry (William Heath), 1828.
(History and Art Collection/Alamy)

4a *Salus Populi Suprema Lex.* Coloured engraving by George Cruikshank,
1832. (Granger Historical Picture Archive/Alamy)

4b *London Bridge, from Southwark Bridge.* Lithograph from *Original Views of
London as It Is*, by Thomas Shotter Boys, 1842. (Album/Alamy)

5a Water carrier. Artist and date unknown. (De Luan/Alamy)

5b *New River Water.* Engraving from *Cryes of the City of London* by
Marcellus Laroon, 1687. (Chronicle/Alamy)

5c A London Turncock. Illustration by Horace Petherick for *London
Characters*, published in 1875. (Chronicle/Alamy)

5d Men laying gas and water pipes in Tottenham Court Road and Francis Street. Brush drawing and grey wash by George Scharf, 1834. (© The Trustees of the British Museum)

6a The Lambeth Water Company's New Works. Engraving from *The Illustrated London News*, 1852. (Granger Historical Picture Archive/Alamy)

6b Giant engine cylinder, *c.*1849. (Photograph courtesy of London Museum of Water and Steam, Kew Bridge.)

7a Filter beds at Hampton Waterworks, *c.*1880. (Courtesy of Thames Water Archives)

7b Joseph Quick (Courtesy of Sally Potts and Neil Quinn)

7c Portrait of Arthur Clay. Drawing by Samuel Cockerell, 1874. (Courtesy of Christopher Clay)

7d Allen Stoneham (Courtesy of Marty Burn)

8a Interior of Crossness Pumping Station, Kent. (Photo © Peter Scrimshaw/Flickr)

8b Sir William Prescott Engine at Kempton Park Pumping Station. (Photo © Stephen Fielding, Kempton Great Engines Trust.)

Acknowledgements

The bulk of this book was written between March and December 2020 – the year of the coronavirus pandemic and multiple lockdowns, when libraries and archives closed and it proved impossible to go on with original research. There was an upside to this: without the closure I might never have started writing. But it also means there are still gaps in my knowledge. I trust the reader will forgive these silent lacunae.

Two archives in particular were invaluable. The London Metropolitan Archives – housed in a building within sight of the original terminus of the New River in Islington – contain the corporate records of all the eight water companies (and their predecessors) taken over by the Metropolitan Water Board in 1904. It is hard to overstate what a precious historical resource this is. Many years ago Geoff Pick and my chum Daniel Beagles (who sneaked me in for a look backstage) physically loaded the whole lot up, vanload after vanload, and ferried it from Thames Ditton to Clerkenwell. Geoff was the Archives' director while this book was being researched: my thanks to him and to his ever-helpful staff.

The London Museum of Water and Steam at Kew Bridge is housed in a handsome set of buildings constructed between 1837 and 1869 as a pumping station for the Grand Junction Waterworks. The site is dominated by an elegant tower which looks like a chimney disguised as an Italian campanile but is in fact a water stand pipe. The museum's displays do a workmanlike job of telling the story of London's water; the real delight is the museum's collection of steam engines. The Kew Bridge archive is small but contains a near-complete run of the *Journal of Gas Lighting, Water Supply and Sanitary Reform* (which is nowhere near as dry as its title and its intimidatingly dense columns would suggest). Until lockdown it was also home to a small team of wise enthusiasts who welcomed an outsider, shared their own knowledge and made many helpful suggestions: this book could not have been written without the advice and assistance of Toby Sleigh, Oliver Pearcey, Bryce Caller and above all the late John Porter, who first told me about Joseph Quick and generously shared the fruits of his own years of research on the Grand Junction's history.

Many others have helped with this book. I spent an entertaining morning with Robin Hutchinson, Bob Phillips and Simon Tyrell of the Friends of Seething Wells, touring the former filter beds and pumping stations of the Lambeth and Chelsea companies; Bob also shared his own research on the history of the site. Martin Rose read a complete early draft and was unfailingly (but not uncritically) enthusiastic, as a good friend should be. Many others provided information, advice, comments and suggestions, acted as sounding boards, supplied pictures, provided access or answered queries; they include (with apologies to anyone I have omitted) Mark Anderson, Marty Burns, Helen Charlton, Christopher Clay, Steve Cowley, Amir Dotan, Stephen Fielding, Duncan Gibbons, Roger Harrabin, Mike Jones, Andrew Marsden, Jim Murray, Anna Nabarro, Anne Quinn, Neil Quinn, Sally Potts, Stanley Root, Boni Sones, James Stewart, Rick Stewart, Becky Trotman, Carry van Lieshout, Zillah Webb, Stuart White. My thanks to them all, though it goes without saying that any errors are my own.

At Headline I owe much to my editor Iain MacGregor and his colleagues – ever helpful and always professional – including Holly Purdham, Caitlin Raynor, Cathie Arrington and Anna Herve: my thanks to them and to my agent Doug Young.

And finally my thanks to my family, and above all to Deborah, for putting up with all this water nonsense for so long.

Index

Index

Index

Index

Index

Index

Index